Advanced Algebra Through Data Exploration

A Graphing Calculator Approach

TEACHER'S GUIDE AND ANSWER KEY

JERALD MURDOCK
ELLEN KAMISCHKE
ERIC KAMISCHKE

KEY CURRICULUM PRESS
Innovators in Mathematics Education

Editor	Crystal Mills
Production Editor	Deborah Cogan
Chief Copy Editor	Greer Lleuad
Copy Editors	John Hammett, Margaret Moore
Editorial Assistant	Jeff Gammon
Production Manager	Luis Shein
Production Coordinator	Susan Parini
Art and Layout	Bev Butterfield, Kirk Mills, Ann Rothenbuhler
Cover Design	Dennis Teutschel
Contributor and Additional Editorial Development	Jennifer North Morris

Publisher
Steven Rasmussen

Editorial Director
John Bergez

This material is based upon work supported by the National Science Foundation under award number MDR9154410. Any opinions, findings, and conclusions or recommendations expressed in this publication are those of the authors and do not necessarily reflect the views of the National Science Foundation.

Key Curriculum Press
P.O. Box 2304
Berkeley, CA 94702
510-548-2304
editorial@keypress.com
http://www.keypress.com

Printed in the United States of America   10 9 8 7 6 5 4 3   01 00 99 98   ISBN 1-55953-226-2

Contents

Advanced Algebra
Through Data Exploration
Teacher's Support Materials

Teacher's Guide and Answer Key

- Overview and philosophy
- Course outlines
- Cooperative learning suggestions
- Assessment suggestions
- Section guides
- Answers for Problem Sets

Teacher's Resource Book

- Transparency and worksheet masters
- Extra projects
- Extra Take Another Looks
- Extra assessment problems
- Data and programs disk for popular calculator models with linking capabilities

Quizzes, Tests, and Exams

- Two quizzes per chapter
- Form A and Form B chapter tests
- Form A and Form B exams (midyear and final) for three different course plans
- Disks with quizzes, tests, and exams formatted for Microsoft Word® for Windows® and Macintosh® computers
- Answers to quizzes, tests, and exams

Solutions Manual

- Complete solutions for Problem Sets
- Project hints and answers
- Take Another Look answers

Blackline Masters for Calculator Notes

- Separate volumes for popular calculator models, keyed to the text

Constructive Assessment in Mathematics
Practical Steps for Classroom Teachers
by David Clarke

- Guide to implementing assessment strategies, including observational assessment, student-constructed tests, group assessment, student self-assessment, student journals, and portfolios
- Tips for recording, interpreting, and communicating assessment information
- Annotated bibliography of assessment resources

Suggested Supplemental Resources

The Geometer's Sketchpad

- Dynamic geometry software for Windows and Macintosh computers

Exploring Trigonometry with The Geometer's Sketchpad

- Add-on module for The Geometer's Sketchpad that teaches students to actively explore trigonometry
- Includes sample activity disks for Windows and Macintosh computers and a book of blackline activity masters

Exploring Conic Sections with The Geometer's Sketchpad

- Add-on module for The Geometer's Sketchpad that deepens students' understanding of the conic sections
- Includes sample activity disks for Windows and Macintosh computers and a book of blackline activity masters

Overview and Philosophy

Mathematics, like art, literature, philosophy, or music, is a journey toward making our chaotic world beautiful by finding and celebrating patterns. Just as poetry is much more than a greeting card that rhymes, mathematics is more than problem sets and symbols. The path you and your students are embarking on is rich with mathematical investigations and applications that encourage the exploration of ideas, data, patterns, and relationships.

Jerald Murdock

Advanced Algebra Through Data Exploration helps you rethink algebra and redefine what good mathematics teachers do in their classrooms. The text and teacher's materials will help you guide and encourage better learning of important mathematics—mathematics that students can immediately use—by featuring important connections among data analysis, quantitative reasoning, mathematical modeling, and algebra. This curriculum, highly influenced by NCTM guidelines and by contemporary curriculum leaders and their initiatives, will help you implement the NCTM *Standards* every day in your classroom.

The teaching/learning model actively engages students in both guided and open-ended mathematical explorations that help them make sense of their experiences. We believe this approach will help your students develop mathematical power so that they can participate fully as productive citizens of our contemporary world.

Ellen Kamischke

Background

As authors, we can trace the development of our innovative book to the mid-80s. We were three high school mathematics teachers working and cooperating together in the same school, Interlochen Arts Academy. We still are! At that time we were searching for classroom materials and computer software that would help make mathematics more relevant to our students' lives. We believed technology was an important tool that could impact what our students learned and how they learned it. We wanted to focus more on processes and conceptual understanding. Then we began writing short units for computer graphing software developed by author Eric Kamischke. Both software and teaching materials were constantly under revision as we continued to look for better visual approaches to learning. We knew that graphs and tables could provide students with "visual spreadsheets" of valuable information.

Eric Kamischke

During this same time period, the NCTM *Standards* were conceptualized and developed. Several successful technology-related curriculum projects were underway, such as Ohio State's Calculator and Computer Precalculus (C^2PC) Project and the North Carolina School of Science and Mathematics' Contemporary Precalculus Through Applications Project. We traded ideas with everyone we could identify as interested in technology and classroom reform—and then graphing calculators became available for high school students.

During the spring of 1991, in a proposal to the National Science Foundation, we formalized the course for our future efforts—to develop instructional materials that would incorporate the use of graphing calculators and provide materials and in-service help to other teachers. Interlochen's 1991–95 NSF-supported (MDR9154410) Graphing Calculator Enhanced Algebra Project (GCEAP) proposed a major reevaluation of both algebra content and instructional strategies to reflect the way people do mathematics with technology. We began writing and piloting prototype units in our own classrooms during the 1991–92 school year.

During the next five years we tested new materials, new technology, and new teaching approaches with our students, in conference sessions, in a variety of workshops, and in several summer institutes. We discovered what worked in our classrooms and were encouraged to continue by our students and by other teachers working with us. We actively participated in the revolution taking place in mathematics classrooms—a revolution involving graphing calculators.

We then sought a publisher that would help us take our book to teachers and students. Since 1993 we have had the good fortune of working with Key Curriculum Press, a leading-edge publisher that provides materials to meet needs not satisfied by the offerings of traditional publishers. Key seeks authors who are also teachers to guarantee that materials will work when they reach the classroom. Together we conducted a national-level field test and then, based on teacher suggestions, revised and improved the text.

What's Different About This Course?

Investigation-Based Relevant Content

During recent years the gap has widened between what has been taught and the algebra required by adults in real-life situations. Traditionally, teachers and students have focused on paper-and-pencil manipulative algebra—simplification of expressions and the solving of equations by formal memorized methods and rules. Thinly disguised "real-world" applications of algebraic techniques just learned were located near the end of various chapters.

In *Advanced Algebra Through Data Exploration* students will study new and different algebra topics applicable in our rapidly changing data-driven, technologically rich society. Recursively defined routines, parametric representations, statistics, data analysis, dynamic simulations, modeling, functions, chance and variation, random process simulations, Markov processes, matrices, and other discrete topics, usually considered as beyond the scope of advanced algebra, play important roles in the course. As NCTM's *Algebra in a Technological World* states, "The content of school algebra will be transformed through changes driven by a variety of perspectives: changes in organization, changes in sequencing, changes in emphasis, changes in focus, changes in representation worlds" (NCTM Addenda Series, 25, 1995).

We believe this curriculum will simultaneously change the pedagogy teachers use, infuse technology (especially graphing calculator related) into the course, and anchor the content of the course in real-world contexts. The curriculum integrates algebra with statistics, data analysis, functions, discrete mathematics, geometry, probability, and trigonometry.

The curriculum guides students through processes of data analysis and helps students relate their findings to the mathematics that models the situation. The curriculum incorporates both open-ended and guided inquiry, posing more questions than it attempts to answer, thus encouraging students to explore relevant ideas and issues beyond the bounds of the course.

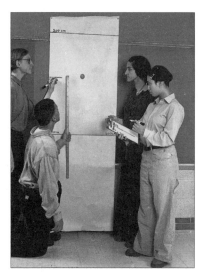

Interesting questions and simple hands-on investigations motivate relevant algebraic concepts and processes, preceding introduction of formulas and symbolic representations. These investigations are accessible to students and teachers in mathematics classes. They use inexpensive and readily available materials, require little technical knowledge, are easy to set up, follow simple procedures, and can be conducted by students without micromanagement by a teacher.

The investigations allow students legitimate opportunities to experiment, hypothesize, measure, analyze, test, talk, write, explain, and justify their ideas. A combination of projects, real-world applications, and appropriate problems emphasizes making sense of numbers, variables, expressions, equations, and algebraic "laws" in

First rebound	
Trial number	Rebound height
1	–?–
2	–?–
3	–?–
4	–?–
5	–?–

contextual situations with real data. Actively involved students make personal and meaningful connections to the mathematics they discover.

Students learn algebra and algebraic thinking as they explore ideas within the context of investigations and nontypical problems. Most *Advanced Algebra* lessons are investigation and cooperative-learning based, encouraging meaningful links to work students have completed in the past. Teachers and students experience mathematics as an activity and a process that encourages use of multiple representations—numerical, graphic, symbolic, and verbal.

Unlike the algebra currently taught in most schools, which is devoid of context, *Advanced Algebra* does not burden students with algebraic manipulations that are being rendered obsolete by technology. The importance and value of what they are learning is clear as they use mathematics to make decisions about the environment, economic and financial conditions, social issues, and science-related technology issues.

Integration of Technology

Changes in technology, science, and mathematical applications in all disciplines necessitate that students study some new and different algebra topics. This curriculum assumes that *Advanced Algebra* students will have graphing calculators at home and at school. Their calculators will be used for more than just confirming answers, investigating graphs, or as an alternative approach after they have mastered paper-and-pencil methods.

Graphing calculators allow students to explore and investigate algebra—combining data exploration with modern, real-world applications. The technology allows students to look at a lot of examples quickly, to solve situations involving difficult computation, and to compare results. They can look at situations from several different perspectives, and the technology allows some students to hurdle unproductive and error-plagued paper-and-pencil barriers.

Because *Advanced Algebra* fully integrates graphing calculators into the mathematical processes, students will not need to learn many obsolete paper-and-pencil routines. Some traditional procedures are de-emphasized in favor of more efficient technology

driven alternatives. The technology allows students to look at graphic, symbolic, and numeric representations of interesting problems and activities. Explorations from these multiple perspectives help students simplify and understand what were formerly difficult algebraic abstractions.

In this course, variables and functions are more dynamic than in a traditional course—students explore variables that actually vary and functions that describe real-world phenomena. Modeling and functions are at the heart of the course. In *Advanced Algebra,* students investigate growth and decay with function models like $y = ax^b$, looking for patterns, shapes, and implications as the parameters a and b change.

Modeling describes the links between mathematics and the real world. This is a powerful motivation, especially for those students who are not attracted to more abstract mathematics. Technology allows students to work with data until they discover the principles that underlie how things behave. Equally important, mathematical modeling lies at the heart of mathematical and scientific inquiry.

Calculators generate numbers very quickly. Knowing how to interpret calculator answers is critically important. *Advanced Algebra* helps students focus on the meaning of the numbers and expressions they enter and of the answers they generate. Finding meaning in numbers, variables, expressions, tables, and graphs is a yearlong challenge for everyone. As the teacher, you will be encouraged to ask for the real-world meaning of a term in a sequence, the slope of a line, the y-intercept, or what happens "in the long run."

In addition, the text incorporates investigations using The Geometer's Sketchpad, a program for exploring mathematics dynamically. Interlochen science instructor Jack Randall has written a book fo calculator-based laboratories (CBL), offering alternative approaches and extensions to *Advanced Algebra* investigations. These powerful tools are not required technology but will be utilized in projects and other optional aspects of the curriculum.

Teaching with *Advanced Algebra* *Through Data Exploration*

The Classroom Environment

The text is adaptable to a variety of individual teaching styles. Most teachers find that a classroom environment based on small cooperative groups is an effective approach. Exercises and investigations have group members interact, plan together, brainstorm, determine and organize tasks, and communicate their individual and collective results.

Students with a wide range of backgrounds and a variety of success stories flourish in a course that catches their interest. The emphasis on technology use and peer interaction are two factors that will help generate that interest. Even students who enter this course with poor computational and manipulation skills will find that through the "eyes" of their graphing calculator screens they can visualize mathematical processes and concepts that previously eluded them.

As students begin to experience success, you may find a new group of class leaders emerge—students who are eager to explain and discuss issues and ideas. Working in groups and with partners to solve problems often enables students strong in team and communication skills to become an important part of the discussions as they gain confidence in their mathematical contributions.

At the same time, students whose computational skills are strong but who have difficulty explaining their ideas may find that the visual representations and the opportunity to reason things out with their peers will help them improve their ability to express their thoughts.

Cooperative investigations allow students time to understand and construct their own knowledge. They learn by doing. They take responsibility for their own learning. The interaction, discussion, questions, suggestions, and ideas offered by students working in teams will benefit all members of the team.

Planning the Lessons

In general, the individual sections in this text are multiday sections, typically consisting of one and a half or more days. New content, motivated by hands-on investigations, is organized in sections designed for multiple periods of 50 minutes or for a single 90-minute class. The text requires reading by students. The writing style and queries are intended to be instructive and a bit incomplete. We have always intended that the teacher's role is to help the students discover mathematics—processes and content.

New topics and questions that encourage thinking and communicating may send you and your students off onto unfamiliar paths. Checking out several options during a thorough exploration takes time. If answers and explanations are provided too quickly, then students continue to expect and depend on them.

Advanced Algebra invites students to think, to problem-solve, to write and verbalize ideas. Students need encouragement and reassurance as they accept more responsibility for their learning. The classroom learning environment is critical. The approach is at least as important as the answer. Everyone must feel that what they have to contribute will be respected so they are encouraged and willing to contribute again.

Although all the investigations in *Advanced Algebra* are valuable to the course, you do not have to do them all to the same depth. Some should be written up and/or presented verbally by students. Others may be completed during class by groups that informally report their results to you. You may choose to omit some investigations because of time constraints. Before you begin a chapter, look through it and make these decisions.

Homework assignments will frequently span two or more sections and two or more days. Students may feel threatened if they are expected to complete a new assignment and turn it in the next day. Often it is better to give an assignment, encourage students to work on it and to come to class the next day prepared to discuss any difficulties or problems they encountered, then continue working on the assignment and turn it in the following day. It is unrealistic to expect all students to complete all the problems. Select those problems that you think will generate student interest and will satisfy your curriculum goals. At times you may want to assign different problems to different groups or individuals; then ask for classroom presentations.

Using Graphing Calculators Effectively

One of the challenges of publishing an innovative textbook like *Advanced Algebra Through Data Exploration* is finding a way to effectively incorporate rapidly changing technology. For example, how does a textbook accommodate students with different— and ever-changing—types of graphing calculators without becoming obsolete? We have met this particular challenge in *Advanced Algebra* by referring to calculators in the student text generically and by providing detailed notes for many different types of calculators in separate book, *Blackline Masters for Calculator Notes.* As new calculator technology is introduced and gains broad acceptance in secondary mathematics classrooms, Key Curriculum Press will create new calculator notes to accommodate it.

NOTE
3A

You and your students will find references to the calculator notes throughout the student text: in the expository writing, in the problem sets, in the Take Another Look sections, and in the projects. For example, on page 97 in Section 3.1 you will find a reference that says "See **Calculator Note 3A**," accompanied by an icon in the left margin. This reference indicates that in Calculator Note 3A there is a helpful hint, a calculator program that will help students use their calculators more effectively, or important information about a procedure. How much your students need these notes will depend on their experience with graphing calculators and with the particular graphing calculator methods used to explore concepts in *Advanced Algebra*. The notes will be particularly useful if your students use many different types of calculators.

Blackline Masters for Calculator Notes, provided for each type of calculator, offers several strategies for copying and distributing the notes to students. The strategy you choose will depend on your students' specific needs, your access to a copy machine, and your duplicating budget. If your students have had limited experience with graphing calculators, an ideal strategy is to distribute a copy of the notes to each student and encourage students to keep the notes in a special notebook section. Another strategy would be to make enough copies for each group of students to have access to one or two copies of the notes, stored in three-hole report covers, which individual students can check out for overnight use. If your students have had a lot of experience with graphing calculators, however, you may need only one or two copies of the notes for classroom reference. Place the copies in binders and make them available for students to check out. If your students use many different calculator brands and models, you'll need to make copies of the notes for each different calculator.

Even if you don't usually copy a complete set of calculator notes for each student, you may find it helpful to distribute copies to all students for particular sections of material. For example, many of the sections in the student text contain special calculator programs. If students input these programs rather than link them, they may need access to a hard copy of the program. For shorter programs you can display the program commands on an overhead display, but if students are using a variety of calculators, you'll probably be better off providing each student with notes for his or her particular calculator. If your students use calculators with linking capabilities and you have access to a computer, the appropriate software, and linking cables, you can take advantage of the programs and data stored on the Programs and Data Disk included in the back pocket of the *Teacher's Resource Book*. You can download programs or data from the disk to a computer and then to a calculator. Students can link their calculators to transfer the data and programs. By downloading programs and data in this way, you and your students can avoid the hassle of debugging programs and checking the accuracy of data input.

Refer to the calculator notes references in the Resources sections of the Section Guides to help you with lesson planning. For example, the reference below appears in the guide for Section 3.1:

RESOURCES
Transparency Masters for Section 3.1: Toothpaste Data and Box Plot

Calculator Notes 3A, 3B, and 3C

Be sure to check these references so that you can provide your students with these notes as needed.

Assessment with Graphing Calculators

Many teachers may be uncomfortable when students are using graphing calculators on assessments, particularly tests or quizzes, because they may feel that students do not really understand concepts when the calculator is doing all the work. This should not be a concern, however, as assessment practices and problems must change from their traditional format and focus. In fact, because the students have access to the technology, you can better assess their understanding of underlying mathematical concepts. However, the problems and the expected responses must be different.

You will find that an assessment device usually contains fewer problems than tests or quizzes given in a more traditional course. In fact, a test designed to fit into one class period may very likely have four or fewer problems. Students will take longer to solve problems because they can check and rework these problems in different ways to convince themselves that they have indeed found a reasonable or correct solution. Because of the technology, students have access to a variety of ways to check both their numeric and symbolic answers. Students are no longer satisfied with just getting an answer; they want assurance that their solutions are correct. And often students cannot get by with providing only an answer as they are asked to explain and interpret answers as well. If we want students to develop problem-solving skills, we must provide them with new situations, and not ask them to just regurgitate and repeat algorithms presented in class. We need to allow students time to think about and reflect on their work.

One way to overcome the time constraint of a class period is to offer a take-home test or at least to allow part of the test to be completed outside of class. Encourage students to get help from peers and adults. When they return to class, have them write about their experiences and answer questions about the process and the results. Make the test a learning experience. You will know how much they understood by reading their answers to the follow-up questions. Students can feel good about solving a difficult problem even if they had a lot of help. Knowing that they will have to explain these answers to you will make them insist on detailed explanations from those who helped them. And in the real world, we don't usually solve real problems in isolation. Learning how and from whom to get help is a valuable lesson.

By allowing the use of class notes and homework when engaged in an assessment task, you encourage and reward students who keep a good record of work they have done. This is something to which we pay lip service but usually don't give students a good reason for doing so—other than telling them "it will help you study for a test." There is very little one can gain from mathematics at this level by memorizing facts or formulas. It is much more useful for students to develop these mathematical skills in a meaningful way so that remembering will be easy.

One way of helping students use their test time more effectively is to provide them with data that will be used for test questions the day before the test. Encourage students to enter the data into their calculators and explore before coming to class. For example, "One question on tomorrow's test will use this data on cigarette consumption and coronary heart disease. Please enter the data into your calculator before coming to class. You are encouraged to graph and explore the data before coming to class to take the test."

Remember that when you evaluate students' work, you are looking for efficiency as well as accuracy. Students may not receive full credit for an answer if they didn't use an efficient method or if they can't justify or explain how they arrived at their solution. Make sure your students are aware of this.

The ability to communicate mathematical ideas is not an easy skill, but it is important. You must assess this communication skill if you want students to realize that it is important and valued. You and your students may feel that this kind of assessment is subject to a certain amount of subjectivity. One way to overcome this feeling is to create grading rubrics and share these with students. You might even engage students in helping to create rubrics for some assessments.

Assessment is much more than only tests and quizzes. In this course, students are constantly investigating, solving real problems, and working together within a group. All of these activities are valuable, and students will be more apt to realize their value if the processes and results are assessed. With the graphing calculator and its accompanying link software, students have the ability to create papers with graphical illustrations. Projects and investigations can be written up similarly to science lab reports. Students can also give oral presentations complete with visual demonstrations using the overhead calculator. In assessing such presentations, you will need to question students to determine whether or not they understand why the buttons are being pressed and to make sure they are not just following a rote procedure. Often you can do this by asking studentswhat would happen if some aspect of the problem were changed. In general, "What if . . ." questions are excellent. Remember, you are looking for depth of understanding.

You will find that it takes longer to grade tests and quizzes, as well as labs, projects, papers, and so on, because you will have to do a lot of reading, comparing, and thinking about student answers. More complex questions are often open to varying interpretations. Students with different backgrounds and different experiences will see problems in a different, but no less valid, way. You may have to give up, or streamline, some of your old practices in order to give yourself time to do this "new kind" of assessment. (Several suggestions for doing this are offered in the assessment section of this *Teacher's Guide* as well as in David Clarke's book *Constructive Assessment in Mathematics.)* Assessment is more than grading, and you will most likely develop a great deal more insight into what mathematical concepts students do and do not understand as well as their problem-solving abilities by employing assessment techniques that complement this new-technology approach to algebra.

The Learning Spirit

Every teacher's challenge is to make mathematics come alive for their students. The learning spirit of the *Advanced Algebra* curriculum—involved students working together in investigations, trying to make sense of what they are discovering—brings life to the classroom.

Advanced Algebra Through Data Exploration decreases the time spent in rote memorization, teacher exposition, extended periods of seat work, and paper-and-pencil drill. It changes the rules for what is expected of students and what they should expect of the teacher. Helping them help themselves is not exactly what some students are looking for—it is not the way the learning game has been played in the past.

Teaching Advanced Algebra Through Data Exploration requires untraditional thinking and behavior, an untraditional classroom, untraditional assessments, and an untraditional teacher. This kind of teaching is a long way up the path from chalk-and-talk lecturing. Success depends on your sensitivity, patience, enthusiasm, and determination.

Overview of Chapters

Advanced Algebra can be used for a variety of different courses. Our students/teachers need three semesters to finish the complete text, but we know of honors algebra classes that have completed all fourteen chapters in two semesters. We begin the course with sequences, examining new and rather complex applications. Students need new and interesting material on day one. Technology-driven recursively defined routines provide them with an easy, yet powerful approach to problem solving. Sequence notations provide access to function notation, and students use arithmetic and geometric sequences to help make sense of linear and exponential functions.

We have written a book that involves the student—investigating, conjecturing, collecting data, searching for models, and so on. The algebra, both processes and content, is embedded in data analysis and real-world applications. The chapter sequence as written allows students to build up a tool kit of functions and problem-solving techniques as they need them. They continue to use all the tools developed and often revisit earlier problems with the new solution approach. For example, matrices are introduced in Chapter 8 and used through-out the remainder of the text.

Study the flow of the text as written. Algebraic paper-and-pencil manipulation has been embedded in the investigations and applications. For example, as students learn the median-median procedure for fitting a best-fit linear model to data, they review, learn, and practice important skills associated with linear functions. If your course outline demands a different order of topics, then you may have to build some bridges.

The goals of Chapter 0 are for students to become comfortable with the technology, to understand how the calculator interprets basic commands, and to become actively involved in the learning process rather than dependent on explanations from the teacher. Students complete some guided investigations and open-ended explorations, and they begin the process of learning to work cooperatively.

Chapter 1 introduces students to recursively defined processes while they explore a variety of sequences and series and continue to learn how to work together as a group.

The chapter introduces new material and new notations and provides interesting applications. Students do not find the material or recursive thinking to be that difficult, but they should not be rushed because the unit establishes one of the solid cornerstones for the course. Many of the problems will be revisited later.

In Chapter 2 students discover and develop explicit formulas for sequences and series as they complete the investigations and problems. They discover important connections between recursive definitions, explicit formulas, linear graphs, exponential graphs, and equations. Because they figure out the patterns and essential components of the formulas, chances are improved that they will understand them, know which one to use, and know where to use it. Throughout the course, students will explore what happens "in the long run."

In Chapter 3 students learn how to organize data using several different one-variable data graphs. They also identify and use concepts, definitions, and vocabulary related to the typical data value in a set of data. They learn to use deviation, mean absolute deviation, and various deviation sums to describe variability. This is the shortest chapter in the text. We have learned not to push through it too quickly because it introduces data analysis, another cornerstone of the course.

Taxable income ($)	Tax ($)
12,000	2,260
16,000	3,260
20,000	4,380
24,000	5,660
28,000	7,100
32,000	8,660

Chapter 4 introduces slope, intercepts, and equations or models of lines in the context of real-world data analysis. Students are asked to think about the real-world meaning of numbers and equations as they work and to "make sense" of answers and predictions. They consider guidelines and criteria for a best-fit line, analyze data pairs, and learn to determine domain and range values that are meaningful. As they learn to calculate the median-median line as a model for a given data set, they practice some meaningful algebraic manipulations. They begin reflecting about a data value and a value predicted by their linear best-fit model.

In Chapter 5 students interpret graphs and decide what it means for a graph to be continuous or discrete. They investigate dynamic relationships between graphs and real-world situations. A basic tool kit of functions—lines, parabolas, square roots, absolute values, circles, and ellipses—is introduced. Graphs of these functions are translated, flipped, stretched, and composed. Students make the transition from u_n or $u(n)$ sequence notation to $f(x)$ notation. They explore and begin to understand compositions of functions.

Transformations of graphs are also a focus of Chapter 6. Students use right-triangle trigonometry to simulate objects in motion by writing appropriate parametric equations and setting conditions that allow control of the movement of a point across the calculator screen. They use these simulations to answer a variety of related motion, time, and position questions. This chapter presents a number of interesting applications that introduce trigonometry and concepts related to vectors.

In Chapter 7 geometric sequences of the form $u_n = u_0 r^n$ are extended to the continuous exponential function form, $f(x) = ab^x$. During their study of this chapter, students study, review, and practice using properties of exponents and roots. Learning to use logarithms completes a list of different problem-solving strategies (including guess-and-check and zooming) that students can use in related situations. Finally, they use the logarithmic function to find best-fit equations for data that are exponentially related.

Chapter 8 introduces randomness, random number processes, and probability. Students find probabilities by constructing and interpreting tree diagrams, devising simulations, and using simulation programs. They use two-dimensional geometric aids, matrices, and network graphs to help organize and present information. Applications for matrices provide meaning for matrix multiplication and introduce the use of matrix multiplication as a strategy for solving problems.

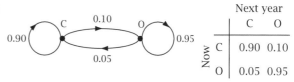

		Next year	
		C	O
Now	C	0.90	0.10
	O	0.05	0.95

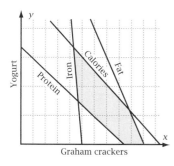

Chapter 9 introduces substitution, elimination, and matrices as techniques for solving systems of equations. Systems of linear inequations, feasible regions, and linear programming are presented in the context of applications that can be examined in a two-dimensional setting. Linear programming is an important real-world tool that provides students with valuable connections to earlier work.

Polynomial functions are the focus of Chapter 10. Finite differences and matrices are used to determine polynomial models. Students study polynomial, vertex, and factored forms and learn how to convert from one form to another. In this chapter, students derive the quadratic formula, use it to find zeros, and make connections between x-intercepts, polynomial zeros, and factors. Finally, complex numbers and synthetic division are introduced.

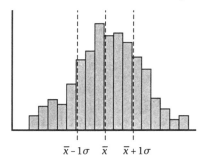

In Chapter 11 students extend earlier notions about probability, counting processes, and tree representations. Permutations, combinations, combination numbers, and binomial expansions lead to binomial distribution investigations. Students discover connections between the standard deviation measure and the normal distribution.

In Chapter 12 students study rational functions and they extend their tool kit of growth models to include a logistics model. Students write distance-time functions and determine optimal values. The last few sections provide connections between equations, table data, and graphs of the conics—circles, ellipses, parabolas, and hyperbolas. Finally, they discover and use a rotation matrix.

Chapter 13 extends definitions of trigonometric functions and introduces the cosecant, secant, and cotangent functions. Students discover some fundamental identities by examining the graphs of function combinations. They apply the Law of Sines and the Law of Cosines in real-world problem settings, and they use inverse trigonometric relations and functions to solve for the variable in periodic and pendulum-type application problems. Polar coordinates and curves, polar form, graphing powers of complex numbers, and iterations of complex numbers are extensively involved in the activities and explorations of the chapter.

Encouraging a Cooperative Learning Environment

Advanced Algebra was designed so that students learn by doing. Students are not given concepts outright; rather, they are asked to conduct investigations in which they discover these concepts. Often they are led to discover new solution strategies and mathematical concepts when working problems in the problem sets. Exploration and discovery require high-level thinking skills and can produce anxiety when students are working alone. Students need ample opportunity to share ideas and communicate the results of their investigative work. Working in cooperative groups reduces individual stress. Investigations can be time-consuming. Sharing tasks with other students speeds up this process. Working in small groups—sharing, discussing, and observing similarities in results—will help students develop an understanding of the mathematics they are constructing. For these reasons we recommend that you use some form of cooperative small group instruction with *Advanced Algebra*.

Cooperative small group instruction, or cooperative learning, refers to classroom techniques in which students work on learning activities in small groups and receive rewards or recognition based partly on the group's performance.

In a cooperative learning environment, the group cooperative skills are themselves an integral part of the curriculum. In a cooperative classroom, the group activities are designed to foster positive interdependence—an environment in which students feel that they need each other. Although students in a cooperative learning situation are assessed in part on their group work, they are also held accountable individually on tests and quizzes and other types of individual assessment.

The ideas presented here represent a synthesis of techniques and information. Use this material as a guide as you organize your class for cooperative learning. If you are interested in reading more about cooperative learning, consult the resource "Additional Readings on Cooperative Learning," which appears after this section. At the end of this section you will also find a summary of the main points discussed here that you can use as a quick reference list.

Benefits of Cooperative Learning

Cooperative group work yields many benefits. Researchers have found that working in cooperative small groups has a positive effect on student achievement and interpersonal relationships. Through cooperative small groups, students increase their contact with and improve their attitudes toward different racial and ethnic groups. Studies have found that low-achieving students spend less time off task in cooperative small groups than in traditionally structured classrooms. Research has also shown that conceptually oriented cooperative small groups (groups designed for long-range projects, brainstorming, and the discovering of new information) promote the learning of abstract processes such as critical thinking skills and problem solving better than traditionally structured classrooms.

Students in cooperative learning groups are usually more active and involved in the learning process and therefore less bored. With cooperative groups, you probably will find it easier to manage a successful learning environment in a large class of 36 or more students because you have the aid of 36 teaching helpers, and you will have to interact only with nine groups rather than 36 individuals. Oftentimes you will be able to spot students' weaknesses and help them without stopping the rest of the class. With cooperative groups, you can establish a more relaxed and comfortable classroom environment, and a comfortable classroom atmosphere reduces student anxiety, which is common in mathematics classes.

Forming Groups

The size of cooperative groups can vary from two to six. Research has shown, however, that three or four is the optimal size for most cooperative learning situations, including the investigations and classwork students undertake in *Advanced Algebra*. If groups are too small, then there may not be enough dialogue, and someone may be left out. If there are too many in a group, then there is too much happening, and managing group cooperation becomes very difficult. For certain types of activities, students in pairs is just right (see "Cooperative Learning Using Pair-Share" later in this section).

Tables usually work best for a cooperative learning classroom because they allow students plenty of work space. If you are unable to beg, borrow, or trade for tables, you can still have an effective cooperative setting with desks. In fact, one obvious drawback to tables is the closeness during tests and quizzes. With desks you can always have the students move the desks into groups of three or four for the cooperative activity and then have the desks returned to a more formal configuration at the end of the period. This type of setup makes it easier to present introductory material (teacher-centered instruction) at the beginning of the period and to give tests and quizzes. When forming groups with desks, be sure that the desks are brought together so that the desk tops form as close to a single surface as possible.

How students are assigned to groups and how often groups are reassigned vary among teachers. You might want to begin with new groups at the start of each grading period, or you might prefer to form new groups each time you begin a new unit. Some teachers feel that it is better to assign students to their groups, others prefer to use a random process, and still others allow students to form their own groups. You may want to try to balance the groups considering ethnicity, race, gender, behavior, and achievement levels of the students. How you form your groups will depend a lot on your particular situation and how much experience you and your students have had working in groups. You might even want to alternate selection processes. There are no hard and fast rules for forming cooperative groups the right way. What works for you and your students is the best way to do it.

Facilitating Cooperative Group Behavior

Depending on how much experience your students have had with cooperative learning situations, you may have to facilitate a discussion concerning appropriate group behavior. Some students may even be reluctant at first to work in a group. If students have never experienced a cooperative learning situation, they may view learning as a competitive endeavor and be reluctant to share what they know and understand for fear that sharing will jeopardize their own academic accomplishments. You will need to help students realize that everyone will benefit in a cooperative learning situation and that in the real world people are expected to work together to solve problems.

Cooperative Group Guidelines

There are several ways you can help to ensure that students will work effectively in groups. First of all, students need to be aware of some basic guidelines and responsibilities. A possible set of guidelines is provided in Section 0.1 and listed below.

When working in groups, each group member has the following responsibilities.

1. Be cooperative and considerate. Never make fun of another person's ideas.

2. Listen carefully, without interrupting, while another group member is talking.

3. Ask questions of others and ask others for help when help is needed. If the group is stuck and can't move on, decide as a group to ask for suggestions or help from your teacher.

4. Help others in your group when asked.

5. Work on a problem until every group member understands it and is ready to describe the solution to the class.

You and your students may want to add to this list or come up with your own set of guidelines, but it is important for students to realize that when they are working in groups they must adhere to certain guidelines if their work is to be productive.

Roles for Cooperative Group Members

In addition to following certain guidelines when working in cooperative groups, students will need to take on a number of roles as group members. Help students to understand what these roles are and guide them toward practicing these roles.

Each group needs to have a *facilitator.* This task can be assigned to a specific student in the group either by the group or by the teacher. The first responsibility of the facilitator is to ensure that the guidelines for cooperative behavior are observed. The facilitator is the one who keeps things moving and keeps the group members focused on the task. The facilitator is usually the only member of the group permitted to leave the group to question the teacher.

The other roles are taken on by all members of the group at various times. These are not assigned roles, and any one member may take on several of these roles simultaneously. The roles in cooperative group learning can include the following:

- *Thinker:* Each group member must be a generator of new ideas.

- *Supporter:* To help ensure that ideas keep flowing, it is important that group members support each other, for example, saying things like, "That's a good idea!"

- *Questioner:* To ensure that ideas are looked at carefully, it is important that group members question each other's ideas, for example, saying things like, "Yes, that's a good idea, but what about . . . ?"

- *Unifier:* One of the more difficult roles group members must play is that of unifier, one who combines or synthesizes the ideas presented by group members into a unified approach to a problem.

Again, these roles are not assigned but rather are roles or behaviors that all members in the group should try to develop.

Necessary Social Skills for Cooperative Learning

In addition to the guidelines and roles of cooperative learning, students should be encouraged to develop good social skills. The development of positive social skills is at the heart of effective cooperative small group learning. It is the observing and recording of good social skills by you, the teacher, that forms the basis of assessment in cooperative learning.

Social skills for cooperative learning can include

- *Using "two-foot" voices.* Encourage students to speak at a volume so that all in the group can hear but not so loud that the discussions from one group disturb the work of another group.

- *Staying on task.* Praise and reward students when they work well with their groups. It is natural and healthy for students to occasionally get off task. When this happens, encourage students to get back to work quickly and praise them for doing so.

- *Asking for help.* Praise and reward students for having the courage to ask for help from others in the group. [one of the guidelines]

- *Being supportive.* Praise and reward students for being supportive to others in the group. This is the easiest social skill to learn and often the first students use on a regular basis. [one of the roles]

- *Asking for reasons.* Praise and reward students for asking the important question "Why?" Other useful questions students should be asking are "How do we know that is true?" and "Why did you do that?" When members of the group habitually ask for reasons rather than accept answers, you have achieved a major goal. [one of the roles]

- *Criticizing ideas, not people.* Praise and reward students for learning to criticize or challenge a group member's idea rather than attacking the group member. In a cooperative setting there is a greater chance of personal attacks because of a greater opportunity for communication among students.

- *Relating present learning to past learning.* Praise and reward students for seeing and pointing out to others the connections between concepts in current lessons and the ideas discovered in earlier lessons. Remind them over and over again how important this skill is and you may see it happening more and more.

- *Having a sense of humor.* Praise students for learning how to have a good time while working and learning. Remind groups that a positive attitude about learning mathematics and solving problems is easier to hold together if humor is used as the glue.

Structuring Group Work
Introducing Your Students to Group Work

Advanced Algebra was designed with cooperative groups in mind. The investigations and many of the problems in the problem sets are quicker, smoother, less anxiety producing, and more fun when done in a cooperative setting.

In Section 0.1, students are introduced to group work through two investigations, the Cross-Number Puzzle and the Camel Crossing the Desert problem. In the Cross-Number Puzzle investigation, they will learn how to input expressions into their calculators. This investigation should provide ample opportunity for students to share discoveries and help each other learn some necessary skills. The Camel Crossing the Desert problem, on the other hand, is not a problem that students will be able to solve immediately. In fact, students may work on this problem over a several-week period. This investigation encourages students to share ideas and strategies and to realize that real problems are easier to solve when several people work together.

At the beginning of the school year, you may have to provide adequate structure so that students will learn some strategies for effective group work. For example, if you use the task cards for Investigation 1.1.1, Shifting Funds, students will have to work together to solve the problem. Cooperative group strategies are embedded in the instructions for some of the investigations. See the cooperative group learning strategies described below for ideas on how to provide the necessary structure. As the school year progresses, students will begin to use strategies that work best for them.

Cooperative Learning Structures

There are many cooperative learning structures that you can employ. The structures described below can be used to fit different learning situations and add variety to the cooperative learning setting.

Cooperative Learning Using Pair-Share

The pair-share method of cooperative learning is probably the most common cooperative learning structure. With pair-share the group of four students is divided into two pairs. One person in each pair (the reader) reads the instructions for the investigation to the partner (the investigator). The investigator performs the steps as directed by the reader. At the same time, the other pair in the group is performing the same task. When each student pair completes the task, they share their results. They then turn to the other pair and share and compare results. As a group of four they make their final conclusions. For another activity the pairs switch partners and roles.

Cooperative Learning Using the Jigsaw Method Within a Group

The jigsaw method of cooperative learning is a very efficient method for performing an investigation or series of investigations within a group. Divide up the investigation tasks among group members; that is, rather than having each student perform a separate investigation and develop his or her own conclusion, have the group assign different parts of the investigation to each group member. After each group member performs his or her part of the investigation, have the group combine their results. Then the group can complete the investigation using all the information collected.

Cooperative Learning Using the Jigsaw Method Among Groups

The jigsaw method of cooperative learning is an excellent method for performing a number of similar or parallel investigations at one time. For example, different parts of an investigation can be assigned to different groups. Then plan time for sharing results with the entire class. This speeds things up, changes the class format, and allows for class presentations by group spokespersons. This technique can also be used when assigning problems in a problem set. Assign different groups different problems. Then ask for class presentations by group spokespersons.

Cooperative Learning Using Numbered Heads Together

Numbered heads together is a cooperative learning reward system that can be used to check on students' understanding of new concepts. After a new concept has been presented, the teacher traditionally asks questions and poses problems to the entire class. When a quick student has the answer, the hand goes up, and the question is answered. The teacher and that one student are ready to move on to new concepts, often leaving the rest of the class behind. With numbered heads together, the teacher again begins by presenting a problem to the entire class.

No shouting out of answers by individuals or groups is permitted. Students work on the problem individually or with the help of their group mates, then they check to make sure that everyone in their group can solve the problem. If each student in a group has an assigned number, you can roll a die or spin a spinner to determine which student in each group will have the privilege of coming up and presenting the solution to the rest of the class. If you want only one or two groups to present, you can use dice or spinners to select the group(s) as well.

Cooperative Learning Using Group Facilitators as Teachers

You can also use groups as an alternative to a teacher-led presentation. Call up the set of group facilitators (one from each group), and in this small group setting, present a mini-lesson with numerous examples. Then send these students back to their respective groups to explain the material. In the meantime, other group members can be reviewing their homework or reading a section in the book preparing for the day's lesson.

The Teacher's Role in a Cooperative Learning Setting

In a classroom using cooperative learning, there are times when the teacher's role is the same as that in a traditional classroom, and there are times when the teacher's role is different. You are no longer the "fountain of all knowledge." A cooperative learning classroom is student-centered rather than teacher-centered. It is more like coaching or guiding the students as they learn.

When you interact with students in a group setting, support the group process whenever possible. If you pass out materials or information, give only one or two sets to each group of students. Then the students will have to work together to be successful. If producing a product is the goal, ask each group to produce a single, joint product. If tasks must be divided between groups members, let them decide how the responsibilities are to be divided. If a report or presentation is required, ask the students to prepare it together. All group products (projects, reports, presentations) should include a description of who did what part, how much time was spent on the product, and how students shared or taught each other the information.

While students are working in their groups, monitor them carefully. Do not stay at your desk catching up on paperwork. Move among the groups, observing their cooperative efforts. As you spend time observing how students function in their groups, share your observations with the group. Be encouraging. Let them know what you like and what things could be improved. Give them your suggestions. Ask them to assess their own progress. Researchers suggest that this sharing process is critical. Even if class time is limited, spend at least a little time with your students discussing how well the groups are functioning. Focus on the contributions that group members make to each other's learning and on the maintenance of effective working relationships in the groups.

Your students will know by your actions that you value good social skills. Let students know that part of your assessment of their progress in this class will be based on group participation and how well they improve their skills of working within a group. A simple and effective way to monitor students' social skills is to walk about the room observing them several times per week. You can carry a copy of the seating chart on a clipboard and record a plus or minus sign for good and bad social skills. You can either move about observing the whole class each time or focus on a different set of two or three groups each time. These plus and minus marks can be part of the basis of your assessment of their group participation.

As the year progresses your observation sheet may include a behavior checklist with such items as contributing ideas, asking questions, giving directions, actively listening, expressing support, encouraging members to participate, summarizing, relieving tension by good-natured joking, talking through problems, and justifying viewpoints. Let your students know when you are looking for specific social skills.

While you are circulating among the groups, offer support, but be conscious of your role and don't do the work of the group for them. Your role is to help the group members function together to achieve their objectives. When asked for help, refuse to give quick answers to questions from the group. Instead, respond with leading questions or direct their questions back to the group. Respond only when the group facilitator assures you that everyone in the group has the same question and that the group has itself made a serious effort to answer the question.

As you circulate, give praise, encouragement, and recognition for a cooperative effort well done. Let students know when they are on track—they need reassurance. Display the products of good group efforts in the classroom. Point out instances of positive group behavior both to the group and to the class as a whole. Show by your example that you are interested in and excited by the problem-solving process.

When certain behavioral norms are clearly lacking in a group, stop and intervene (but use restraint and give the group members ample opportunity to work out the problem among themselves first). Most often, you will simply have to remind the group to get back on task. A gentle tap on the shoulder or an inquiry about their progress usually suffices. On occasion you will need to point out or even review the guidelines for cooperative behavior. You can also help students clarify the various roles that they can play within a group. In cases where the behavior of one member is disrupting the functioning of the group, you may have to work with the group to help them resolve the problem and pull the student back into the group process. In extreme cases, you may have to speak to a student privately concerning his or her role. When this happens, be sure to make a point of speaking to the other members of the group privately as well, reminding them that it is the responsibility of the entire group to establish and maintain the cooperative atmosphere. Sometimes it helps to point out that the groups will change and that they'll have a chance to work with a different set of classmates soon.

If there are several members of the class whose behavior and/or absenteeism doesn't allow them to participate as functioning members of a group, then you may have to separate these students and let them form a group of their own. By removing unproductive students from the mainstream groups, the groups are not burdened with trying to work with uncooperative, often absent, group members. Of course the students who are assigned to special groups are still expected to work to improve their social skills, and the hope is that they eventually will be able to rejoin a mainstream group. Some of these students will start working to earn their way back when they see how much more interesting and fun the mainstream groups are. If they improve their attendance and make good enough progress catching up, they can be reassigned to a mainstream group the next time groups are reassigned or even added to an existing group if that group agrees to let the student join their group.

There are many other techniques you can employ to foster cooperation. One technique is to assign a particular problem to a group asking them to prepare to present their results to the class. Let them know that the presenter will be chosen randomly. That way everyone in the group must be prepared to present. This forces them not only to get the answer but also to make sure that everyone in the group understands the solution and can explain it.

Success with Cooperative Learning

Many of you have already successfully introduced cooperative learning into your classes. For those who have not, we hope that these suggestions will help. Keep in mind that you can ease yourself and your students into cooperative learning.
It might be anxiety producing to adopt a new textbook and begin teaching based on cooperative small group instruction all at the same time. However, you will have success with *Advanced Algebra* using even a few of the cooperative small group instruction techniques that have been suggested.

Have an exciting and rewarding time with *Advanced Algebra* this year.

Good luck!

Jerald Murdock   Ellen Kamischke   Eric Kamischke

Cooperative Learning Summary

Benefits of Cooperative Learning

- Affects positively a student's achievement and interpersonal relationships
- Improves attitudes toward different racial and ethnic groups
- Helps low-achieving students spend less time off task
- Involves students more actively in the learning process
- Helps the teacher to spot student weaknesses and to assist these students more quickly
- Creates a more relaxed and comfortable classroom environment

Forming Groups

- Form groups of four when possible, as groups of this size work best.
- Randomly assign students to groups at first, use teacher-assigned groups, allow students to select their own groups, or alternate selection processes.
- When possible balance groups by gender, race, ethnicity, behavior, and achievement levels.
- Change groups at designated time intervals or at the beginning of a unit.

Facilitating Cooperative Group Behavior

- Explain and model the guidelines, roles, and social skills of cooperative behavior.
- Provide more structure for group work at the beginning of the year, less as the year progresses.

Cooperative Group Guidelines

- Be cooperative and considerate. Never make fun of another person's ideas.
- Listen carefully, without interrupting, while another is talking.
- Ask questions of others and ask others for help when help is needed. If the group is stuck and can't move on, decide as a group to ask for suggestions or help from your teacher.
- Help others in your group when asked.
- Work on a problem until every group member understands it and is ready to describe the solution to the class.

Roles for Cooperative Group Members

- Facilitator keeps the group members focused on the task.
- Thinker generates new ideas.
- Supporter says, "That's a good idea!"
- Questioner says, "Yes, that's a good idea, but what about . . . ?"
- Unifier combines the ideas presented by group members into a unified idea.

Necessary Social Skills for Cooperative Learning

- Using two-foot voices
- Staying on task
- Asking for help
- Being supportive
- Asking for reasons
- Criticizing ideas, not people
- Relating present learning to past learning
- Having a sense of humor

Cooperative Learning Structures

- Pair-share
- Jigsaw method within a group
- Jigsaw method among groups
- Numbered heads together
- Group facilitators as teachers

The Teacher's Role in a Cooperative Learning Setting

- Establish clear objectives.
- Support the group process.
- Monitor students carefully.
- Refuse to give quick answers.
- Give praise, encouragement, and recognition for cooperative behavior.
- Intervene when necessary.
- Employ techniques to foster cooperation.

Additional Readings on Cooperative Learning

We have included in this list both readings that are general to cooperative learning, selected for their applicability to secondary classrooms, and resources that are specific to teaching mathematics in a cooperative high school classroom. More comprehensive bibliographies, titled *The 1993 Cooperative Learning Resource Guide,* and *The 1995 Supplement to the Cooperative Learning Resource Guide,* are available through the International Association for the Study of Cooperation in Education (IASCE), Box 1582, Santa Cruz, CA 95061-1582.

Abrami, Philip, Bette Chambers, Catherine Poulsen, Christina de Simone, Sylvia d'Appollonia, and James Howden. *Classroom Connections: Understanding and Using Cooperative Learning.* Toronto, Ontario: Harcourt Brace, 1995. 221 pages. ($24.95, Canadian, Harcourt Brace & Co., Canada, 55 Horner Avenue, Toronto, Ontario M8Z 4X6, Canada) A thoughtful book that clarifies the purposes, theory, and methods of cooperative learning. The first section focuses on theory and research, the second on practical implementation issues, the third on particular methods and how they can be complementary.

Bellanca, James, and Robin Fogarty. *Blueprints for Thinking in the Cooperative Classroom.* Second Edition. Arlington, IL: Skylight, 1991. 384 pages. ($45, IRI/Skylight Publishing, Inc., 2626 Clearbrook Drive, Arlington Heights, IL 60005, 800-348-4474) This comprehensive manual combines cognitive research perspectives with cooperative learning approaches to promote creative problem solving and higher-order thinking skills. Includes model lessons for secondary students and a lengthy section on authentic assessment.

Bennett, Barrie, Carol Rolheiser-Bennett, and Laurie Stevahn. *Cooperative Learning: Where Heart Meets Mind.* Edina, MN: Interaction Book Co., 1991. 345 pages. ($29, Interaction Book Co., 7208 Cornelia Drive, Edina, MN 55435, 612-831-9500) An eclectic approach that integrates cooperative learning and teaching with current educational theory from Glasser, Joyce, Fullen, and the thinking-skills movement. Helps teachers make strategic decisions based on their own and their students' experience and on the context and purpose of the activity.

Brubacher, Mark, Ryder Payne, and Kemp Rickett, eds. *Perspectives on Small Group Learning.* Mississauga, Ontario: Copp Clark Pitman Press, 1990. 342 pages. ($23, Dominie Press, 11568 Sorrento Valley Road, Suite 12, San Diego, CA 92121) A collection of 25 excellent articles by leaders in the fields of both collaborative and cooperative learning. The authors teach high school and espouse an eclectic mix of perspectives, with an emphasis on "constructivist" theory and cooperative practice.

Clarke, Judy, Ron Wideman, and Susan Eadie. *Together We Learn.* Scarborough, Ontario: Prentice-Hall Canada, 1990. 216 pages. ($20, U.S., order through IRI/Skylight Publishing, Inc., 2626 Clearbrook Drive, Arlington Heights, IL 60005, 800-348-4474) A general introduction to cooperative and collaborative learning that is practical and especially oriented for the secondary student. This book combines the importance of exploration with the need for careful structuring of groups for effective learning. Particularly helpful is the large section on assessment and evaluation methods.

Cohen, Elizabeth G. *Designing Groupwork: Strategies for the Heterogeneous Classroom.* Second Edition. New York: Teachers College Press, 1994. 224 pages. ($17.95, Teachers College Press, Box 2032, Colchester, VT 05449, 800-488-2665) A classic for the cooperative group work called "complex instruction," this edition includes new material on skill building for advanced students, developing roles for older as well as younger students, and treatments for equalization of status within cooperative groups.

Davidson, Neil, ed. *Cooperative Learning in Mathematics: A Handbook for Teachers.* Menlo Park, CA: Addison-Wesley, 1990. 416 pages. ($26.84, Addison-Wesley Alternative Publication Division, Route 128, Reading, MA 01867, 800-447-2226) A collection of essays covering all the major approaches to teaching mathematics in cooperative groups to students of all ages, with chapters by leaders in the field. Includes sample activities and specific strategies for using computers with small groups.

Dishon, Dee, and Pat Wilson O'Leary. *A Guidebook for Cooperative Learning: A Technique for Creating More Effective Schools.* Second Edition. Holmes Beach, FL: Learning Publications, 1994. 168 pages. ($19, prepaid, Cooperation Unlimited, P.O. Box 68, Portage, MI 49081, 616-327-2199) A revision of a popular handbook that guides teachers to understand the fundamentals of cooperative learning and to make conscious choices of goals and practices.

Ellis, Susan S., and Susan F. Whalen. *Cooperative Learning: Getting Started.* Jefferson City, MO: Scholastic Books, 1990. 72 pages. ($10, Scholastic Books, 2931 East McCarty Street, Jefferson City, MO 65102, 800-325-6149) For teachers new to cooperative learning, this short, simple, and straightforward presentation helps them get rolling and includes advice on dealing with typical implementation problems.

Erickson, Tim, et al. *Get It Together: Math Problems for Groups Grades 4–12.* Berkeley, CA: EQUALS Project, 1989. 180 pages. ($15, EQUALS, Lawrence Hall of Science, University of California, Berkeley, CA 94720, 510-642-1823) Using the jigsaw method of cooperative learning for problems in logic, number, geometry, algebra, probability, measurement, and functions, this book builds in student responsibility for learning. These problems can be solved only by sharing information. The book includes useful tips for creating a cooperative classroom.

Graves, Nan (now Liana Forest), and Ted Graves. *A Part to Play: Tips, Techniques and Tools for Learning Cooperatively.* Second Edition. Victoria, Australia: Latitude Media, 1995. 186 pages. ($28, Kagan Cooperative Learning, 27134 Paseo Espada, Suite 303, San Juan Capistrano, CA 92675, 800-933-2667) A guide for teachers at all levels. Includes fundamentals of cooperative learning, model lesson plans, and cooperative activities in different subject matters, including mathematics. Because the activities are designed to be used with adults in professional development settings, they are easily adapted for secondary school use.

Hemmerich, Hal, Wendy Lim, and Kanwai Neel. *Prime Time: Strategies for Life-Long Learning in Mathematics and Science in the Middle and High School Grades.* Portsmouth, NH: Heinemann, 1994. 126 pages. ($12, Heinemann, 361 Hanover Street, Portsmouth, NH 03801-3912, 800-541-2086) Fourteen strategies to involve students not ordinarily interested in mathematics through cooperative methods, activating prior knowledge, multiple intelligences, and active learning techniques.

Herr, Ted, and Ken Johnson. *Problem Solving Strategies: Crossing the River with Dogs.* Berkeley, CA: Key Curriculum Press, 1994. 372 pages. ($19.95, Key Curriculum Press, Box 2304, Berkeley, CA 94702, 510-548-2304) High school students take responsibility for their own learning in 17 chapters, each of which illustrates a different strategy for solving nonroutine types of problems. Students use examples of strategies to work together to solve other problems, explore methods of solution, and demonstrate to the class.

Johnson, David W., and Roger T. Johnson. *Learning Together and Alone: Cooperative, Competitive, and Individualistic Learning.* Fourth Edition. Boston, MA: Allyn and Bacon, 1994. 242 pages. ($25, Interaction Book Company, 7208 Cornelia Drive, Edina, MN 55435, 612-831-9500) This popular classic presents both theory and practical application of the Johnsons' cooperative learning methods contrasted with competitive or individualistic learning. It covers social skills, assessment, group process, conflict resolution, strategies for at-risk students, creating a multicultural classroom, and challenging the gifted.

Johnson, David W., Roger T. Johnson, and Edyth Holubec. *The New Circles of Learning: Cooperation in the Classroom and the School.* Alexandria, VA: Association of Supervision and Curriculum Development, 1994. 111 pages. ($13.95, Association of Supervision and Curriculum Development, 1250 North Pitt Street, Alexandria, VA 22314-1453, 703-549-9110) An updated old favorite now includes not only fundamental components for a successful cooperative learning program but also steps for making existing lessons cooperative.

Kagan, Spencer. *Cooperative Learning.* San Juan Capistrano, CA: Kagan Cooperative Learning, 1994. 392 pages. ($35, Kagan Cooperative Learning, 27134 Paseo Espada, Suite 303, San Juan Capistrano, CA 92675, 800-933-2667) A comprehensive and eclectic resource that places many different methods of cooperative learning into a structural perspective. Updated version not only includes team building, class building, thinking skills, communication skills, mastery, and information sharing, but adds new material and structures as well. This book imparts theoretical insight along with practical step-by-step guidance.

Schmuck, Richard, and Patricia Schmuck. *Group Processes in the Classroom.* Seventh Edition. Dubuque, IA: William C. Brown, 1997. 336 pages. ($33.06 or $22.80 to schools, Wm. C. Brown, Co., 2460 Kerper Boulevard, Dubuque, IA 52001, 800-338-5578) A classic book integrating theory and research with a practical guide for developing a well-functioning cooperative classroom.

Sharan, Shlomo, ed. *Handbook of Cooperative Learning Methods.* Westport, CT: Greenwood Publishing, 1994. 374 pages. ($75, Greenwood Publishing Co., 88 Post Road West, Westport, CT 06881, 203-226-3571) A collection of essays by major developers and practitioners presenting eight generic methods of cooperative learning applicable to a wide variety of subject matter. This extensive resource book is also practical for teachers.

Slavin, Robert. *Cooperative Learning: Theory, Research and Practice.* Des Moines, IA: Prentice-Hall, 1990. 173 pages. ($27, Prentice-Hall, P.O. Box 11071, Des Moines, IA 50336-1071, 515-284-6751) This text covers most of the basic approaches to cooperative learning, including research evidence on achievement and other outcomes and a practical guide to implementation focusing mainly on Johns Hopkins Student Team Learning and Group Investigation methods.

Slavin, Robert E., Shlomo Sharan, Spencer Kagan, Rachel Hertz-Lazarowitz, Clark Web, and Richard Schmuck, eds. *Learning to Cooperate, Cooperating to Learn.* New York, NY: Plenum Press, 1985. 472 pages. ($60, Plenum Press, 233 Spring Street, New York, NY 10013, 800-221-9369) A compilation of major writings in the field, covering theory, research, and implementation in general cooperative learning; how to create a cooperative environment; and applications to mathematics and science and the multiethnic classroom.

Suggestions for Assessment

Assessment is an opportunity for you to learn more about your students. Through assessment you can discover what students know and understand, how they think, what they still need to learn, and how they feel about their learning. Assessment is also an opportunity for students to learn more about themselves.

Assessment does not always mean recording a grade. You assess students when you read their journals or when you observe them interacting with other members of a group.

You might be one of the many teachers who structure mathematics classrooms and lessons differently from traditional methods. For this reason you need assessment practices that match your changing classroom. For example, teachers argue that if students work cooperatively, we should assess the work they do in groups. If we ask students open-ended questions, we should use open-ended questions as assessment items. If students connect mathematics with the world outside their classroom, we should evaluate projects that make these connections.

Teachers want assessment methods that are genuinely helpful to themselves and their students. They are finding that this kind of constructive assessment requires more than grading the results of a paper-and-pencil test. The *Advanced Algebra* assessment materials can help you use multiple modes of assessment to create a more accurate portrayal of students' learning. These materials consist of the following:

Constructive Assessment in Mathematics: Practical Steps for Classroom Teachers

This new book by David Clarke, which Key Curriculum Press provides as part of the *Advanced Algebra* teacher's materials, offers a good overview of assessment as well as some guidance in specific assessment strategies. You might want to read Clarke's book first for background, then look over the Assessing What You've Learned sections following each of the first seven chapters of *Advanced Algebra*. Finally, come back to this section of the *Teacher's Guide* to find more specific suggestions about the assessment strategies that interest you.

Advanced Algebra Student Text

Because *Advanced Algebra* engages students as active learners, it provides ample opportunities to assess student learning in the normal course of instruction. While you move around your classroom helping and observing students as they work in cooperative groups, you are engaging in what Clarke describes as observational assessment (see Clarke, Part 2). Investigations provide opportunities for performance assessment (assessment that focuses on students' "process"). Journal-writing prompts in exercise sets and Take Another Look problems can stimulate portfolio entries and presentations. Projects in the student text give students opportunities to demonstrate their learning in new contexts.

Besides the diverse tasks found in the student text, every chapter ends with a section called Assessing What You've Learned. Each of these sections provides general suggestions to the student for using various methods of assessment. Their central purpose is to give you and your students flexibility in approaching assessment. They introduce new assessment strategies that might not be familiar to students, and they alert students to ways in which they can take responsibility for assessing their own learning.

These sections are not meant to stand alone, and they're not meant to be completed in their entirety, one after another. You and your students should choose discriminatingly from these assessment suggestions. You may also need to provide students with more guidance on how to go about the suggested tasks.

There is some logic to the order in which the Assessing What You've Learned sections introduce assessment strategies, since in most cases the strategy presented is well suited to the content of the particular chapter. However, you do not need to use these strategies in the order they appear in the student text. For example, you could have students give group presentations at the beginning of the year, even though the student text describes group presentations for the first time at the end of Chapter 6. If you like to plan ahead, you might want to read all the Assessing What You've Learned sections when you make your assessment plan at the beginning of the year. Then you can decide which idea or ideas you want to try and when you want to try them.

Advanced Algebra Quizzes, Tests, and Exams

This volume contains quizzes, chapter tests, and midyear and final cumulative exams. These materials are also provided on disk so that teachers using Microsoft Word or a compatible word-processing program (Windows or Macintosh) can customize them.

This Section of the *Teacher's Guide and Answer Key*

The remainder of this section presents practical suggestions and support materials for using a number of assessment strategies, including portfolios, journals, notebooks, performance assessment, open-ended questions, presentations, projects, and tests and quizzes. The discussion of each strategy includes at least one specific example of how an *Advanced Algebra* teacher used that assessment technique, together with any evaluation forms or rubrics the teacher created. Many strategies are cross-referenced with David Clarke's *Constructive Assessment in Mathematics*.

A word of caution, though: Be careful about trying new assessment strategies. Don't try to do too much too fast. Assessment should enhance the quality of your interactions with students, not tire you out. Fortunately, the discovery approach and the diversity of tasks in *Advanced Algebra* make constructive assessment possible without sacrificing too much instructional time or too much of your personal time. Before proceeding to discuss individual techniques, let's take a quick look at some strategies for optimizing the time you spend on assessment.

Strategies for Saving Teacher Time and Work

Teaching can be a very time-consuming job. Many of us face larger and more challenging classes than ever. For this reason, using new assessment techniques can sometimes feel more like an extra burden than like an interesting opportunity to learn more about our students. With this in mind, here are some time-saving tips for how you can spend less time on assessment and involve your students in assessment work. You will see specific examples of how teachers have used some of these strategies when we discuss individual assessment strategies.

1. ***Don't always collect material from every student. Instead, select a random subset of material to read or grade.***

   Strategy 1: Roll a die. Collect work only from the row or group that corresponds to the number on the die. This strategy works especially well if your classroom has six rows, six columns, or six groups. Students love to be the one to roll the die, and because the outcome is random they need to be prepared to show their work at any time. It's a good way to teach about probability and sampling. You can also use a random number generator as discussed in Section 8.1.

   This strategy works well for evaluating homework, notebooks, and journals. You can also use it to pick a sample group of students for a particular performance assessment task.

   Strategy 2: Use playing cards to assign groups, then collect work from students or groups at random by choosing a card. To assign groups, hand each student a card as he or she enters the classroom and display the seating chart on the overhead projector (showing where the aces sit, and so on). You might need to watch out for illicit card swapping. Once students have found their places, fill in their names on the seating chart, with each student's card designated alongside his or her name. (Even better, have a student fill out the seating chart.) To use the cards to call on people, just shuffle the deck and have a student pick a card. In this way you can randomly call on individuals ("Two of hearts, it's your turn"), groups ("I want to look at notebooks from the nines today"), or individuals from each group ("I want the hearts from each group to present their group's solution to this problem"). It's also easy to adjust the probabilities by taking cards out of the deck or by shuffling in more cards from a second deck.

   Strategy 3: Have each group turn in only one written response to an assigned task. This strategy could reduce the number of items you read from thirty to six. To ensure individual accountability, you might require each student in the group to be responsible for different parts of the task. For example, give a four-question group quiz, and have the first student in each group responsible for the response to the first question, the second student responsible for the second question, and so on.

An alternative strategy is to let the students know that only one of the quizzes will be selected at random to be collected and graded. This technique makes the quizzes a little faster to grade and requires each student to put his or her best effort into the entire quiz.

Strategy 4: Inform each group that you are going to look at the work of only one member of their group. You will select the work randomly. Some teachers have every student put work in the middle of the group's table, then go around the room drawing one piece of work randomly from each pile. Other teachers have students paper-clip together work from their group and then use some random process to determine which number in the pile to read. Teachers find this strategy helps promote cooperation because it encourages students to make sure every member of their group produces good work.

Some teachers use these strategies to assign grades. Although this practice can work well, be careful about assigning grades to individuals based on the work of the whole group or another student in the group. You might want to describe this strategy first to parents and administrators—and certainly to students—before you plan to use it. Make sure the task really requires group cooperation and could not be done easily by individuals so that the purpose of the group effort and shared group grades is more meaningful to students.

2. ***Don't read everything from a given assignment. Instead, select a random subset of material to read or grade.***
   Find a part of the assignment or problem that you think is crucial, important, or interesting and simply skip over the rest. Open-ended questions and research questions are especially good choices to focus on. Let students know that you will do this, but don't tell them ahead of time which part or problem you are going to look at. This strategy works well with homework, notebooks, and journal entries.

3. ***Observe students working in cooperative groups instead of individually.***
   We know that there are many reasons to have students work cooperatively, but we don't often realize that it can save us assessment time. Teachers find that observing groups discuss a problem or project gives them insight into what the students understand. By the time they collect any written material from a group, teachers claim they often already have a good idea how they will evaluate this material because of the assessment they accomplished as they observed students during class time. (Think how little you learn about your students' mathematical understanding as they take individual tests silently.) For suggestions on recording

your insights, see David Clarke's section on observational assessment in Part 2 of *Constructive Assessment in Mathematics.*

4. *Have each student assess herself or himself.*
Self-assessment can be as simple as having students correct a traditional quiz or test against an answer key and figure out their own grade. Remember, even if you choose not to "count" the grade itself, you and the student have still gathered information about the student's understanding of the material. Hint: Before students correct their own quizzes, have them put away the pencils they used in taking the quiz. Then hand out colored pencils or pens to use in correcting the work. Because their original responses will still be identifiable, this method allows them to put in corrections.

Some teachers have students determine their own grades for an entire project or even an entire unit, usually with the understanding that the teacher has the last say and may change the grade. Students must defend their suggestion for their grade in writing and possibly also by demonstrating their mathematical knowledge in a portfolio of work.

Before using this method, you need to consider what you will do if you disagree with a student's self-determined grade and feel obliged to exercise your prerogative to change it. In such cases, communication is essential to prevent resentment on the part of the student. You will need to explain your decision, perhaps in writing or through a brief one-on-one conference with the student. Also, you may find that good students tend to be harder on themselves than you would be, whereas poor students may be more lenient. Because of the work you will be putting into communicating with students about their self-grading, this particular technique may not be a time-saving device. Of course, you may choose to use it for other reasons.

5. *Have students assess one another.*
Peer assessment can result in tricky group dynamics, so use it with caution. It can work very well with the right group of students if the class establishes an atmosphere of fairness. Students often evaluate one another using either unfairly high standards or unnecessarily low standards, so watch out for these tendencies. You'll need to provide some guidance and examples to help them strike a balance.

Strategy 1: Have different groups evaluate each other. You can have groups exchange work or have each group evaluate the group on their right. It's a good idea to use a rubric, especially if the evaluation is an important one. You might design the rubric together as a class. This strategy can work well for any sort of group project, group presentation, or open-ended response.

Strategy 2: Have a sample of students evaluate a presentation, project, or other assignment, but have each of these students respond as an individual, without discussing their feedback together. It may be best to keep these responses anonymous, and you might decide that you will be the only one to read them. Because many students are sensitive about having others see their work, you might also elect to have students mark their papers with an identification number—such as their school ID numbers or numbers you assign—rather than their names to keep the papers themselves, as well as the evaluators' responses, anonymous.

You can also collect individual response forms from everyone but select only a random sample to read. Sometimes it works best to have a selected but rotating "jury" responsible for evaluations. The class could even select the jury itself. Beware of having everyone in a class evaluate everyone else individually, since this could result in $30 \cdot 30 = 900$ evaluations and will not save you time at all! Of course, make it clear that you have the last say about the final evaluation or grade.

Strategy 3: Students can assess each other by deciding as a group how to split up a certain allotted number of points among their group members. This strategy works better if the number of total points is not divisible by the number of students in the group so that students must choose at least one student who deserves more points than the others. It's best to have students justify their allotment of points in writing. This strategy works well for evaluating any assessment done cooperatively. Teachers often count these points as only a part of the evaluation or grade.

Strategy 4: Have other group members "sign off" on a student's work to record that a certain task or set of tasks is complete. For a specific example of how a teacher used this strategy, see the sample notebook assessment forms later in this section. This strategy helps promote honesty and accountability among each group of students and also saves you time.

6. ***Have students write their own assessments.***
   Students can learn a lot from designing their own test questions, open-ended problems, and projects. The assessments also feel less arbitrary to students if they have a hand in making them. You will want to have the students design the corresponding answer key or rubric. You will definitely need to look over the student suggestions before assigning them, so this strategy may not be a big time-saver. Be aware that students typically design assessment items that are harder than the ones you would have made.

Portfolios

What Is a Portfolio?

Following the example of professional artists, the use of portfolios has blossomed in education, initially in the field of writing. Mathematics teachers have learned from their English teacher colleagues that an emphasis on revising work until it is good enough to put into the portfolio focuses students' attention on taking responsibility for the quality of their work in ways that they otherwise might not have contemplated.

The word *portfolio* means different things to different people. Most people use the word to signal a purposeful selection of student work, in contrast to a cumulative folder or notebook. As David Clarke indicates in *Constructive Assessment in Mathematics,* there are two major kinds of portfolios—developmental and standards-based. The purpose of the developmental portfolio is to show growth or development over time. The purpose of a standards-based portfolio is to show accomplishment. It's possible to combine these goals, but it's important to be clear with students what their goals are as they collect their work. The description of portfolios at the end of Chapter 2 in *Advanced Algebra* is open enough to allow you to use this assessment tool however you'd like to.

Where to Learn More About Portfolios

David Clarke discusses portfolios in the Assessment Activities section in Part 2 of *Constructive Assessment in Mathematics.* His discussion includes a description of the system developed by New Standards, a cooperative effort by a number of states and localities to create a standards-based portfolio. Also see the end of Chapter 2 in *Advanced Algebra.*

Hints for Using Portfolios

First, you will want to think about the way you organize your course and what you are trying to accomplish. If you want students to focus on how *Advanced Algebra* approaches the study of algebraic concepts, you may want to specify categories for their portfolios that correspond to the different kinds of assignments they will encounter and tell them that their portfolio should include one of each type: project, investigation, test, homework, chapter review, Take Another Look, Geometer's Sketchpad investigation. If you want students to focus on the way this course contributes to their overall development in mathematics, you may want to specify categories for their portfolios that correspond with more general standards for mathematics learning, such as the New Standards categories described more fully in the Clarke book: conceptual understanding, problem solving, putting mathematics to work (projects), skills, and communication.

Name _____ Period _____ Date _____

For all problems you are expected to show your work. If you use your calculator, you must still show equations that you enter or other procedures that you use. Full credit will not be given if you only provide an answer without an explanation of how you got your answer.

1. a. Give an example of an arithmetic sequence in which 5 and 59 are both terms. Justify your answer.

    b. List the first four terms of an arithmetic sequence in which 2 is the first term and 83 is the tenth term.

2. Give an example of a problem or situation that involves geometric sequences. Make it clear!

3. Consider the sequence 1, 1, 1, ...

    a. Explain why it is arithmetic.

    b. Explain why it is geometric.

4. You have a decision to make as to what to do with $10,000. Here are your options:

    i. Your current car has only about 2 years left in it and virtually no trade-in value, so you can use the money to buy a new car now—no loans, just pay cash for it.

    ii. You can put the money into a bank account earning 3.75% annual interest, compounded quarterly. Then in 2 years, you can buy the car. (Inflation for the next 2 years is expected to be about 3.5% compounded yearly.)

    iii. You can use $5,000 as a down payment on the car, financing the balance due at 6.4% interest over 5 years, and put the remainder into a savings account earning 3.75% annual interest, compounded quarterly.

    What would you do? Justify your answer completely and state any assumptions that you make.

5. Consider the sequence defined by $u_n = \begin{cases} a & n=1 \\ \left(u_{(n-1)}\right)^2 & n>1 \end{cases}$.

    a. If $a = 4$, what are the first five terms of this sequence?

    b. If $a = 1$, what are the first five terms?

    c. If $a = 0.999$, what are the first five terms?

    d. For each of the a-values in parts a–c, explain what happens to the terms in the long run.

Name _____ **Period** _____ **Date** _____

For all problems you are expected to show your work. If you use your calculator, you must still show equations that you enter or other procedures that you use. Full credit will not be given if you only provide an answer without an explanation of how you got your answer.

1. Consider this formula for a sequence: $u_n = 5n - 4$.
   a. Name the first five terms of this sequence.
   b. Is this sequence arithmetic, geometric, both, or neither? Justify your answer.
   c. Does the formula $u_n = 5n - 4$ define a sequence recursively or explicitly? Justify your answer.
   d. If you were to graph this sequence, what would the graph look like? Justify your answer (and not by graphing it!).

2. In your new job your annual salary will be $18,000. Each year you can expect a 4% raise.
   a. How much will your annual salary be in 10 years?
   b. What will be your total earnings in this 10-year period?
   c. How long will you work at this job before you have earned 1 million dollars?

Advanced Algebra Through Data Exploration: Quizzes, Tests, and Exams
©1998 by Key Curriculum Press

Name _____ **Period** _____ **Date** _____

For all problems you are expected to show your work. If you use your calculator, you must still show equations that you enter or other procedures that you use. Full credit will not be given if you only provide an answer without an explanation of how you got your answer.

1. Write a convincing argument explaining why $\sqrt{A^2 + B^2} \neq A + B$.

2. Find $\sqrt[4]{228886641}$.

3. Rewrite $(1.25)^5$ in fraction form.

4. Evaluate $\dfrac{2x + y}{x + y}$ for $x = 14.6$ and $y = 1.8$.

5. If $A = 4.2$, $B = 5.62$, and $C = 10.9$,

   a. find $\dfrac{-B + \sqrt{B^2 - 4AC}}{2A}$ (or describe the dilemma).

   b. find $\dfrac{-B - \sqrt{B^2 - 4AC}}{2A}$ (or describe the dilemma).

6. a. Sketch a graph of $y = -1.5x^2 + 7$, and name a good viewing window.

   b. Find the corresponding y-values when $x = 3, 5,$ and -13.

Name _____ **Period** _____ **Date** _____

For all problems you are expected to show your work. If you use your calculator, you must still show equations that you enter or other procedures that you use. Full credit will not be given if you only provide an answer without an explanation of how you got your answer.

For each sequence named in Problems 1–3, identify the sequence as arithmetic, geometric, or neither. Then find the indicated term.

1. 29, 18, 7, $^-$4, ... Find the eighth term.

2. 5, $^-$5, 5, $^-$5, ... Find the 102nd term.

3. $1, \frac{1}{2}, \frac{1}{3}, \frac{1}{4}, \ldots$. Find the tenth term.

4. Suppose $1,000 is deposited into an account that earns 5.5% annually.

a. If the interest is compounded monthly, what is the monthly rate?

b. Write a recursive routine that provides the monthly balances.

c. Find the balance after 2 months. Find the balance after 2 years.

Advanced Algebra Through Data Exploration: Quizzes, Tests, and Exams
©1998 by Key Curriculum Press

Name _____ **Period** _____ **Date** _____

For all problems you are expected to show your work. If you use your calculator, you must still show equations that you enter or other procedures that you use. Full credit will not be given if you only provide an answer without an explanation of how you got your answer.

1. List the first five terms of the sequence defined by $u_n = \begin{cases} -2 & n=1 \\ -4\left(u_{(n-1)}\right)+3 & n>1 \end{cases}$.

2. Find S_{12} for the sequence 0.5, 1.5, 4.5, ...

3. Leif Raker has a problem. It's fall, the leaves are falling, and he has fallen behind in his leaf-raking chores. He estimates that 30,000 leaves are covering his front lawn. With his new rake he can rake and dispose of 30% of the leaves each day. Unfortunately, 3000 new leaves fall every day. He has a little over a month before it starts to snow and the leaves stop falling. If there are no more than 4000 leaves by the time it starts to snow, Leif thinks that he can get all of the leaves raked. Do you think Leif will win the "battle of the leaves"? Explain why or why not.

Chapter 1 Test

Form A

Name _____   Period _____   Date _____

For all problems you are expected to show your work. If you use your calculator, you must still show equations that you enter or other procedures that you use. Full credit will not be given if you only provide an answer without an explanation of how you got your answer.

1. To build a solid staircase, Bill Ditt must stack cement blocks as shown at the right. List the number of cement blocks in the top row, second row, third row, . . . , tenth row.

    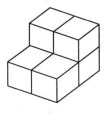

    a. Write a recursive routine for the terms of the sequence you wrote above.

    b. If the steps are to be 22 layers high, and each block weighs 5 pounds, how much will the stairs weigh?

    c. If a city ordinance allows stairs to weigh no more than 2000 pounds, how many "levels" can there be?

2. Consider the sequence 1120, 560, 280, ...

    a. Is this sequence arithmetic or geometric? Justify your response.

    b. What is the ninth term of the sequence?

    c. Which term (if any) is the first term that is less than 0.1?

    d. Find S_{10}.

    e. Make an educated guess as to what S_{100} is. Justify your guess.

3. Suppose $100,000 is invested in an account that pays 6.75% annual interest compounded monthly.

    a. How much will be in the account after 10 years?

    b. Suppose instead that an additional $100 is added to the account every month just after the interest is compounded. Now what would be the balance after 10 years?

4. Suppose a mortgage of $100,000 is to be paid off in exactly 30 years. At 9.25% annual interest, what will be the monthly payment?

5. There are 220 million people living in the United States. Each year about 3% of these people die or leave the country. Also each year the population increases by 8.1 million people due to births and immigration. If this pattern continues, what will be the population in 5 years? What will be the population in the long run?

Advanced Algebra Through Data Exploration: Quizzes, Tests, and Exams
©1998 by Key Curriculum Press

Second, you will want to think about your standards for students. Are you interested in their progress, in their level of accomplishment, or both? If you're interested in progress, you'll need to get students to gather baseline data in the first month or two of the course so that they can show growth over time. If you're interested more in their accomplishment, you may want to wait until most students can identify their best work according to criteria you have discussed with them.

Comparison of Developmental and Standards-Based Portfolios

	Developmental portfolio	Standards-based portfolio
Purpose	Shows growth over time	Shows accomplishment
Entries	• Early work that establishes students' performance baselines • Benchmark items that demonstrate best performance to date	• Sample work in described areas of performance, such as problem solving, that show mastery • Commentaries that show how the performance descriptions are reflected in the work samples

Portfolios are especially useful for collecting examples of artwork and write-ups of extended projects. Students will be more motivated to revise work if they have already invested significant time in it or if it represents original thinking or a unique form of expression. In contrast to recopying homework assignments to correct answers or to improve their appearance, *revision* involves testing the work against expressed standards of completeness, depth, clarity, and logical organization, as well as accuracy and neatness. The revision process allows students to capture the insights they have *after* the bulk of the assignment is completed, perhaps after class discussion. It promotes pride, fosters retention of the concepts involved, and more accurately mirrors a real-world work process.

If you want students to consider revising work before they include it in their portfolios, you'll want to list, explain, and give examples that meet the criteria you'd like them to apply during the revision process. You may want to prepare a handout listing your criteria as a guide for assembling the portfolio as a whole or as an entry slip to accompany each student work sample included in the portfolio.

Constructive Assessment in Mathematics lists and comments on the three types of exhibits (work samples) of the New Standards portfolio system—conceptual understanding, problem solving, and putting mathematics to work (projects)—as well as a "virtual exhibit," which is essentially an index of skills and styles of communication to be found in work samples entered in the first three exhibits.

The New Standards system suggests that a file be kept for each student containing one folder for each of the four exhibits and a fifth work-in-progress folder. The sample forms at the end of this discussion of portfolios include a New Standards entry slip for the **Conceptual Understanding Exhibit for Functions and Algebra.** Also provided are additional entry slips you can use or adapt for **Development Portfolios and Standards-Based Portfolios.**

To provide motivation and closure for the effort of assembling portfolios, you may want to provide an opportunity for students to share portfolios or for parents to see them. The **Portfolio Review Form** is one that you can use or adapt for students' peer critiques, for parents' viewing, or for your own evaluation.

Conceptual Understanding Exhibit

Name _____ Date _____

Functions and Algebra

Enter two or three pieces of evidence that show you understand the concepts listed below. Identify the concept or group of concepts for which you are providing evidence. Show that you can use the concepts to solve problems.

_____ Model given situations with linear, exponential, or quadratic functions and interpret given functions in terms of situations.

_____ Work with functions: evaluate, find slope, find local maxima and minima.

_____ Use arithmetic and geometic sequences.

_____ Define and use variables, parameters, constants, and unknowns in work with both functions and equations.

_____ Solve equations both symbolically and graphically, especially linear, quadratic, and exponential equations.

_____ Represent functional relationships in formulas, tables, and graphs, and translate among them.

_____ Represent the structure of the number system algebraically.

_____ Use equations to represent curves such as lines, circles, ellipses, and parabolas.

_____ Use functions to represent patterns.

Show your understanding of variables and state the relationship between variables as a function. For example, you might: describe the relationship using words and a labeled diagram, formulate the function algebraically, give numerical examples in a table and graph the function, discuss the behavior of the function.

Title of Piece   **Circumstances (Mark all that apply.)**   **Where Is It?**

_____ Alone   _____ Group   _____ Here (attached)

_____ Homework _____ w/feedback   _____ Not Here. Look in

_____ Other   Exhibit _____

                                                                          Entry _____

_____ Alone   _____ Group   _____ Here (attached)

_____ Homework _____ w/feedback   _____ Not Here. Look in

_____ Other   Exhibit _____

                                                                          Entry _____

_____ Alone   _____ Group   _____ Here (attached)

_____ Homework _____ w/feedback   _____ Not Here. Look in

_____ Other   Exhibit _____

                                                                          Entry _____

From *New Standards™ High School Mathematics Portfolio.* © 1995 by National Center on Education and the Economy. Used by permission.

Developmental Portfolio   **Benchmark Entry Slip**

Name _____ Date _____

The title of the work I am replacing _____

Its date _____

The title of this new entry is _____

This entry shows that I understand these concepts:

1.

2.

3.

This entry is an improvement over the one it replaces in these categories:

     Accuracy   Clarity of communication

     Depth   Logical organization

     Completeness   Appearance

My comments on the effort or creativity I put into this entry:

I credit these people for helping me with this entry:

Standards-Based Portfolio

Performance Area Entry Slip

Name _____ Date _____

Title of this entry _____

This entry is evidence of my work in this performance area:

Recursive sequences and series	Functions
Explicit sequences and series	Parametric equations
Discrete mathematics	Trigonometry
Patterns	Exponential functions
Statistics	Logarithmic functions
Probability	Polynomials
Data analysis	Inverse functions
Investigations	Systems of equations

This entry is a good example of my work in this performance area because

Using numbers from 1 (low performance) to 5 (high performance), I rate my work on this entry according to these criteria:

Accuracy	Clarity of communication
Depth	Logical organization
Completeness	Appearance
Planning	Creativity

I credit _____ for helping me with this work.

The kind of help I got was

Portfolio Review Form

Date _____

I have examined the portfolio prepared by _____

In my opinion, the best entry is

_____

because

Overall, the strong points of this portfolio seem to be

There could be some improvement in

The effort of assembling this portfolio was worthwhile because

Signed _____

Print name _____

Journals

What Is a Journal?

A journal is a place where students can record and reflect on their experience learning math. Students can use their journals to express frustrations and anxieties, as well as pride in their accomplishments. They can write freely and privately about concerns regarding other people in the class or in their lives, and they can also record interesting and valuable mathematical ideas. Students who are quiet in class can be quite expressive in their journals, thus giving you a chance to get to know them. Teachers also find that journal writing can help relieve math anxiety.

Where to Learn More About Journals

The student text introduces journal writing at the end of Chapter 1. David Clarke describes using journals in Part 2 of *Constructive Assessment in Mathematics.*

Hints for Assigning Journal Prompts

Have students write in their journals regularly, but keep in mind that you will need to read their responses—and that takes time. Some teachers have found that reserving the last 15 minutes or so of class on Friday for writing in journals provides students with an opportunity to reflect on their week of mathematics learning. (See the form following this discussion for an example of one teacher's weekly journal prompts.) Other teachers find that one journal entry per unit is all they have time to read. Even having students reflect on their learning a few times a year can provide you with some valuable assessment of your students' feelings and thoughts.

There are many ways of storing student journals. If you have students fill out forms for their entries (such as the one shown in Clarke's book or the ones available on the next few pages), have a folder for each student where they store these forms. You can also have students use a special notebook. It helps to have a specific place in your classroom where students know they can find their journals so that they can read them and write in them any time they wish. Some teachers have students use part of their class notebook as their journal. This way students can write in their journal at any time, even when they are not in their math classroom.

One teacher used the **Sample Journal Entry Form for the Beginning of the Year** for one of the first few days of school. The intention of the form was to gather information about each student, as well as to get students accustomed to writing down their feelings about a math class. The form asks for students' birthdays because the teacher kept track of them during the year and used them in story problems. **The Sample Weekly Journal Prompts** form was used for weekly journal entries. If students are writing in notebook journals, you could show these prompts on the overhead instead of handing them out. You might not require students to respond to every prompt, but have them use the prompts as suggestions to help them start writing.

Some teachers prefer to have more precise journal prompts, often that relate specifically to mathematics content ("Summarize what your group learned today from Investigation 1.4.1"). Others prefer vague prompts, with the intention of simply getting students to express their feelings ("What could you have done this past week to help yourself learn more algebra?").

Since writing is difficult for many students, let your students know that journal entries can include pictures, diagrams, and concept maps. Some teachers make it clear that they are not concerned about spelling and grammar in journals. Other teachers use journal writing as an opportunity to help students improve their writing skills and practice correct spelling and grammar.

Hints for Reading and Assessing Journals

In order for students to feel comfortable expressing themselves honestly, it's best not to grade journals. But you do need to read them. Reading every student journal can be very time-consuming if your students write in them frequently. Nevertheless, some teachers find journal reading so worthwhile that they choose to spend time this way rather than on other tasks (for example, checking over homework).

You don't need to read every journal entry, and if students' journals become truly personal there may be some entries they will not want you to read. You could have students highlight one entry per month that they especially want you to see.

Sample Journal Entry Form for the Beginning of the Year

Name _____ Date of birth _____

Home phone _____

Favorite food _____

Favorite TV show _____

Favorite school subject _____

Career goal _____

Someone in class that you wish to be in a group with sometime during the year:

Someone in class that you wish never to be in a group with during the year:

Do you have difficulty hearing or seeing or have some other special needs
that I should know about? Explain.

What do you like a math teacher to do in a math class?

What do you hate for a math teacher to do in a math class?

How can your math teacher be more helpful?

Complete the sentence below (tell me something that happened and how you felt about it).

One time in a math class . . .

Sample Weekly Journal Prompts

My name is

_____

My fellow group members are

_____

Journal entry for the week of _____ to

_____

The most important mathematical concept I learned this week is

A question I still have about what we investigated this week is

Something I think my group did well this week is

The group behavior or social skill I would like to see my group work to improve is

Notebooks

What Is a Notebook?

The students' notebooks are where they organize important mathematical ideas. Students should bring their notebooks to class every day and should have them outside of class to use for homework.

Where to Learn More About Notebooks

The student text contains suggestions for organizing notebooks at the end of Chapter 0.

Hints for Assessing Notebooks

An organized notebook helps students think more clearly and work more carefully. For this reason many teachers find it worthwhile to evaluate student notebooks in order to show that they are an important part of the course. Making sure that students keep organized notebooks can be a big nuisance for a teacher. Here is a strategy one *Advanced Algebra* teacher used: During review work at the end of a unit or at the end of a semester, he had students work in groups on review material. This freed him up to interview individual students about their notebooks. He required the students to present their notebooks and demonstrate that they had fulfilled certain requirements. For example, he might require a summary for each chapter, check the notebook for overall neatness, correct homework assignments, review complete investigations, assign projects, or check important handouts. He did not ask to see every item from every student, but rather examined a sample of each student's work.

Another teacher required that each notebook consist of a folder divided into four sections: one section for notes and homework, one for group work, one for projects, and one for investigations. This teacher then created very specific forms for evaluating student notebooks every six weeks. The *Advanced Algebra* **Notebook Evaluation Sheet** that follows is a sample of one of these forms. Notice that the form includes writing requirements and, in this way, is similar to a journal. Notice also that this teacher saves herself time by making fellow students responsible for verifying that a notebook meets certain requirements.

Another teacher has a more elaborate list of sections for notebooks: (1) Notes and Chapter Summaries, (2) Investigations, (3) Tests and Quizzes, (4) Projects and Other Activities, (5) Journal Entries, and (6) Homework, Warm-ups, and Classwork. This teacher finds the Investigations section especially valuable. The students do each investigation in a lab write-up format including the hypothesis, procedure, data collection, and conclusions.

Advanced Algebra Notebook Evaluation Sheet
(For first six-week grading period)

Name _____ Date _____ Period _____

Group members' names _____

Homework/notes section	Ch 0	Ch 1	Ch 2	Two group members sign-off	
HW assignments completed	_____	_____	_____	(initials) _____	(initials) _____
Number of HW assignments	(3)	(7)	(7)	(points) _____ (40)	(points) _____ (40)

Investigations section	Ch 0	Ch 1	Ch 2	Two group members sign-off	
Investigations completed	_____	_____	_____	(initials) _____	(initials) _____
Number of investigations	(3)	(7)	(5)	(points) _____ (40)	(points) _____ (40)

Chapter 0 investigations: 0.1.1: Cross-Number Puzzle; 0.1.2: Camel Crossing the Desert; 0.2.1: Fractions and Decimal Numbers

Chapter 1 investigations: 1.1.1: Shifting Funds; 1.2.1: Pyramid Investment Plan; 1.2.2: Investing with Meg Abux; 1.3.1: Color Concentration; 1.4.1: Uncle Scrooge's Investment; 1.5.1: The Tower of Hanoi; 1.6.1: Wheat on a Chessboard

Chapter 2 investigations: 2.2.1: Arithmetic Series Formula; 2.2.2: Toothpick Trapezoids; 2.3.1: Bouncing a Superball; 2.4.1: Explicit Geometric Series; 2.5.1: Counting Beans

Select your "best" section from Chapter 1 and your best section from Chapter 2. Write an essay for each section on a separate sheet of paper, explaining what makes the section your best section of that chapter. Describe what you did in each of your best sections. What did you learn? Give an example of how to use or apply what you learned in the section. What do you mean by "best"? Is it your best because it was easy or because it was interesting or useful?

Best section in Chapter 1: _____ Points for Chapter 1 essay _____ (10)

Best section in Chapter 2: _____ Points for Chapter 2 essay _____ (10)

Notebook grade _____ (100)/grade

Performance Assessment

What Is Performance Assessment?

Some skills are difficult to assess by simply looking at the product of your students' work. Instead, you can learn more about the students' understanding by observing the *process* they use when carrying out a particular task. This is especially true of physical tasks like measuring or constructing. It's also true of investigations, where you want to see not only what conjectures students make but also how they arrived at the conjectures.

Where to Learn More About Performance Assessment

The student text introduces performance assessment at the end of Chapter 3. Although *Constructive Assessment in Mathematics* does not have a specific section devoted to performance assessment, the section on observational assessment offers suggestions relevant to carrying out performance assessment.

Hints for Using Performance Assessment

The **Sample Performance Assessment Tasks** list contains some appropriate performance tasks an *Advanced Algebra* teacher used. The list is simply a collection of examples, so feel free to add to it or change it. You can assign tasks like these to groups of students, or you can assign them to individuals. You can evaluate students' completion of each task by simply checking it off on a checklist, or you can grade their performance using more detailed criteria. Your assessment method will depend on what you think is important and what you have time for. Since the material on this list spans most of the *Advanced Algebra* curriculum, you could hand out a list of this kind near the beginning of the year and let students know they should be able to do any task on the list by the end of the year.

The student text contains plenty of ideas for performance assessment tasks, so don't feel you need to make them up yourself. Look at the projects, the Take Another Look problems, Geometer's Sketchpad investigations, and the section investigations and problem sets.

To avoid competition among students, some teachers choose not to assign each student or group of students the same task. You could assign tasks randomly or allow students to pick the one they think they can perform best.

Be careful about putting individual students on the spot. It might be best not to require individuals to perform tasks before the entire class, although you no doubt have a few students who would love to do so. For more suggestions on having students present to the entire class, see the discussion of presentations later in this section.

Sample Performance Assessment Tasks

- Give students two different salary plans or two different loan-payoff strategies, and have them analyze them and find advantages of one or both of the plans. (Chapter 1)

- Have students make a physical model with sticks or strips of paper that shows the sum of infinite geometric sequence with r less than 1 is finite. (Chapter 2)

- Give students the scores from last year's basketball season or the school PSAT scores, and have them prepare a report complete with statistical measures and graphs. (Chapter 3)

- Given a set of data, students should find a best-fit line and give a real-world meaning to the slope and one of the intercepts. (Chapter 4)

- Have students make a face or some other simple picture on graph paper using each of the five functions at least once and applying each of the transformations. Write the equations of each of the functions in the picture. (Chapter 5)

- Given a map of their state, have students calculate the course direction and time needed to fly a small plane at 250 mph between two cities. (Chapter 6)

- Give students data from the city, county, state, or some other near region that is exponential, and have them prepare a presentation, posters, models, and predictions for that data. (Chapter 7)

- Have the students create a carnival game and analyze the probability of winning. (Chapter 8)

- Have students explain several methods of solving a system of linear equations. (Chapter 9)

- Given a piece of graph paper, have students find the largest volume box they can create and show using an equation that their box is the largest. (Chapter 10)

- Have students determine the number of trials and the probability of success given a histogram of binomially distributed data. (Chapter 11)

- Have students make a picture titled "The Park" on graph paper using each of the five curves (circle, ellipse, parabola, hyperbola, rational) at least once. Write the equations of each curve appearing in the graph. (Chapter 12)

- Have students find the distance to some distant or high object, such as the height of the peak of the gymnasium ceiling from two points on the bleachers, by indirect measurement using the Law of Cosines or the Law of Sines. (Chapter 13)

Open-Ended Questions

What Is an Open-Ended Question?

An open-ended question has more than one correct answer. It is worth distinguishing between truly open-ended questions and open-response questions. An open-response question probably does have a best solution, but different paths of reasoning can be followed to arrive at the solution. Students need to make intelligent assumptions and use logical reasoning to solve open-ended and open-response questions. Because most problems students come across in their everyday lives will not have a single correct answer, or a single method of finding an answer, the ability to solve these kinds of questions is an important skill.

Where to Learn More About Open-Ended Questions

The sections marked Take Another Look in the student text contain open-ended questions. The student text introduces the Take Another Look questions at the end of Chapter 4.

Although *Constructive Assessment in Mathematics* does not have a specific section devoted to open-ended questions, the section "Establishing the Criteria for Quality Mathematics Performance" in Part 3 describes one way of assigning and assessing an open-ended question.

Hints for Assigning and Assessing Open-Ended Questions

Encourage students to provide thorough and well-written answers to open-ended questions. Give students ample time to respond to these questions, and don't assign too many at a time.

Don't formally grade open-ended responses until your students are comfortable with your expectations. You might want to first evaluate, or have students evaluate, a few open-ended questions before assigning a question that you plan to grade.

To describe the attributes of a good response, you might want to show students one of the sample rubrics from the following pages. You can have students respond individually to open-ended questions, but they also make excellent group problems.

A teacher assigned **A Sample Open-Response Question: Two Perspectives of Sequences and Series** following Chapter 2. The teacher created a rubric for "Two Perspectives of Sequences and Series" to evaluate the students' methods of analyzing and solving the problem, as well as the correctness of their conclusion. The teacher based the form on his experiences with previous student responses to the same question because it is difficult to make such a detailed rubric the first time you assign such a problem. Each group of students in the class was required to turn in a single response to the problem. Students did not see the assessment form ahead of time. When the teacher graded responses, he recorded the same grade for each student in a group. He weighted the grade the same as a traditional quiz grade.

Advanced Algebra contains plenty of open-ended problems. You will always find open-ended problems in the Take Another Look sections and sometimes in the problem sets. Many of the projects can be treated like open-ended questions. Some *Advanced Algebra* teachers require students to write up and turn in a certain number of Take Another Look problems as part of a unit exam or a semester exam. This guarantees that students perform some open-ended work at least every unit or every semester.

Using rubrics to assess responses to open-ended questions can be difficult at first, but the task becomes easier with experience. When you're starting out you might try grading with other teachers at your school, if you have appropriate and willing colleagues. Note also that it isn't necessary to provide a rubric as elaborate and detailed as the one that goes with this teacher example. Some general rubrics for evaluating open-ended questions follow this more specific one.

A Sample Open-Response Question: Two Perspectives of Sequences and Series

Group names _____

You have finished Chapter 2 and have studied sequences from two perspectives. Explain the differences between recursive definitions and explicit formulas and why you need to learn about both. You are free to give examples as needed. I expect the paper to be *at least* a page in length, and yes, spelling and grammar do count. This is not a group assignment, but you may talk to other people about your ideas.

Assessing "Two Perspectives of Sequences and Series"

1. Mathematical correctness   Points

No errors in the calculations	5
Minor errors or omissions in calculations	3
Significant errors in calculations or calculations not shown	1
No calculations included	0

2. Explanation of differences

Proper terms used, clear and concise explanations	5
Explanations somewhat confusing or incomplete	3
Does not demonstrate an understanding of the differences	1
No explanation attempted	0

3. Statement of need to learn both types of formulas

Clear explanation of a need to learn each type	5
Only one type justified	3
Some reason given for learning formulas in general but not specific to the types	1
No reasons given for learning formulas	0

4. Definitions of formula types

Definitions clear, uses mathematical language correctly but are not simple copies of textbook definitions, also explains in their own words	5
Terms defined but does not make use of mathematical language or just copies from the textbook, does not include explanation in their own words	3
Definitions unclear, not correct, but attempted	1
No definitions given	0

5. Thoroughness of answer

Both arithmetic and geometric examples are discussed, series and sequences of both types are used	5
Both arithmetic and geometric examples are discussed, does not use both series and sequences	3
Discusses only one type, arithmetic or geometric	1
Discusses only one type, arithmetic or geometric, sequence or series	0

TOTAL POSSIBLE POINTS   **25**

     SUGGESTIONS FOR ASSESSMENT

Sample Form for Evaluating a Response to an Open-Ended Question

Name _____

I have indicated my rating in each criterion with a mark somewhere on the number line.

Did you investigate the problem completely?

|———————————————————————————|
Incomplete   Complete

Comments:

Did you communicate your ideas clearly?

|———————————————————————————|
Unclear and confusing   Clear and articulate

Comments:

Did you use mathematics correctly and appropriately?

|———————————————————————————|
Incorrectly used   Correctly used

Comments:

Did you include original or creative insights into the problem?

|———————————————————————————|
No original thoughts   Includes several original thoughts

Comments:

Overall grade and additional comments:

Sample Rubric for Evaluating a Response to an Open-Ended Problem

This rubric shows descriptions of responses at levels 5, 3, 1, and 0.

A 4 is somewhere between a 5 and a 3, and a 2 is somewhere between a 1 and a 3.

5: A superior response

Completeness
  - Is complete in responding to all aspects of the problem
  - Focuses on all the important elements of the problem

Understanding
  - Shows mathematical understanding of the problem's ideas and requirements
  - Includes only minor computational errors, if any
  - Shows strong reasoning

Presentation/Communication
  - Includes examples or diagrams when appropriate
  - Communicates ideas effectively

Creativity
  - Offers a unique explanation or representation of the problem

3: An adequate response

Completeness
  - Is not totally complete in responding to all aspects of the problem

Understanding
  - Shows some deficiencies in understanding aspects of the problem
  - Indicates some understanding of required mathematical ideas, but misconceptions are evident
  - May present information that is only partially correct
  - Exhibits incomplete reasoning
  - Contains computation errors, either major or minor

Presentation/Communication
  - Is somewhat confusing or unclear
  - May include examples or diagrams that are unclear or inappropriate
  - May not offer a unique explanation or representation of the problem

1: An inadequate response

Completeness
  - Attempts but fails to answer or complete the question

Understanding
  - Shows very limited understanding of the problem
  - Contains major computational errors
  - Focuses on the wrong mathematical idea or procedure
  - Includes explanations or reasoning that is not understandable

Presentation/Communication
  - Shows copied parts of the problem with no attempt at a solution
  - Contains work, examples, or diagrams that do not reflect the problem

Creativity
  - Does not offer a unique explanation or representation of the problem

0: No response
  - No attempt was made to respond to the problem

Presentations

What Is a Presentation?

In a presentation, individual students or groups of students present their work or perform a task in front of the entire class. Presentations can be formal and result in a recorded evaluation or grade, or they can be an informal opportunity for students to share their work.

Where to Learn More About Presentations

The student text introduces group presentations at the end of Chapter 6. Look at the section "Group Assessment" in Part 2 of *Constructive Assessment in Mathematics* for a description of methods for grading group presentations.

Hints for Assigning and Assessing Presentations

Presentations give students responsibility for presenting mathematics in front of the class and take the spotlight off the teacher. Be prepared to accommodate students who are shy, especially if they will feel awkward for linguistic or cultural reasons. Remind students that being able to present ideas clearly before an audience is a valuable skill both for everyday life and for a job. Be severe with students who tease or harass the presenters. Explaining mathematics before one's peers is difficult enough without any extra discouragement.

If you have students present in groups, you relieve some of the pressure of a presentation. The outgoing student can do most of the talking, but the others still participate by helping with planning, handing out materials, typing up the overheads, doing research, preparing the poster, and so on. It works well to have each group describe briefly to the class how each member contributed to the presentation ("Sarah and Conn made the poster," "Lexie found the books from the library," etc.).

A good time for group presentations is at the end of a chapter or group of chapters, or at the end of the semester, for review. You can divide the chapter or chapters into a number of topics equal to the number of groups in your classroom, then have each group present the review for its assigned topic. One advantage of this method is that it is easier to make time for presentations, because the group work can substitute for any other review you had planned.

Be aware that presentations can take a lot of class time. An advantage of group presentations is that you can get through all the students in less time—having every student make a presentation could take several days. Another way to save time is to have the presentations in a visual form, such as a poster. You can designate the first part of class as a time for students to pin up work and then to wander around the classroom and observe one another's work. This gives a nice ambiance to your classroom and gets students out of their seats. Then, after everyone has had a chance to see all the work, you can have each person or group spend a few minutes explaining the highlights of their poster. One teacher calls this time the "museum tour." It also works well to have students present the highlights of one another's posters. This makes them responsible for looking carefully at other students' work during the first part of class. If you are having students evaluate one another's presentations, you can use this observation time for evaluation as well. Have students include an envelope beside each presentation for peer evaluation forms. (For some cautions about using peer evaluation, see the earlier section "Strategies for Saving Teacher Time and Work.")

Another technique that works well for some types of presentations is to give each presenter an overhead transparency ahead of time for writing his or her notes. The transparency provides a motivation for the presenters to organize their thoughts.

You can also have individuals present material only to the other members of their group. This strategy saves time since you can have many presentations going at once. It also avoids putting students on the spot in front of the whole class. Of course, it also makes it harder for you to monitor the presentations, since so much student activity is going on at the same time.

If you have the technology available, try having students prepare electronic presentations. The Geometer's Sketchpad allows the user to annotate sketches with both visual text and recorded commentary. Other software applications such as Hypercard and Digital Chisel allow students to design creative and dynamic presentations. The TI Graph Link is a valuable tool for students to print out their data sets and graphs.

One teacher used the **Sample Evaluation Form for a Group Presentation** that follows when her students evaluated a group presentation. Every student evaluated every group. (Be aware of the amount of paperwork this will require. A single class of 30 students with 6 groups presenting will need 180 forms. You may want to have a smaller "jury" of students responsible for the evaluations. This jury could be randomly selected and could also rotate.) She looked through the forms for each group herself and wrote a summary form to give back to the group. Then she had student teaching assistants average the last set of scores from each form for each group and used these numbers to determine a grade for the group.

Sample Evaluation Form for a Group Presentation

Fill out this evaluation form to evaluate a group presentation. Be fair. Remember, others will be doing the same for you. Do not put your name on this sheet. Your teacher will be the only person who will read these evaluations.

Topic _____

Names of group members _____

_____

For parts 1–4, decide how strongly you agree or disagree with each statement. Circling a **5** means you strongly agree with the statement. Circling a **1** means you strongly disagree with the statement. Circling a **3** means you don't feel strongly either way.

1. The presentation explained the material well and helped me understand the topic.

Strongly disagree				Strongly agree
1	2	3	4	5

2. The group was well prepared and put in a lot of hard work.

Strongly disagree				Strongly agree
1	2	3	4	5

3. The group appeared to cooperate well with equal participation among members.

Strongly disagree				Strongly agree
1	2	3	4	5

4. The presentation made the topic interesting and fun.

Strongly disagree				Strongly agree
1	2	3	4	5

5. Now give a general rating for the whole presentation.

Needed a lot of improvement	Needed improvement	O.K.	Good	Great!
1	2	3	4	5

6. Use the space below and the back of this sheet for any additional comments.

Projects

What Is a Project?

A project is a multistep assignment students complete over an extended period of time, both inside and outside of class. A project allows students to investigate mathematical ideas in a new context and often involves a series of related investigations, problem-solving situations, library research, demonstrations, and presentations. In the Geometer's Sketchpad investigations in *Advanced Algebra,* students explore related mathematics using dynamic drawing tools. Projects can take a lot of time, but teachers find they increase students' understanding of the material and their enthusiasm for learning. Because projects provide opportunities to investigate and express ideas using different modes of interaction and communication, they can address the needs of many different learning styles.

Where to Learn More About Projects

The student text contains several projects in every chapter. In *Constructive Assessment in Mathematics,* look at the Mathematical Projects section in Part 2.

Hints for Assigning and Assessing Projects

There are many projects available in *Advanced Algebra.* You don't have to invent your own unless you want to. Don't expect to get to every project in the text. Assigning students one project per chapter could give you a great deal of work if you plan to read a project from every student. If you assign one project per group, you will not have as much to read, but it still might be more reasonable to assign only one project per grading period or even one per semester. Some teachers use peer evaluation to help evaluate the projects. This strategy helps students take responsibility for one another's work, and it saves teacher time. Many teachers weight a project grade about the same as a test grade.

It's fun for students to pick the projects they find the most interesting. This way different students or groups of students complete different projects, and you can have them present or display their results to the rest of the class when they are done. To prepare yourself and your students for a project, try some of the following suggestions:

- Give students plenty of advance notice for a project. Talking about projects ahead of time can generate enthusiasm and ideas.
- Clearly explain your expectations of a completed project. Try to give students copies of an assessment rubric ahead of time.
- Have samples of past projects available if you can.
- Have some resource materials available in your classroom if you can.

It helps if your students have some experience with writing activities that stress revisions of earlier drafts. You may need to explain to students what you expect in a draft. For example, a draft might include indications of what they are planning for artwork and diagrams, and a preliminary list of their resources. It also helps if your students have previous experience researching in a library and on the World Wide Web.

Hints for a Good Time Frame for Projects

One teacher used the following time frame to guide students' project work:

- By the end of the first week, students should have done some library research and should have selected a topic.

- By the end of the second week, they should have outlined their projects.

- By the end of the third week, they should have a first draft. Each draft should be proofread for general understanding and correct mathematics by one other group member if the project is an individual project or by all group members (or a different group) if the project is a group project.

- By the end of the fourth week, they should have a second draft. If students are presenting their projects, they also need to outline their presentations. Each draft should be proofread for spelling, style, clarity, grammar, and punctuation by two group members if the project is an individual project or by all group members (or a different group) if the project is a group project.

- The final versions and presentations, if they are being done, are due during the fifth week.

If you can make the time, it's a good idea to provide feedback on each major step in the development of the project so that projects stay on track and reflect an accurate understanding of the assignment and the mathematics.

Hints for Group Projects

If you have students complete projects in groups, it helps ensure individual accountability to have each student respond to the following:

- Write a complete description of (1) what you did in this project, (2) how you did it, (3) when you did it, (4) who did what part, and (5) what algebra concepts you learned.

- Include a group self-evaluation of how well you completed the task and how well you worked together.

One teacher assigned the following project while her students were working through Chapter 3. The project was due at the end of the chapter. The page that follows the project outline is the **Project Evaluation Form** the teacher used for evaluating the project.

The last page in the section on projects contains a general **Sample Checklist for Evaluating a Project.** A checklist provides you with a fast way of evaluating an assignment. Notice that there is room after each entry for comments so that you can give a more detailed response as well. Also, you can record numbers or grades in the blanks instead of checks if you want to record more precise measurements of the criteria.

Chapter 3 Project

Your project involves making a conjecture comparing a behavior among two or more groups of people. For example, "Theater people skip more meals than nontheater people" or "Juniors get more sleep than seniors." The project should include the following as a minimum:

- One statement of what you are trying to show

- Numeric data from 40 people (20 from each of two groups)

- The mean, median, and mode of each set

- The range, interquartile range, and mean absolute deviation of each set

- A graph containing box plots of each set

- Graphs of histograms of each set

- Analyses of the data comparing and contrasting the sets

- Conclusions based on the analysis (was your assumption right, or wrong, or based on the data it needs further study?)

These are, of course, the minimum. Feel free to collect as much data as you can and to look at more than two groups if you wish. Your grade will depend on both the mathematical correctness of the information and the way that it is presented. As an idea you may wish to consider presenting the information in a binder as an executive might give to his or her boss. Or you might choose to prepare a poster displaying the information. The use of color, organization, and ease of reading along with creativity will play a part in your grade. Meet with your group and get started early. This project may take a while. I need to see at least rough drafts of your box plots and histograms in two weeks.

Assessing Chapter 3 Project

1. Conjecture
	Points
The conjecture is clearly stated in the opening of the project.	4
The conjecture is vaguely stated.	2
The conjecture is hard to find.	1
There is no conjecture.	0

2. Data
The data values are given with units.	5
The data is given without units.	3
Some of the data is given.	1
There is no data given.	0

3. Procedure
The paper explains in detail how the data was collected.	3
The paper sort of explains how the data was collected.	2
No explanation of procedure is given.	0

4. Measures of center
The three values for the measures of center are correctly calculated.	4
All of the values are there and two are correct.	3
Only one value is correct.	2
None of the three values are there.	1

5. Measures of spread
The three values for the measures of spread are correctly calculated.	4
All of the values are there and two are correct.	3
Only one value is correct.	2
All three values are not there.	0

6. Box plots
The box plots are drawn correctly, with axis labeled with values and units, both drawn to the same scale, and drawn together.	10
The box plots are drawn correctly, with axis labeled with values and units, both drawn to the same scale, but drawn separately.	8
The box plots are drawn correctly, with axis labeled with values and units, but drawn to different scales.	6
The box plots are drawn correctly, without axis labels or values and units.	4
The box plots are not quite correct.	2
There are no box plots.	0

SUGGESTIONS FOR ASSESSMENT

7. Histograms

	Points
The histograms are drawn correctly, with axis labeled with values and units, both drawn to the same scale.	8
The histograms are drawn correctly, with axis labeled with values and units, but drawn to different scales.	6
The histograms are drawn correctly, without axis labels or values and units.	4
The histograms are not quite correct.	2
There are no histograms.	0

8. Conclusion

The conclusion is clearly stated, and the data justify the conclusion.	8
The conclusion is clearly stated but is not justified by the data.	6
The conclusion is stated in a confusing manner and is not justified.	4
No conclusion is stated even though one is possible from the data.	2
No conclusion is stated or an incorrect conclusion is stated.	0

9. Overall appearance and clarity

The project is displayed in an attractive manner and is readily understandable.	4
The project is somewhat confusing in appearance.	2
The project is disorganized and difficult to understand.	0

TOTAL POSSIBLE POINTS   **50**

Sample Checklist for Evaluating a Project

Name _____

_____ Your project is complete in responding to all these requirements:

     _____ Requirement 1 _____

     _____ Requirement 2 _____

     _____ Requirement 3 _____

     _____ Requirement 4 _____

     _____ Requirement 5 _____

_____ Your project communicates your ideas effectively.

_____ Your project includes examples or diagrams when appropriate.

_____ Your project includes only minor computational errors, if any.

_____ Your project offers some unique insight into the topic.

Overall comments and grade _____

Tests and Quizzes

What Is a Test or Quiz?

A test or quiz is a structured and usually written assignment that poses specific, often closed-ended problems and questions designed to test students' mastery of specific subject matter and skills. This section describes how to use traditional tests and quizzes, and where to find them. Typically, students work on these tests and quizzes individually and are expected to complete them during a limited amount of class time.

The advantage of traditional tests and quizzes is that they provide a simple tool for rating a student's understanding of the material. You can usually translate a test result into a numerical grade fairly easily. This gives you, students, and parents seemingly objective feedback on how well the students are doing.

Where to Learn More About Tests and Quizzes

The separate volume *Advanced Algebra Quizzes, Tests, and Exams* contains quizzes, chapter tests, and midyear and final cumulative exams. These materials are also provided on disk so that teachers using Microsoft Word or a compatible word-processing program (Windows or Macintosh) can edit them.

The student text explains to students how to write their own test items at the end of Chapter 5. For more tips, see the section "Student-Constructed Test Items" in Part 2 of *Constructive Assessment in Mathematics*.

Hints for Assigning and Assessing Tests and Quizzes

Beware of giving tests and quizzes too frequently. A teacher recently shared a joke about a rancher who tried to fatten up his cattle by weighing them more often. Don't try to increase your students' learning by testing them more often. Remember to mix traditional forms of assessment with some of the other assessment strategies described earlier in this section.

It is difficult and probably unfair to ask very broad, investigative, or open-ended questions on an individualized, timed test (although it's a good idea to include at least one question that tests students' analytical skills). Timed, individualized tests and quizzes demonstrate how well a single student performs during a limited time on certain tasks. For this reason, tests don't generally provide a complete measure of student understanding.

Besides testing a limited set of skills, assessments of this kind are stressful for many students. Some students suffer from enough test anxiety that they simply cannot complete tests. (Of course, there are also those students who perform at their best in these situations.)

Here are some ideas for making traditional testing less stressful. One strategy is to allow students to create and bring a "cheat sheet"—a collection of notes on a note card or sheet of paper that they can reference during a test. Teachers find students do some useful review in putting together their "cheat sheets." Beware of students truly using the note card to cheat by copying information from students who took the same test earlier. Also, you might want to require that each note card be in the student's own handwriting so students don't borrow or duplicate those of other students. Some teachers collect the note cards and count them as part of the test grade. Students often find that they hardly ever look at their note card during the test, but they feel better having it handy.

Some teachers allow students to use their notebooks during tests and quizzes. This encourages students to keep their notebook organized. Sometimes teachers even allow students to use their textbook during a test. This encourages them to become familiar with their mathematics book ahead of time. Remind students that good problem solving involves knowing how to use the proper resources.

You can also alleviate test anxiety by allowing students to retake tests. The disadvantage to this strategy is that it requires extra time for you to make and correct a second set of tests. Some teachers require students to correct their first test completely before they are allowed a retake. Generous teachers allow students to keep the highest grade from the two tests, but many prefer to average the grades or require that the second grade count as the only grade (this last technique cuts down on the number of students who opt for the retake test).

It is not a good idea to test students on how quickly they can perform mathematics. Good mathematical reasoning is a slow and thoughtful process. For this reason, it is fair to allow students extra time to finish a test if they need it. This is especially true for students who may have linguistic, physical, emotional, or psychological needs that slow them down. It can be hard to find the extra time to allow students to finish. Sometimes it's worth having them come in after school or at lunchtime to allow them the few extra minutes they need. Beware of students who misuse this privilege and discuss test questions outside class before they return to finish.

It's always best to mix traditional testing with a few of the other assessment strategies we have reviewed. A good mix helps accommodate the different learning styles and needs of your students, and it allows you to stress that there are many different ways of performing and learning mathematics. Remember, too, that assessment can be an integral part of instruction. Always try to give assessment tasks that allow students to learn more mathematics as well as assessing what they already know.

For a sample mix of strategies, see the **Sample Semester Assessment and Grading Form** that follows. This strategy was used by an *Advanced Algebra* teacher already experienced in some of the newer assessment strategies. Although this teacher used cooperative problem-solving activities and open-ended problems for her group tests and group quizzes, notice that there are still no specific references to portfolios or journals. Nobody can do it all at once! Remember, add only one or two new strategies at a time to your overall assessment plan. As David Clarke emphasizes in *Constructive Assessment in Mathematics,* the goal should be not more assessment, but better assessment.

Sample Semester Assessment and Grading Form

For this semester of advanced algebra, I will calculate your grade based on the following requirements and points. Typically, your semester grade will be averaged from about 350 total points. This will vary slightly based on how I see the class working and progressing. For example, if I see the whole class working very hard on a project, I might decide it would be more fair to weight the project as 25 points.

- Nightly homework assignments (1 point each)

- Approximately six chapter tests (20 points each)

- One group test (20 points)

- One final exam (40 points)

- Approximately ten quizzes, including individual quizzes and group quizzes (10 points each)

- One project for a group grade (20 points)

- One project for an individual grade (you will have a chance to revise each of your projects) (20 points)

- A notebook grade (you will determine this, but it must be approved by two group members and myself) (20 points)

Additionally, I'll carry out what I call "observational assessment." This means I will write down comments about how I see you behaving, communicating, helping, working, and cooperating in class. I will collect five comments per student per semester. I will use these comments to determine your progress and to report progress to your parents. They will not influence your grades. You can see your comments or learn your current grade average at any time after school. I will not show you this information during the school day.

Course Outlines

There are 14 chapters in *Advanced Algebra Through Data Exploration* and 108 sections. Many sections will take one day, but several might take two. A few sections may be extended to three or four days. Clearly, you will not be able to discover all of the sections in a typical two-semester school year. By selecting different routes through the text, you can customize your courses to the needs and goals of your class. Four different courses have been outlined below.

These courses are outlined with only ten days per semester for tests, quizzes, and any catch-up that may be necessary. The course outlines are written for an ideal teaching situation. An ideal teaching situation means one in which there is no need for reteaching; there are no shortened days, no special schedules, no days set aside for standardized testing, no rallies, no field trips or illnesses that wipe out your class roster; and chapter tests never happen to fall on Mondays. For some schools, ten days may be adequate to cover tests and so forth. For others, you may have to adjust the schedule by reducing the number of lessons covered or shortening and combining lessons.

In most sections, there are investigations, Take Another Look problems, and projects that enhance and extend the mathematical concepts. These activities have been designed so that students can work on them independently or in cooperative groups, even if students do not use regular class time for them. You may want to give extra credit to students who take on the projects.

Advanced Algebra (Algebra 2) with Trigonometry Course

The content of this course in intended for a standard Algebra 2 course. Since there are so many lessons and some concepts take two days to develop, it is impossible to complete the entire book. Students will explore and discover mathematical concepts by completing investigations and projects in each chapter. The optional sections have been left out of this outline. If you have additional time at the end of the semester, you may wish to return to those sections that are skipped.

Fall Semester

Chapter	Lessons	Days
0 Intro the Calculator	1–3	4
1 Patterns & Recursion	1–7	15
2 Sequences & Explicit Form	1–5, 7	12
3 Introduction to Statistics	1–4, 8	7
4 Data Analysis	1–6, 9	14
5 Functions	1–10	15
6 Parametric/Trigonometry	1–5, 7	14
Projects/Catch-up/Final		9
	Total	**90**

Spring Semester

Chapter	Lessons	Days
7 Exponentials/Logarithms	1–8, 10	16
8 Discrete Math	1–3, 5–8	13
9 Systems of Equations	1–7, 9	11
10 Polynomials	1–7, 9	13
11 Probability & Statistics	1–3, 7	8
12 Functions & Relations	12, 4–7, 10	12
13 Trigonometric Functions	1– 5, 8	12
Projects/Catch-up/Final		5
	Total	**90**

Advanced Algebra Honors Course

Honors students should have the opportunity to work with the tools of data analysis to discover algebraic properties, thus discovering their own creative powers. *Advanced Algebra* offers your honors students enrichment without the use of other supplementary material. The course outlined below is a fast-paced, accelerated, and enriched program and is designed for students who will take Precalculus and Advanced Placement courses the following years.

Fall Semester

Chapter	Lessons	Days
0 Intro the Calculator	1–3	3
1 Patterns & Recursion	1–7	13
2 Sequences & Explicit Form	1–7	13
3 Introduction to Statistics	1–4	9
4 Data Analysis	1–7, 9	12
5 Functions	1–10	13
6 Parametric/Trigonometry	1–7	16
Projects/Catch-up/Final		11
	Total	**90**

Spring Semester

Chapter	Lessons	Days
7 Exponentials/Logarithms	1–10	13
8 Discrete Math	1–8	13
9 Systems of Equations	1–9	12
10 Polynomials	1–9	13
11 Probability & Statistics	1–7	12
12 Functions & Relations	1–8, 10	13
13 Trigonometric Functions	1– 5, 8	9
Projects/Catch-up/Final		5
	Total	**90**

Year-and-a-Half Advanced Algebra with Trigonometry Course

This course includes all of the sections in the book and can be used for an Algebra 2 and first-semester Precalculus course. Plenty of time is given to complete all investigations and several extension problems for each chapter. Students explore and discover each concept with extra time.

Fall Semester

Chapter	Lessons	Days
0 Intro the Calculator	1–3	6
1 Patterns & Recursion	1–7	16
2 Sequences & Explicit Form	1–7	15
3 Introduction to Statistics	1–4	8
4 Data Analysis	1–9	20
5 Functions	1–10	20
Projects/Catch-up		5
Total		**90**

Spring Semester

Chapter	Lessons	Days
6 Parametric/Trigonometry	1–7	14
7 Exponentials/Logarithms	1–10	20
8 Discrete Math	1–8	16
9 Systems of Equations	1–7	15
10 Polynomials	1–9	20
Projects/Catch-up		5
Total		**90**

First Semester–Precalculus Course

	Lessons	Days
10 Polynomials	1–9	15
11 Probability & Statistics	1–7	15
12 Functions & Relations	1–10	20
13 Trigonometric Functions	1– 8	20
Projects/Catch-up		20
Total		**90**

Note: Chapter 10 is repeated as the first unit in the third semester.

Advanced Algebra with Discrete Math (Fourth Year) Course

Students will review advanced algebra concepts while exploring discrete mathematics. This course may be used to follow Algebra 2 as an elective course or as a prerequisite to an Advanced Placement Statistics course. Students should be familiar with the functions of a graphing calculator.

Fall Semester

Chapter	Lessons	Days
1 Patterns & Recursion	1–7	10
2 Sequences & Explicit Form	1–7	10
3 Introduction to Statistics	1–4	8
4 Data Analysis	1–9	15
6 Parametric/Trigonometry	1–5, 7	10
7 Exponentials/Logarithms	1–7, 10	11
8 Discrete Math	1–8	20
Projects/Catch-up		6
Total		**90**

Spring Semester

Chapter	Lessons	Days
9 Systems of Equations	1–9	16
10 Polynomials	1–9	15
11 Probability & Statistics	1–7	15
12 Functions & Relations	1–10	18
13 Trigonometric Functions	1–8	18
Projects/Catch-up		8
Total		**90**

Problem Matrix

The following problem matrix provides suggestions for how to assign and use problems contained in the problem sets. The matrix also suggests how to us problems and investigations for assessment purposes. The first column of the matrix lists problems that may be more appropriately assigned for *individual* work. The second column does the same for problems that can be assigned for *groupwork*. Often the groupwork problems are designated as such because they require several different levels of thinking, or because the problem might be overwhelming to an individual student but can be solved readily by a group of students working together.

The third column lists problems that are *essential* to some courses. These are problems that may be revisited throughout the course, they may extend concepts that were introduced in the section, or they may introduce new concepts that weren't specifically discussed in the section. This list of problems should not be considered as a minimum assignment for the section. In fact, for some sections, no essential problems have been listed. This does not mean that no problems from the section should be assigned.

When thinking of *performance assessment* items, we often think of skills such as "construct an angle bisector," which is easily demonstrated. However, many algebraic skills can be quickly and easily demonstrated, such as "Find the mean of these data points: 23, 45, 67, 89." We have included problems such as these in the fourth column.

In the *portfolio* column, we have included some problems and/or investigations that could be included in student portfolios. But for some of these problems and/or investigations to be considered for a portfolio assignment, we would expect students to do a complete and thorough write-up of the problem and the solution. In addition, some of the problems listed in this column can easily be extended. Problems that encompass several important skills are included here as well. Project write-ups are also excellent to include in student portfolios.

Some sections of the text contain problems that are specifically written as *journal prompts*. These are noted in the Problem Set Notes in the section guides. However, often there are other problems that can lend themselves to this purpose. In the final column of the matrix, there are references to these problems as well as to those problems that have been specifically written as journal-writing prompts.

	Individual	Group	Essential	Performance assessment	Portfolio	Journal
Chapter 0						
Problem Set 0.1	1, 3, 4, 5	2, 6		1	Inv. 0.1.2, 5	3d
Problem Set 0.2	1–5, 9	6–8		1, 2	5, 6, 7	3, 9
Problem Set 0.3	3, 5, 6, 7, 8	1, 2, 4		5		7, 8
Chapter 1						
Problem Set 1.1	1–5	6–8		3	Inv. 1.1.1	
Problem Set 1.2	1, 3, 4, 6	2, 5		4	Inv. 1.2.1, 2, 6	2
Problem Set 1.3	4, 6, 7, 9, 10	1–3, 5, 8	5, 9	2, 3	6, 7	
Problem Set 1.4	1–3	4–6			Inv. 1.4.1, 4	4
Problem Set 1.5	1, 2, 4, 7, 9	3, 5, 6, 8	6, 7	1	5, 7	9
Problem Set 1.6	1–5, 9, 10	6–8		1, 2, 8	Inv. 1.6.1, 7, 9	10
Problem Set 1.7	1–7			7		
Chapter 2						
Problem Set 2.1	1, 2, 4, 6, 7, 9	3, 5, 8, 10	3, 4, 9	1, 2	10	
Problem Set 2.2	1–6	7–9	9	1, 2, 3	8	
Problem Set 2.3	1, 2, 4–6, 10	3, 7–9	2	1, 4, 6		10
Problem Set 2.4	5–8	1–4	1	1, 4		
Problem Set 2.5	1–4, 10, 11	5–9	4, 6	1	5, 8, 9	11
Problem Set 2.6	4	1–3			4	
Problem Set 2.7	1–11			2, 4		
Chapter 3						
Problem Set 3.1	1–3, 8, 9	4–7, 10	4	1	Inv. 3.1.2	2
Problem Set 3.2	1, 2, 4, 5, 10	3, 6–9	1, 4	4		10
Problem Set 3.3	3–6, 8	1, 2, 7	1, 6	3, 4	Inv. 3.3.1, 8	6, 8
Problem Set 3.4	1–8				8	
Chapter 4						
Problem Set 4.1	1, 2, 4, 7	3, 5, 6	1–3	2		7
Problem Set 4.2	1–4, 6	5, 7, 8	3, 4	1, 2, 3, 4		
Problem Set 4.3	1, 2, 4–8	3, 9, 10	7	1, 4	9	
Problem Set 4.4	1–7, 12	8–11	1, 3, 9	1, 2, 3	11	9, 12
Problem Set 4.5	1–3, 7	4, 5, 6	3, 5, 7	1, 7	Inv. 4.5.1	
Problem Set 4.6	1–5, 11, 12	6–10	1, 5		10	8, 9, 12
Problem Set 4.7	1–5, 10	6–9		1, 2, 3	Inv. 4.7.1	10
Problem Set 4.8	1–4	5–8	1			3
Problem Set 4.9	1–27			1, 2, 3		

	Individual	Group	Essential	Performance assessment	Portfolio	Journal
Chapter 5						
Problem Set 5.1	2, 12–21	1, 3–11	3	2, 4–21	Inv. 5.1.1	
Problem Set 5.2	3–6, 9	1, 2, 7, 8	6, 8	9		
Problem Set 5.3	1–3, 6, 8, 9	4, 5, 7, 10, 11	1, 2, 5	2	Inv. 5.3.1	
Problem Set 5.4	1–7	8–12	2–4, 6, 9, 12	5, 8		9
Problem Set 5.5	1–5, 8, 11	6, 7, 9, 10	1, 5–7	1, 3, 7	9	
Problem Set 5.6	1–7, 9–11	8, 12–14	1–4, 7, 9, 12	3, 7	13	
Problem Set 5.7	1–8, 15	9–14	1–3, 7, 9, 14	2	13	15
Problem Set 5.8	1–7, 13	8–12	1, 2, 7, 8, 10	1, 2		8, 13
Problem Set 5.9	4–7	1–3, 8–10	1, 2, 4, 5, 8	4		10
Problem Set 5.10	1–7			1, 2, 3		
Chapter 6						
Problem Set 6.1	3–6	1, 2	1, 2, 4, 5	1		
Problem Set 6.2	3, 5–7	1, 2, 4	3, 4, 5, 7	2		
Problem Set 6.3	1, 2, 6, 7, 9, 10, 12	3, 4, 5, 8, 11	1, 2, 4, 10–12	1, 2	Inv. 6.3.2	
Problem Set 6.4	1, 4, 6, 7, 9, 10	2, 3, 5, 8	1, 3, 4, 6–8	6	Inv. 6.4.1	
Problem Set 6.5	4, 5, 7, 8, 10, 11	1–3, 6, 9	1, 4, 6		8, 11	10, 11
Problem Set 6.6	6–9	1–5			7	9
Problem Set 6.7	1–12			1, 5		12
Chapter 7						
Problem Set 7.1	1, 5–7	2–4	3		Inv. 7.1.1	
Problem Set 7.2	3–7, 10	1, 2, 8, 9, 11	3, 4, 9	3, 4, 6		9
Problem Set 7.3	1–5	6–11	5, 6, 9, 11	1, 2, 5		
Problem Set 7.4	1, 2, 4, 6, 8, 9, 12, 13	3, 5, 7, 10, 11	2, 5, 8, 9	1, 8		13
Problem Set 7.5	1, 2, 4–6, 10	3, 7–9	7	1, 2	Inv. 7.5.1	10
Problem Set 7.6	1–6, 10	7–9	1, 2	1		10
Problem Set 7.7	4–10, 13	1–3, 11, 12	1–3	1, 2		5, 13
Problem Set 7.8	1–4	5–10	2	3	10	
Problem Set 7.9		1–8	4–6			
Problem Set 7.10	1–7			1, 2, 3		7
Chapter 8						
Problem Set 8.1	6, 7	1–5, 8	4, 6, 7		Inv. 8.1.2	
Problem Set 8.2	1–4, 7	5, 6, 8, 9	6			
Problem Set 8.3	1–6	7–11	6–8	2, 3		

	Individual	Group	Essential	Performance assessment	Portfolio	Journal
Problem Set 8.4	3, 5, 7, 8, 9	1, 2, 4, 6	1, 2		Inv. 8.4.1	8
Problem Set 8.5	1–3	4, 5	2, 3		Inv. 8.5.2	
Problem Set 8.6	1–4	5, 6	1, 3, 4			
Problem Set 8.7	1, 3–6, 9, 10	2, 7, 8	1, 4, 9	1, 4, 6		10
Problem Set 8.8	1–12					11, 12
Chapter 9						
Problem Set 9.1	3–6	1, 2, 7, 8	2, 8		8	8
Problem Set 9.2	3, 4, 6–10	1, 2, 5, 11				
Problem Set 9.3	1–5	6–11	1, 3	1, 2, 3	8	11
Problem Set 9.4	1–7	8–11	4	1, 2, 6	8–11	
Problem Set 9.5	1, 2, 4, 6, 8, 9	3, 5, 7	8	2		9
Problem Set 9.6	4	1–3	1			
Problem Set 9.7	4, 5	1–3			4, 5	
Problem Set 9.8	4–6	1–3		1		5, 6
Problem Set 9.9	1–12			1, 3, 4		11, 12
Chapter 10						
Problem Set 10.1	3, 5, 6	1, 2, 4	1, 2		Inv. 10.1.2, 6	
Problem Set 10.2	5–8	1–4, 9, 10	1, 2, 4, 5	1, 2	9, 10	
Problem Set 10.3	1, 2, 8–11	3–7	1, 2, 7–9	1, 4		
Problem Set 10.4	5, 8, 11, 12	1–4, 6, 7, 9, 10	3, 5	1, 2	Inv. 10.4.1	12
Problem Set 10.5	1, 2, 4, 6, 9	3, 5, 7, 8		1		
Problem Set 10.6	1, 4, 7, 8	2, 3, 5, 6	1, 2, 4	1	Inv. 10.6.1, 8	
Problem Set 10.7	1, 2, 4, 8, 9	3, 5–7	1, 2, 5	1, 4		
Problem Set 10.8	3, 5–7	1, 2, 4	2	3	Inv. 10.8.1	6, 7
Problem Set 10.9	1–7			2, 4		6, 7
Chapter 11						
Problem Set 11.1	2, 3, 5	1, 4, 6, 7	2, 3	1a, 2, 5	7	
Problem Set 11.2	1–4, 7, 10	5, 6, 8–9	1, 5	2, 3	Inv. 11.2.1, 5	8, 10
Problem Set 11.3	1, 2, 4, 8	3, 5–7	1, 8	2		7
Problem Set 11.4	1–3	4–8	7, 8		Inv. 11.4.1	
Problem Set 11.5	2–5, 9	1, 6–8	5, 6			
Problem Set 11.6	1–4	5–7	7		5, 6	
Problem Set 11.7	1–10			1, 4, 9		2
Chapter 12						
Problem Set 12.1	1–3, 5, 6	4, 7, 8	2	1	Inv. 12.1.2, 8	
Problem Set 12.2	2, 5–8	1, 3, 4, 9	1, 2, 4	1, 3	9	

PROBLEM MATRIX

	Individual	Group	Essential	Performance assessment	Portfolio	Journal
Problem Set 12.3	1–3, 6	4, 5, 7, 8	1		8	
Problem Set 12.4	2, 4, 5	1, 3, 6, 7	3		3, 6	
Problem Set 12.5	1–3, 7	4–6, 8, 9	3, 6	1, 3		
Problem Set 12.6	1–3	4–6		1, 2	Inv. 12.6.2	
Problem Set 12.7	2–5, 8	1, 6, 7	3	1	7	8
Problem Set 12.8	1, 3, 4, 8	2, 5–7	2, 6	1		8
Problem Set 12.9	1, 2, 4, 8	3, 5–7				
Problem Set 12.10	1–9			1	8	2, 9
Chapter 13						
Problem Set 13.1	1, 2, 4, 5, 8	3, 6, 7, 9	3, 5	1	Inv. 13.1.1	
Problem Set 13.2	1–5	6–9	1, 3, 9	2	Inv. 13.2.1	
Problem Set 13.3	1, 3, 5–7	2, 4, 8, 9	1, 3, 5, 6		2	
Problem Set 13.4	1–3	4–8	1, 2	1	2	2
Problem Set 13.5	1, 3–5, 9	2, 6–8, 10	1, 2	1	10	8
Problem Set 13.6	1–4, 8	5–7	1, 2, 4, 5	1, 8	Inv. 13.6.1	
Problem Set 13.7	1–6	7–11	1–5	1, 2, 5	11	
Problem Set 13.8	1–11			1, 2, 5, 9		6

Section Guides

Introduction to the Section Guides

Advanced Algebra Through Data Exploration: A Graphing Calculator Approach has 14 chapters with 108 sections. Each section will take from one to three days to complete. You and your students will not be able to cover all of the sections in a two-semester school year. You should expect to be able to present about 9 to 12 chapters depending on the type of course you choose (see the Course Outline section of this book), your school's daily schedule, and your school calendar. The 108 section guides included here are useful for all four types of algebra courses suggested for *Advanced Algebra.*

The section guides consist of an overview of each chapter followed by a detailed guide for each section in the chapter. The chapter overview discusses the philosophy or intent of the chapter including the content and flow of the presentation.

Each section is identified by the section number and title.

Section Guide 4.3
Real-World Meanings

Each section guide is divided into parts. The first part is **Objectives,** in which the mathematical objectives are stated.

OBJECTIVES
- To analyze data pairs and determine which are independent values and which are dependent values, thus finding the domain and range values
- To interpolate and extrapolate with a linear model and to identify inherent difficulties involved
- To provide real-world meanings for values and variables of a linear model and for answers obtained with the model

The next two parts are **Materials** and **Resources.** Under materials you will find a list of items needed or recommended for use with the section, usually for the investigation(s) in that section. Under resources you will find references to transparencies and worksheet masters in the *Teacher's Resource Book* as well as tests and quizzes, which are in the book of tests and quizzes.

The fourth part, **Teaching Notes,** describes the concepts introduced in the section. Sometimes suggestions will be provided for how to organize the class and how much time you might expect to spend on the section. Background information that might be helpful for the teacher is also provided. Within this part you will also find helpful hints and answers for the investigations. Investigations that are marked with an asterisk are essential to the course. If you omit any of these investigations, then you need to be sure to provide an alternative introduction or activity.

The fifth part, **Problem Set Notes,** describes things to look out for in the problem sets. For example, you may not want to assign Problem 5 if students haven't done Problem 3. This part also includes the information from the problem matrix on how different problems can be used and assigned.

The last part, **Extensions,** offers a variety of ideas for further investigation. These may include additional Take Another Look activities or projects that can be found in the *Teacher's Resource Book.*

In the section guide for the Chapter Review section, you will find a reference to the Assessing What You've Learned section found at the end of each chapter.

Chapter 0
Introducing the Calculator

Overview

Understanding the order of operations is essential if students are to know how to enter expressions into the calculator and what to expect for an answer. The goal of this chapter is for students to become comfortable with the technology, to understand how the calculator interprets basic commands, and to become actively involved in the learning process rather than dependent on explanations from the teacher. As students become familiar with the keypad, encourage them to verbalize how the calculator interprets entries.

You can demonstrate keystroke entries and solutions using a classroom overhead calculator. Students can copy the instructions on their calculators and produce the same display you have. Or, even better, if one of your students is an "expert" already, she or he can enter the instructions on the classroom device.

It is probably not necessary to do any formal end-of-chapter assessment for Chapter 0. The investigation write-ups and individual assessments of how members of their group are contributing are important considerations. Look at individual writing styles and provide suggestions for more creativity, better writing, and longer and more inclusive arguments.

Some assessment of homework, including accuracy, creativity, completeness, organization, and presentation, is valuable information for you and your students during the chapter. Making frequent entries in journals during the last five minutes of class can be valuable to your students and to you. It gives them an opportunity to reflect on difficulties and to express themselves, and it can provide you with future direction.

Section 0.1
Using the Calculator for Basic Operations

OBJECTIVES
- To become familiar with basic calculator use involving simple arithmetic, squaring, cubing, parentheses, square roots, negation, and π
- To explore menus in order to locate and use functions
- To review the rules for order of operations and to discover how the calculator treats implied multiplication

MATERIALS

Posters of the keypad for the calculators used in your classroom

RESOURCES

Transparency/Worksheet Master for Section 0.1: Investigation 0.1.1

Calculator Notes 0A and 0B

TEACHING NOTES

Turn students loose in this section. Encourage them to work together in their groups. Students will get the answers, but perhaps not on the first try. They will quickly learn the keypad and calculator menus and remember locations. If necessary, develop alternative examples or explanations for the most difficult problems. Try to become comfortable working with small groups and the dynamics involved. Five responsibilities that each group member should follow are introduced in this section. Students will find these helpful throughout the course. You might want to encourage students to dedicate a special section of their notebooks for notes about using their calculators so that they can refer back to these notes when they have forgotten a certain calculator procedure.

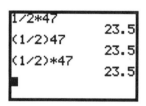

Your calculator may connect directly with a computer to produce printouts for classroom use. This graphic at left is a computer printout generated using software that emulates the calculator showing different ways the expression $\frac{1}{2}(47)$ can be entered. On most calculators, you will have to enclose a fraction in parentheses or else the the number or variable that follows the denominator will be included as part of the denominator. Sometimes a multiplication symbol must be used to separate the two quantities. Implied multipli-cation with fractions will need to be treated again and again throughout the course. For example, the graph of $y = \frac{1}{2}x$ should not be a hyperbola. Most student errors are caused by the omission or misuse of parentheses.

Ask students to describe when parentheses are needed and when they are not. Rule of thumb: If you are unsure, put them in. Explain error-handling difficulties in an expression like $\sqrt{137 - 2.4^7}$. Be sure that students understand why an error occurred.

Extra Examples:

2π or $2 \cdot \pi$ or $2(\pi)$ or $(2)(\pi)$: Some calculators will also allow $(2)\pi$.

24^2 or 24^2: Some calculators will have an x^y key instead of the ^ key.

Expression	Calculator answer
$\sqrt{2+\pi}$	$2.2675\ldots$
$\sqrt{2\pi}$	$2.5066\ldots$
$\sqrt{2}\cdot\pi$	$4.442229\ldots$
$\frac{1}{2}(47)$	23.5
$\frac{1}{3+\pi}$	$0.16282\ldots$
$\sqrt{137-2.4^7}$	ERROR, because $137-2.4^7 < 0$ (The complex answer is $17.9345i$.)

Investigation 0.1.1: Cross-Number Puzzle

This investigation gives you an opportunity to observe the students. There is a worksheet master available for this investigation. Move around the classroom, helping when asked, but, in general, allow students to help each other. Everyone will learn from previous mistakes and make necessary adjustments.

Investigation 0.1.2: Camel Crossing the Desert

This investigation is difficult. The problem seems unrelated to the rest of the chapter, but it is a good problem or investigation for introducing the dynamics of groupwork. Hopefully, you will be surprised by the variety of approaches. The investigation is always worth some class time even if groups don't arrive at the optimal answer.

Students are not used to problems that they can't solve immediately, and they often think there is something wrong with the teacher, the problem, or themselves if a solution isn't apparent in a few minutes. Start this problem in class. Then give students several days to come up with a strategy and solution. Periodically allow them class time to work on this investigation. Ask groups to present their solutions to the class or to write them up more formally. These presentations can be acted out using some creative manipulatives.

An "improved" group solution should pass two tests: (1) Is the process correct? and (2) Is the proposed answer bigger than the previous best answer?

The following answer is not necessarily the best; it is just the best that the authors could find. *You will better appreciate the problem if you don't look at the solution until you and your students have first done some exploration.*

Take 1000 bananas, go 200 miles, leave 600 bananas, return to start. Take 1000 more bananas, go 200 miles, pick up 200 more bananas, go $333\frac{1}{3}$ miles, leave $333\frac{1}{3}$ bananas, return to 200-mile mark, pick up 200 bananas, return to start. Take the last 1000 bananas, go 200 miles, pick up 200 bananas, go $333\frac{1}{3}$ miles, pick up $333\frac{1}{3}$ bananas, go $466\frac{2}{3}$ miles to the other side of the desert. You have $533\frac{1}{3}$ bananas left.

PROBLEM SET NOTES

Encourage students to work on their homework with partners. By working together, students overcome some of the frustrations they may experience as they try to solve nonroutine and real-world problems. Although it may not apply in this section, demand that students record their work as well as their answers. If they say, "I did it all on the calculator," ask them to record the entry process, difficulties encountered, the graphing window used, a sketch of the graph, several terms of the sequence, and so on. The homework paper should reflect their processes, organization, and pride in their effort; it should be usable later when they refer back to a problem. If you allow students to use their homework on certain assessments, they will find that answers alone are not very helpful.

Suggested Assignments

Individual	Group	Essential	Performance assessment	Portfolio	Journal
1, 3, 4, 5	2, 6		1	Inv. 0.1.2, 5	3d

Section 0.2
Fractions, Decimal Numbers, and Scientific Notation

OBJECTIVES

- To explore methods for converting fractions to decimals and decimals to fractions
- To convert between scientific and normal (decimal) notation

MATERIALS

None

RESOURCES

Calculator Notes 0B and 0C

TEACHING NOTES

Some students will be familiar with much of this material from previous courses, so they can present it to other students. Ask good questions, and allow thinking time before allowing anyone to give an answer. Consult with the chemistry and physics teachers to see how they use scientific notation. Coordinating teaching strategies and objectives will be helpful to all. Students have the tendency to copy the calculator screen as their answer. Encourage them to translate some answers into scientific notation without using their calculators.

Investigation 0.2.1: Fractions and Decimal Numbers

This investigation takes a lot of calculator time, which is one of its goals. More time spent with the calculator now will help students use the machine better later on.

Recognizing the repeating unit in part 1 of the investigation may be difficult for some students. The last digit displayed will be rounded. Review with students the concept that any fraction, when converted to a decimal number, will result in either a terminating or a repeating decimal.

In part 2c, students may have difficulty finding the correct denominator by which to multiply. A systematic plan for finding these denominators is helpful. For example, don't try 2, 5, 8, 10, and so on. Encourage students to look at the decimals obtained from fractions with denominators of 3 and 6.

Part 1

a. 2 and 5

b. Any number that does not have a factor of 2 or 5

c. If the denominator of a fraction has only factors of 2 or 5, the fraction will be a nonrepeating decimal. If the denominator contains any other factors, the fraction will be a repeating decimal.

Part 2

a. The result is the numerator of the original fraction.

b. $\frac{4}{33}$

c. i. $\frac{2}{11}$ ii. $\frac{19}{11}$ iii. $\frac{5}{14}$

PROBLEM SET NOTES

In Problem 1, don't expect students to know or understand these formulas. However, they should be able to evaluate them for given values of the variables. The following are explanations for what each formula represents.

a. This is the Lorenz contraction for the length of an object of rest length *L*, traveling at velocity *v* (where *c* is the speed of light).

b. This is Planck's constant as determined from electrons of voltage *V* with charge *e*, which give off X-rays of wavelength *L*.

Problem 3 involves writing about scientific notation. For Problem 6, the distance from Lake Michigan to Lake Erie is about 170 miles. For Problem 8, the masses of a hydrogen atom and an electron are listed in the paragraphs immediately before Example 4. Problem 9 requires students to write about the advantages and disadvantages of groupwork in the course thus far.

Suggested Assignments

Individual	Group	Essential	Performance assessment	Portfolio	Journal
1–5, 9	6–8		1, 2	5, 6, 7	3, 9

Section 0.3
Using the Graphing Calculator

OBJECTIVES
* To gain familiarity with the procedures for setting a specific graphing window
* To enter a function, set an appropriate graphing window, and graph the function

MATERIALS
None

RESOURCES
Calculator Notes 0D and 0E

Review quiz for Chapter 0 to be given after this section

TEACHING NOTES
In Example 1, let the students generate (*base, area*) data points and, as a group, determine a good window to display these points. Students are beginning the process of determining an appropriate graphing window for a particular situation. Encourage explanations and discussions describing why certain graphing windows are more appropriate than others. Students will also review the concept of absolute value and look at the graph of this function.

PROBLEM SET NOTES

For Problems 2 and 3, there should be some discussion as to which is the best window and why. Encourage students to verbalize their reasoning. It is important that the students sketch the graphs neatly, include units on the axes, and label significant points in the graph. Students need to realize the importance of making accurate sketches rather than a crude copy of the graphing calculator screen. Do not become alarmed if students are unfamiliar with the formulas. In this text, formulas and equations are not normally presented for students to use. In general, students generate data or are given data, and then they are asked to model the situation with an equation. Problems 7 and 8 ask students to describe problems in which they have found graphing calculators to be helpful.

Suggested Assignments

Individual	Group	Essential	Performance assessment	Portfolio	Journal
3, 5, 6, 7, 8	1, 2, 4		5		7, 8

Assessing What You've Learned—Organizing Your Notebook

This section asks students to assess their own work. It is suggested that they review their work to make sure they demonstrated their knowledge of the concepts learned in each section.

In this course, students will complete investigations, groupwork, assignments, journal writing, calculator methods, and projects. They may wish to divide their notebooks into sections that reflect these categories.

Chapter 1
Patterns and Recursion

Overview

Chapter 1 introduces students to exploring patterns using recursively defined sequences. They will explore and discover the methods for finding arithmetic and geometric sequences and series. Writing recursive routines to generate sequences will seem very natural to your students. Most of the sequences and series they will work with can be applied to a variety of interesting application problems and investigations.

Encourage students to find solutions by exploring the situation rather than by using a formula. When students are asked to find a growth rate that causes a given initial population to increase to a certain level, or a payment that allows a loan to be paid off in a given amount of time, encourage them to use a creative and productive guess-and-check approach.

From the home screen they will enter computations and routines like 4 $\boxed{\text{ENTER}}$ Ans + 6 $\boxed{\text{ENTER}}$. When students tire of pushing $\boxed{\text{ENTER}}$ to find terms well into a sequence, they are ready for the RECUR program. This short program can be adapted by students to find solutions to very difficult problems. Expect a lot of trial-and-error. The RECUR program is officially introduced in Section 1.5, but it probably would be most appropriately introduced when your students beg for some relief from pushing $\boxed{\text{ENTER}}$ repeatedly. This may occur in the later stages of Section 1.3 or in Section 1.4. The RECUR program is clearly outlined in Calculator Note 1C.

The investigations in this chapter serve two purposes. They give students a way to explore and discover recursively defined sequences and series while introducing them to working in groups. Because working as a team is such an integral part of this course, several opportunities for groupwork have been provided in this first chapter to expose students to the benefits of working together.

Section 1.1
Recursively Defined Sequences

OBJECTIVES

- To recognize and visualize mathematical patterns
- To understand, use, and write recursive definitions for arithmetic, geometric, and other sequences

MATERIALS

Introductory Example Demonstration

    Square tiles, toothpicks, coffee stirrers, or graph paper

RESOURCES

Worksheet Masters for Section 1.1: Investigation 1.1.1

TEACHING NOTES

Use Investigation 1.1.1 to introduce this section. Allow students time to gain familiarity and practice with arithmetic and geometric sequences. Introduce situations that involve adding a common difference and multiplying by a common ratio. Give them time to explore how to convert these expressions to Ans + d or $r \cdot$ Ans form they have used on their calculators.

Investigation 1.1.1: Shifting Funds

Use this investigation to introduce students to the concept of recursion. Students need no prior knowledge of recursively defined sequences and should be given time in their groups to discover their own methods to complete this investigation. One way to do this investigation is to provide each group with a set of clue cards and instructions. After the groups have completed the investigation, have them share their methods, findings, and success as a group with the class.

	Car "Lotta" Doe	Les Cache	Hollie Hacker
Start or Seed	2000	470	0
1st night	1950	510	10
. . .			
17th night	**1150**	**1150**	**170**
. . .			
25th night	750	1470	250
26th night	**700**	**1510**	**260**
Routine	Ans − 50	Ans + 40	Ans + 10

PROBLEM SET NOTES

Problems 2 and 3 make use of recursive routines similar to the one used in Problem 1. Problems 4, 6 and 8 are bathtub-related problems.

Suggested Assignments

Individual	Group	Essential	Performance assessment	Portfolio	Journal
1–5	6–8		3	Inv. 1.1.1	

EXTENSION

Project: Interest, the Bank, and Rounding Off (in the *Teacher's Resource Book*)

Section 1.2
Modeling Growth

OBJECTIVES

- To solve problems by writing and using recursive routines using the Ans function
- To begin identifying the initial terms in real-world sequences as the *y*-intercept

MATERIALS

None

TEACHING NOTES

Use Investigation 1.2.1 to introduce this section. Investigation 1.2.2 is essential for explaining and demonstrating the core material. If you haven't done so earlier, introduce the $u_n = u_{(n-1)} + d$ and $u_n = r \cdot u_{(n-1)}$ notation and show students how they can convert to the Ans $+ d$ or $r \cdot$ Ans form they have used on their calculators.

When approaching difficult problems, encourage students to calculate the first few terms using as many steps as needed. They should write these steps down, try to combine the steps into one line, and then use the previously calculated answers to check that their routine is correct.

Investigation 1.2.1: Pyramid Investment Plan

Round number	1	2	3	4	5	6
Letters sent	200	2,400	28,800	345,600	4,147,200	49,766,400
Responded	12	144	1,728	20,736	248,832	2,985,984

a. 12   b. 144   c. See completed table.

d. Yes; $14,929,920   e. 2,400   f. 54,290,600 households

g. $1.94 \cdot 10^{15}$ households   h. 92,000,000

i. Answers will vary. Chain letters and pyramid schemes are productive for those who initiate the scheme. The schemes quickly consume all potentially interested households.

Investigation 1.2.2: Investing with Meg Abux

a.

Elapsed time (yr)	0	1	2	3	4	...	7	...	10	...	n
Balance ($)	2,000	2,140	2,289.80	2,450.09	2,621.59	...	3,211.56	...	3,934.30	...	$u_n = \text{Ans}(1 + 0.07)$

b. 17 yr

c.

Elapsed time (yr)	0	1	2	3	4	...	7	...	10	...	n
Balance ($)	2,000	2,170	2,354.45	2,554.58	2,771.72	...	3,540.28	...	4,521.97	...	$u_n = \text{Ans}(1 + 0.085)$

d. 14 yr

e. Answers will vary. It takes only 14 yr for the balance to grow to at least $6,000 at 8.5%. It takes 17 yr for the balance to grow to at least $6,000 at 7%.

f. This number is the decimal form of the monthly interest rate.

g. $2,176.78; $2,806.53; $3,618.46; 13 yr; it occurs in 13 yr rather than 14 yr.

PROBLEM SET NOTES

Problem 2 is a follow-up to Investigation 1.2.1. As an extension of Problem 5, Problem 6 requires students to research information about the student's city, county, or state.

Suggested Assignments

Individual	Group	Essential	Performance assessment	Portfolio	Journal
1, 3, 4, 6	2, 5		4	Inv. 1.2.1, 2, 6	2

Section 1.3
A First Look at Limits

OBJECTIVES

- To experiment with sequences that introduce the concept of a limit
- To predict and identify limits of real-world sequences

MATERIALS

Investigation 1.3.1

> One large clear plastic or glass container (fishbowl or 2-liter soda bottle)
>
> One large measuring cup or beaker
>
> One small measuring cup
>
> Large spoon or ladle
>
> Liquid food coloring
>
> Water
>
> Two pails

TEACHING NOTES

In this section, students are introduced to recursive notation for sequences. This notation is more abstract and may confuse some students at first until they realize that $u_{(n-1)}$ is *the previous answer* (Ans on their calculator).

$$u_n = \begin{cases} 450 & \text{if } n = 0 \\ 0.75 \cdot u_{(n-1)} + 210 & \text{if } n > 0 \end{cases}$$

A demonstration of Investigation 1.3.1 is an effective concrete example to introduce recursive notation and the concept of limit.

*Investigation 1.3.1: Color Concentration

Students will remember this investigation and classify many future problems or situations as "like the Color Concentration Investigation." It takes planning and effort to round up materials, but this investigation is essential to the course.

- Use one of the pails to hold water.

- Invite four students to act out or perform the roles of nurse, patient, medical recorder, and calculator technician.

- Ask the class to visualize a nurse-patient situation and to keep track of the amount of medicine (the food color) in a patient's blood supply.

- The *patient* holds one large container to represent his or her blood supply.

- The *nurse* gives the patient a spoonful of medicine (food color and water) from the small measuring cup.

- The patient's kidney removes one-fourth of the total solution. (The patient uses the large spoon or ladle to put the eliminated portion into one of the pails.)

- The *recorder* keeps track of the changing amounts of medicine.

- The *technician* works the overhead calculator.

The entire scenario (it can be light and humorous) can be presented in a short time period. Exact measurements are not important. Keeping track of the theoretical medicine amounts in a table is important.

Part 1

a.

Time period	Amount of clear liquid (mL)	Amount of colored liquid (mL)
0	984	16
1	988	12
2	991	9
3	993.25	6.75
long run	1000	0

b. Amount of clear liquid: $u_0 = 984$; $u_n = u_{(n-1)}(1 - 0.25) + 250$

Amount of colored liquid: $u_0 = 16$; $u_n = u_{(n-1)}(1 - 0.25)$

c. 10 hours

d. Clear liquid: 1000 mL; Colored liquid: 0 mL

Part 2

a.

Time period	Amount of clear liquid (mL)	Amount of colored liquid (mL)
0	984	16
1	972	28
2	963	37
3	956.25	43.75
long run	936	64

b. Amount of clear liquid: $u_0 = 984$; $u_n = u_{(n-1)}(1 - 0.25) + 234$

Amount of colored liquid: $u_0 = 16$; $u_n = u_{(n-1)}(1 - 0.25) + 16$

c. No. Answers will vary.

d. Clear liquid: 936 mL; Colored liquid: 64 mL

PROBLEM SET NOTES

Students need to do Problems 1 and 2 before doing Problem 3. Problem 8 extends work initiated in Investigation 1.3.1. Problems 5 and 9 will be revisited and extended repeatedly during the year. Problem 7 is a continuation of Problem 6. Problem 10 is a continuation of Problem 4.

Individual	Group	Essential	Performance assessment	Portfolio	Journal
4, 6, 7, 9, 10	1–3, 5, 8	5, 9	2, 3	6, 7	

EXTENSIONS

Take Another Look 1.3

Project: Automobile Depreciation

Project: Fibonacci's Rabbits (in the *Teacher's Resource Book*)

Section 1.4
Graphing Sequences

OBJECTIVES

- To display, organize, and visualize sequences with graphs
- To understand the connection between points on a graph and (n, u_n)
- To represent and understand graphs of sequences as discrete graphs

MATERIALS

Investigation 1.4.1

Graph paper

RESOURCES

Calculator Notes 1A and 1B

Quiz covering Sections 1.1 to 1.3

TEACHING NOTES

Students are introduced to graphs (point plots and scatter plots) of sequences and begin making important connections between tables, graphs, and symbolic representations of sequences. Instructions on scatter plots and point plots are available in Calculator Notes 1A and 1B.

Investigation 1.4.1: Uncle Scrooge's Investment

a. The balance does not earn interest.

Time	Now	After 1 yr	After 2 yr	After 11 yr	After 12 yr	After 15 yr	After 16 yr
Balance	$50,000	$40,000	$32,000	$4,294.97	$3,294.97	$294.97	0

Explanations will vary. However, 20% of the previous balance is withdrawn during each of the first 11 years because that amount is greater than $1,000. During years 12–15, $1,000 is removed. The final $294.97 is removed during the sixteenth year.

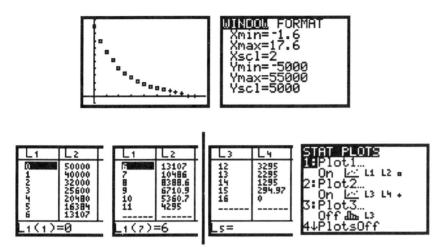

b. The balance earns 8% annually. (This interpretation assumes 20% is withdrawn and then the remainder earns 8% over the next year.)

Time	Now	After 1 yr	After 2 yr	After 16 yr	After 17 yr	After 21 yr	After 22 yr
Balance	$50,000	$43,200	$37,324.80	$4,821.59	$4,127.32	$748.57	0

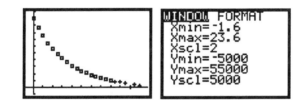

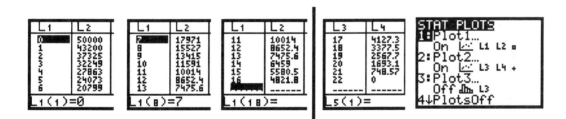

PROBLEM SET NOTES

Problem 3 is an extension of Problem 2. Problem 4 offers an extension of Investigation 1.4.1. Problem 5 is an extension of Problem 5 in Problem Set 1.3. Problem 6 is similar to Investigation 1.3.1.

Suggested Assignments

Individual	Group	Essential	Performance assessment	Portfolio	Journal
1–3	4–6			Inv. 1.4.1, 4	4

EXTENSIONS

Take Another Look 1.4

Take Another Look 1.4a (in the *Teacher's Resource Book*)

Project: The Gingerbread Man (Calculator Note 1E needed)

Section 1.5
A Recursive Routine for Sequences

OBJECTIVE

• To enter, alter, execute, understand, and use a calculator program for a recursive routine that can quickly provide answers that otherwise would involve a long tedious process

MATERIALS

Investigation 1.5.1

   Tower of Hanoi puzzles

RESOURCES

Transparency Master for Section 1.5: Calculator Note 1C

Calculator Note 1C

TEACHING NOTES

Your students either have been using the RECUR program already or will begin to use it in this section. It is found in Calculator Note 1C. After students are comfortable with the original version of the program, add the program line that plots the (N, Ans) values. Students should enter and edit the program repeatedly to make it work for them. This process keeps them in touch with the meaning of the numbers and points that are produced and with the meaning of the lines of code that make up the program.

Calculators designed since 1983 have a built-in sequence mode that is better on some calculators than others. This feature is improving on newer calculators. You will have to decide if your students are better off using the RECUR program or the built-in sequence mode. Specific advice is given in the calculator notes for each calculator.

Investigation 1.5.1: The Tower of Hanoi

If you don't have the puzzles, students can can move a poker chip, a half dollar, a quarter, a nickel, a penny, and a dime, or they can use different-sized washers, which can be purchased inexpensively at a hardware store. Use three X marks drawn on paper to substitute for the pegs. Begin this investigation by demonstrating the puzzle to the class and then ask the students for predictions about how long it would take for the priests to move all 64 disks. Let them complete the investigation in groups and then discuss their methods and results.

Part 1

a.

Number of disks	1	2	3	4	5	6	7
Number of moves	1	3	7	15	31	63	127

b. Moves needed for 3 disks + 1 (for the bottom disk) + moves needed for 3 disks; moves needed for 4 disks + 1 (for the bottom disk) + moves needed for 4 disks; moves needed for $(n - 1)$ disks + 1 (for the bottom disk) + moves needed for $n - 1$ disks.

c. 1 ENTER

   2 • Ans + 1 ENTER repeatedly

d. $1.84467441 \cdot 10^{19}$ moves

Part 2

a. $\{3, 5, 7, 9, \ldots\}$

b. 129 in.

c. Answers will vary, but students should be able to defend their answers. The average diameter would be 66 in. (more than 5 ft). Undoubtedly the time should be more than 1 min because of the distances, the stack heights, and the weight of the disks. The answers to parts d and e assume a time of 1 min.

d. $1.84467441 \cdot 10^{19}$ min, or about $3.51 \cdot 1013$ yr

e. About $3.51 \cdot 10^{13}$ yr after 3000 B.C.

PROBLEM SET NOTES

Problem 3 is another look at Problem 5 in Problem Set 1.3. Problem 7 is a first look at the California Problem, which students will revisit throughout the course.
Problem 9 asks students to analyze their role as a group member during the course so far.

Suggested Assignments

Individual	Group	Essential	Performance assessment	Portfolio	Journal
1, 2, 4, 7, 9	3, 5, 6, 8	6, 7	1	5, 7	9

EXTENSIONS

Take Another Look 1.5

Project: Recursive Midpoint Games (Calculator Note 1F needed)

Have students construct their own Tower of Hanoi puzzles

Section 1.6
A Recursive Look at Series

OBJECTIVES

- To identify similarities and differences between sequences and series
- To find the sum of recursively defined sequences
- To recognize, understand, and use different representations of sequences and series

MATERIALS

Investigation 1.6.1

    Chessboards

    Small supply of grain or rice

    Paper or cardboard

    Tape

    Rulers

    Scissors

    Resources for students to research volume formulas for containers

    Geometric solids (optional)

RESOURCES

Transparency Master for Investigation 1.6.1

Calculator Note 1D

TEACHING NOTES

Introduce the concept of partial sums (or series) using the garbage statistics in the introductory paragraph. Let students experiment with the program in Calculator Note

1D. Students will figure out the difference between a sequence and a series and learn how and when to use each. Have students complete Investigation 1.6.1 in groups. Consider using part 2 of Investigation 1.6.1 as an out-of-class longer-term project, or use it as an extra-credit project.

Investigation 1.6.1: Wheat on a Chessboard

This investigation will be referred to in later chapters, so it is important for students to do at least the first part of the investigation.

Before students begin this investigation, ask them to predict how many grains the inventor will receive on the 64th square and how big the container will have to be to hold all the grains. Students will be surprised by the rapid growth of the number of grains required for a square. You can use rice grains and a transparent grid to demonstrate this problem on an overhead projector. Geometric solids may be helpful for your students when designing the containers. Please note that students should be aware that it is very difficult if not impossible to constuct all eight containers.

Part 1

Number of squares	1	2	3	4	5	6	7	8	64
Number of grains	1	2	4	8	16	32	64	128	$9.22337204 \cdot 10^{18}$

Row number	1	2	3	4
Total number of grains	$2^8 - 1$	$2^{16} - 1$	$2^{24} - 1$	$2^{32} - 1$
Volume	1 cm^3	$(6.4 \text{ cm})^3$	$(41 \text{ cm})^3$	$(2.6 \text{ m})^3$

Row number	5	6	7	8
Total number of grains	$2^{40} - 1$	$2^{48} - 1$	$2^{56} - 1$	$2^{64} - 1$
Volume	$(16 \text{ m})^3$	$(104 \text{ m})^3$	$(0.66 \text{ km})^3$	$(4.19 \text{ km})^3$

PROBLEM SET NOTES

Problems 5, 7, and 9 ask students to find the sum of a series in a real-world context. The other problems deal with series in a more abstract sense. Problem 10 asks students to reflect on the use of the graphing calculator in the course.

Suggested Assignments

Individual	Group	Essential	Performance assessment	Portfolio	Journal
1–5, 9, 10	6–8		1, 2, 8	Inv. 1.6.1, 7, 9	10

EXTENSIONS

Geometer's Sketchpad Investigation: Constructing a Sequence

Section 1.7
Chapter Review

OBJECTIVE

• To review the mathematical terms, concepts, and problem-solving skills in Chapter 1

RESOURCES

Quiz covering Sections 1.4 to 1.6

Test on Chapter 1 to be given following this section

TEACHING NOTES

Review the important concepts of the chapter. Assign the chapter review and allow the students to work together to solve the problems while you circulate to answer questions. Students may wish to present their solutions to the class as part of the review.

Suggested Assignments

Individual	Group	Essential	Performance assessment	Portfolio	Journal
1–7			7		

Assessing What You've Learned—Journal Writing

Journal writing is formally introduced at the end of this section. Several problems throughout each chapter are journal prompts. They usually appear as the last problem in a section. Students are asked to look back at Problem Sets 1.5 and 1.6 for examples.

Students are reminded to make sure their notebooks are kept organized and to record calculator techniques in their notebooks that they found helpful in this chapter.

Chapter 2
Sequences and Explicit Formulas

Overview

This chapter contains more problems involving arithmetic and geometric sequences and series. Students will discover and develop the explicit formulas as they complete the investigations and problems. If they have personally figured out the patterns and essential components of the formulas, chances are much better that they will understand them, know which one to use, and know where to use it. Encourage students to work problems both explicitly and recursively, especially if they are reluctant to move away from comfortably familiar recursive approaches.

Section 2.1
Explicit Formulas for Arithmetic Sequences

OBJECTIVES

- To discover some limitations of a recursive definition

- To find and use explicit formulas to describe arithmetic sequences

- To explore some connections between recursive definitions, explicit formulas, and linear graphs and equations

MATERIALS

None

RESOURCES

Transparency Master for Section 2.1: Sequences

Calculator Note 2A

TEACHING NOTES

Students will gain more familiarity and practice with arithmetic sequences, but this time they will use and write formulas that make a connection between the index n and u_n. A transparency master is available for these sequences.

The first table is determined by $u_n = n^2$; so $u_{10} = 100$ and $u_{17} = 289$:

n	1	2	3	4	5	6	7
u_n	1	4	9	16	25	36	49

The table in Example 1 is determined by $u_n = 2(1 + 3n)$:

n	1	2	3	4	...	11	...	25	n
u_n	8	14	20	26	...	68	...	152	$2(1 + 3n)$

The pattern in this table is the first letter of the number name:

n	1	2	3	4	5	6	...	10	...	11	...	18	19
u_n	O	T	T	F	F	S	...	T	...	E	...	E	N

The pattern in this table involves squaring:

n	1	2	3	4	...	11	...	20	...	n
u_n	2	5	10	17	...	123	...	401	...	$n^2 + 1$

In the formula in Example 2, $u_n = 6n - 4$, the slope (or common difference) is 6 and the intercept is −4. Students plot the points and see that the explicit formula contains the slope and intercept values, specifically, the u_n-intercept. Now students can find specific terms like u_{22} by substitution rather than by relying on the RECUR program in Calculator Note 1C.

There are several ways the calculator can be used to evaluate expressions. On a TI-82, students can enter 22→n: $6n - 4$ [ENTER]. (On a TI-81, this is a two-line routine because the [:] command isn't available. Therefore, they would have to enter 22→n [ENTER] and then $6n - 4$ [ENTER].)

PROBLEM SET NOTES

It is very likely that your students won't discover the explicit formula $u_n = slope \cdot n + vertical\ intercept$ until they work with the problem set. Problems 3 and 4 force them to think about and test some important connections that lead to this explicit formula. Problem 5 introduces arithmetic means.

Suggested Assignments

Individual	Group	Essential	Performance assessment	Portfolio	Journal
1, 2, 4, 6, 7, 9	3, 5, 8, 10	3, 4, 9	1, 2	10	

EXTENSIONS

Take Another Look 2.1

Section 2.2
Explicit Formulas for Arithmetic Series

OBJECTIVES

• To recognize the difference between a sequence and a series

• To discover and use an explicit formula for arithmetic series

• To use sigma notation for an arithmetic series

MATERIALS

Investigation 2.2.2

  Toothpicks or coffee stirrers

TEACHING NOTES

As students study Example 1 and do the investigations, they will invent and use an explicit formula for arithmetic series—probably some form of $S_n = \frac{n(u_1 - u_n)}{2}$.

This section also introduces sigma notation for finding the sum. Students will find this very difficult at first, but with practice, by the end of the chapter they will be proficient with sigma notation.

Investigation 2.2.1: Arithmetic Series Formula

Before splitting into groups, have each student write down an arithmetic series consisting of 10 to 20 terms different than any they have seen before. Have them identify the start value and the common difference. Students should work on the investigation in groups.

a. Answers will vary.

b. Students should check their work using the method introduced in Section 1.6.

c. Students might first find u_{15} by using a slope of 2,000 and a u_0 value of 16,400.

   Entering $S_{15} \rightarrow n$: $2000n + 16400$ as the value of u_{15}.
   Therefore, $S_{15} = 18{,}400 + 20{,}400 + 22{,}400 + \cdots + 46{,}400$, or
   $\qquad S_{15} = 46{,}400 + 44{,}400 + \cdots + 18{,}400$ (The series written backwards)
   $\qquad 2S_{15} = 15 \cdot (18{,}400 + 46{,}400)$ (There are 15 pairs with the same sum), or
   $\qquad S_{15} = 486{,}400.$

Investigation 2.2.2: Toothpick Trapezoids

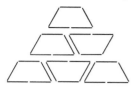

This investigation helps students recognize the difference between a sequence and a series. Some students learn better when they use manipulatives. If toothpicks or stirrers aren't available, students can draw the trapezoids.

	Term	Sum
$n = 1$	5	5
$n = 2$	9	14
$n = 3$	13	27

The sum of all the toothpicks used must be less than or equal to 1000. Though it is always difficult to predict solution strategies, students probably will use either the recursive or the explicit form of the Series Program in Calculator Note 1D. Inserting a Pause command after the display line is an efficient way of controlling the outcome.

a. If n equals 21, $u_n = 4n + 1$ becomes $4(21) + 1$, or 85 toothpicks in the last row.

b. 21 rows

c. The total number of toothpicks used in all 21 rows is

$$5 + 9 + 13 + \cdots + 85 = \frac{21 \cdot (5 + 85)}{2} = 945 \text{ toothpicks.}$$

d. One explanation is that each row of toothpicks represents a term of the sequence. The series is the sum of the number of toothpicks in all the rows.

PROBLEM SET NOTES

Encourage students to solve each problem both recursively and explicitly. Problem 3 is necessary for students to practice sigma notation.

Suggested Assignments

Individual	Group	Essential	Performance assessment	Portfolio	Journal
1–6	7–9	9	1, 2, 3	8	

EXTENSIONS

Have students create a problem similar to Problem 8 that fits your own school auditorium.

Section 2.3
Explicit Formulas for Geometric Sequences

OBJECTIVES

- To find and use an explicit formula to describe a geometric sequence

- To explore, compare, and contrast recursive definitions, explicit formulas, and related graphs

MATERIALS

Investigation 2.3.1

> One superball per group
>
> One meter stick or tape measure for each group
>
> Several 200 cm sections from a roll of butcher paper (optional)

RESOURCES

Quiz covering Sections 2.1 to 2.2

TEACHING NOTES

In this section, students gain more familiarity and practice with geometric sequences. They will write explicit formulas that make a connection between the index n and u_n.

One interpretation of the first paragraph of this section is to assume that the program is transferred from the teacher's calculator to one student's calculator during the first 20 seconds. During the next 20 seconds, each of the two calculators is used to transfer the program to two new calculators. In the next time period, four new calculators receive the program, and so on. During $(5 \cdot 20)$, or 100, seconds, more than 25 students would have received the program $(1 + 2 + 4 + 8 + 16 > 25)$, and within $(8 \cdot 20)$, or 160, seconds, more that 250 students $(1 + 2 + 4 + 8 + 16 + 32 + 64 + 128 > 250)$ would have received the program.

Number of calculators receiving	1	2	4	8	16	32	. . .
Time (seconds)	20	40	60	80	100	120	. . .

Investigation 2.3.1: Bouncing a Superball

This investigation introduces a real-world application of a geometric sequence. It is an integral part of introducing the explicit formula for a geometric sequence. Give the students time to determine their own strategy for conducting this experiment before gathering their materials and collecting data.

Remind your students that consistency is important. They need to think about how and where the ball is dropped and how and where to calculate the height of the rebound. If, for example, they ask if they can drop the ball from other heights, ask them, "Do you think it will make a difference? How would you test to see if it does make a difference?"

Each group should conduct their own experiment and use their own data. Students might have to collect data in the gym, cafeteria, or hallway because the floor needs to be level, without cracks, and not carpeted. One option is to tape 200 cm strips of paper to the wall or against the lockers so that they can mark the heights of the bounces. The most efficient procedure is to collect data for the first rebound height from ten trials, then data for the second rebound height for ten trials, and so on. This helps eliminate the "Twister Game effect." However, to help develop problem-solving skills, let the groups develop their own procedures and strategies.

a. Tables will vary. Here is one example of the first three bounces.

Trial number	First rebound height	Second rebound height	Third rebound height
1	160	120	100
2	155	118	91
3	153	116	82
4	151	119	92
5	154	119	89

b. If the ratio is 0.77, an "ideal" completed table will look like the table below. Experimental results will definitely show the pattern, but entries will not be as exact or consistent as these.

Rebound number	Average height	Ratio
0	200	
1	154	0.77
2	118.6	0.77
3	91.3	0.77
4	70.3	0.77
5	54.1	0.77
6	41.7	0.77

c. Answers will vary. For the above example, $r = 0.77$, or 77%, rebound

d. The most influential factors are the ball and the type of floor. Other factors might be the way the ball is dropped, the temperature, and so on.

e. $u_0 = 200; u_n = 0.77 \cdot u_{(n-1)}$

f. An expression for the second term is $u_2 = 200 \cdot r^2$.

g. $u_5 = 200 \cdot r^5$

h. $u_n = 200 \cdot r^n$

i. In general, the nth term of a geometric sequence is $u_n = u_0 \cdot r^n$.

PROBLEM SET NOTES

Students need to do Problem 2 before Problem 3. Problem 7 uses the bouncing-ball results. Problem 10 works well as a journal entry.

Suggested Assignments

Individual	Group	Essential	Performance assessment	Portfolio	Journal
1, 2, 4–6, 10	3, 7–9	2	1, 4, 6		10

EXTENSIONS

Project: Instant Money

Project: AIDS Epidemic (in the *Teacher's Resource Book*)

Section 2.4
Explicit Formulas for Geometric Series

OBJECTIVES

- To recognize the difference between a sequence and a series

- To discover and use an explicit formula for geometric series

- To use sigma notation for a geometric series

MATERIALS

None

TEACHING NOTES

In Investigation 2.4.1, students will discover the explicit formula for the sum of a geometric series. This is the only place where this explicit formula is developed. Example 1 and Example 2 use a particular form of the explicit formula for a geometric series. Students should test it, as well as the formula they generated in the investigation, and explore the advantages and disadvantages of each formula. This section also gives students more practice with sigma notation.

*Investigation 2.4.1: Explicit Geometric Series

If students don't do this investigation, then an alternative investigation needs to be provided.

Here is a sample response using June 4 as the birth date: $r = 6$ and $u_1 = 4$.

a. 4, 24, 144, 864, 5184, 31,104

b. 24, 144, 864, 5184, 31,104, 186,624

c. 4, 186,624

d. $4 - 186{,}624 = -186{,}620$

e. $\dfrac{4 - 186{,}624}{1 - 6} = \dfrac{-186{,}620}{-5} = 37{,}324$

f. $4 + 24 + 144 + 864 + 5184 + 31{,}194 = 37{,}324$

g. In this case, you have $\dfrac{u_1 - u_7}{1 - r}$ or $\dfrac{u_1 - u_1 \cdot r^6}{1 - r}$.

   In general, $S_n = \dfrac{u_1 - u_{n+1}}{1 - r}$ or $\dfrac{u_1 - u_1 \cdot r^n}{1 - r}$ or $\dfrac{u_1 \cdot (1 - r^2)}{1 - r}$.

h. It won't work because $r = 1$ makes the divisor zero.

PROBLEM SET NOTES

Problem 7 is related to Investigation 1.6.1 in Section 1.6.

Suggested Assignments

Individual	Group	Essential	Performance assessment	Portfolio	Journal
5–8	1–4	1	1, 4		

EXTENSIONS

Project: Living in the City

Section 2.5
In the Long Run

OBJECTIVE
• To investigate what happens to sequences and sums "in the long run"

MATERIALS
Investigation 2.5.1

    A small cup of 150–200 beans or other counters for each group

RESOURCES
Worksheet Master for Section 2.5

TEACHING NOTES
Your students have developed some form of each of the four explicit formulas high-lighted in this section. This is the first time these formulas have been listed in print for students. In this section, students are exposed to a variety of applications where they have to think about the long-run (or infinite) situation. The concept of a limit is introduced in Investigation 2.5.1.

The sequence of falling distances for the bouncing ball is represented by 200, 160, 128, 102, 82, . . . , 0. The calculator soon rounds these decreasing values to zero even though they are actually tiny positive falling distances. Encourage your students to find out where their calculator gives up and rounds $200 \cdot (0.80)^n$ to zero. Encourage them to think about r-values that allow r^n to go to zero as n increases.

Because the falling distances are becoming smaller (approaching zero), the sum of these falling distances will approach a limiting value as the ball continues to bounce.

Encourage your students to play with increasing values of n to see what happens to $\frac{200[1 - (0.80)^n]}{1 - 0.80}$. This gives them an opportunity to see that if $(0.80)^n \to 0$, then the geometric sum approaches $\frac{200[1 - 0]}{1 - 0.80}$, or 1000 cm. In fact, the calculator will eventually give 1000 cm as the sum.

Investigation 2.5.1: Counting Beans
In this investigation, students explore limiting values with different start values and percentages. You will need to judge in how many of the five parts of the bean investigation you want students to actually manipulate the beans. For some students, moving beans in part a only might be sufficient.

Number of beans in the pile	10	18	24	29	33	. . .	48
Number of transactions	1	2	3	4	5	. . .	∞

Below are two calculator routines that will produce the table entries above.

   i. In the MODE menu, select 0 decimal places rather than the usual float setting. A recursive routine is:

      10 $\boxed{\text{ENTER}}$

      Ans(1 − 0.20) + 10 and press $\boxed{\text{ENTER}}$ repeatedly.

   ii. In the usual float setting,

      10 $\boxed{\text{ENTER}}$

      round(Ans(1 − 0.20), 0) + 10 and press $\boxed{\text{ENTER}}$ repeatedly.

The command round(expression, 0) rounds Ans(1 − 0.20) to zero decimal places. In the long run, the number of beans in the pile is 48.

a.

Number of beans in the pile	150	130	114	101	91	. . .	50
Number of transactions	1	2	3	4	5	. . .	∞

If you start with 150 beans, and each time remove 20% and add 10 beans, the long-run number of beans in the pile is 52.

b. i. The results would have been decimal parts of beans.

    ii. The final outcome is 50. However, it takes much longer to arrive at this answer.

    iii. 20% of 50 beans will equal the 10 beans added each turn. Therefore, the final result will be the same.

c.

Number of beans in the pile	10	13	15	17	19	. . .	25
Number of transactions	1	2	3	4	5	. . .	∞

If you start with 10 beans, and each time remove 20% and add 5 beans, the long-run number of beans in the pile is 25.

d.

Number of beans in the pile	150	125	105	89	76	. . .	25
Number of transactions	1	2	3	4	5	. . .	∞

If you start with 150 beans, and each time remove 20% and add 5 beans, the long-run number of beans in the pile is 25.

e.

Number of beans in the pile	10	18	23	27	31	. . .	40
Number of transactions	1	2	3	4	5	. . .	∞

If you start with 10 beans, and each time remove 25% and add 10 beans, the long-run number of beans in the pile is 40.

f. The equilibrium or long-run value, x, must satisfy the equation $x(1 - t) + g = x$, where t is the take percentage and g is the give value. This equation simplifies to $x = \frac{g}{t}$.

PROBLEM SET NOTES
Problem 3 uses the results of Investigation 2.5.1 to revisit Problem 5 in Problem Set 1.3. Problem 11 is a journal-writing prompt.

Suggested Assignments

Individual	Group	Essential	Performance assessment	Portfolio	Journal
1–4, 10, 11	5–9	4, 6	1	5, 8, 9	11

EXTENSIONS
Take Another Look 2.5

Geometer's Sketchpad Investigation: Seeing the Infinite Sum

Section 2.6
Fractal Patterns

OBJECTIVES
• To investigate and create fractal patterns

• To think about what happens to the patterns "in the long run"

MATERIALS
Rulers and protractors

RESOURCES

Transparency/Worksheet Masters for Section 2.6: Fractal Problems

TEACHING NOTES

This is an optional section. It includes problems that apply the concepts that have been introduced in this chapter. It is better for students to work together on these explorations. Encourage students to make neat drawings and to carefully measure line segments and angles with rulers and protractors. Their work will need to be organized if they are going to figure out the patterns. The drawings can also be done on a computer. Using a dynamic geometry program like The Geometer's Sketchpad is an effective way to generate the drawings for these problems.

PROBLEM SET NOTES

Consider assigning the problems (or some of them) as extended individual or group projects that can be completed over a longer time period, written up, and presented to the class.

Suggested Assignments

Individual	Group	Essential	Performance assessment	Portfolio	Journal
4	1–3			4	

EXTENSIONS

Take Another Look 2.6

Project: Sierpiǹski Carpet

Section 2.7
Chapter Review

OBJECTIVE

• To review the mathematical terms, concepts, and problem-solving skills in Chapter 2

RESOURCES

Quiz covering Sections 2.3 to 2.5

Test on Chapter 2 to be given following this section

TEACHING NOTES

Review the important concepts of the chapter. Assign the chapter review and allow the students to work together to solve problems while the teacher circulates to answer questions. Students may wish to present their solutions to the class as part of the review.

Suggested Assignments

Individual	Group	Essential	Performance assessment	Portfolio	Journal
1–11			2, 4		

Assessing What You've Learned—Portfolios

Portfolios are formally introduced at the end of this section. Students learn the difference between their journals and entries in their portfolios. Prompts are provided for the students to document their entries in the portfolio.

Students are also reminded to review their journal entries in Problem Sets 2.3 and 2.5 and to organize their notebooks.

Chapter 3
Introduction to Statistics

Overview

Graphing data is critical to understanding the data. Pictures tell us a great deal, but no one picture can tell us everything. In this chapter, students learn how to depict data using several kinds of one-variable data graphs. They study some numerical measures of data that will help them better understand and interpret information.

From this point on, students will occasionally work with very large data sets. Every calculator has its limitations by design or available memory. Read Calculator Note 3A to find out specific information on the limitations of various calculators.

Section 3.1
Box Plots and Measures of Center

OBJECTIVES
- To explore random sampling concepts
- To identify and use concepts, definitions, and vocabulary related to the typical data value in a set of data
- To construct and recognize important elements of box-and-whisker plots

MATERIALS
Human Box Plot Activity
    Numbered index cards, chalk, or masking tape
    100 ft of clothesline

Investigation 3.1.1
    Decks of playing cards

Investigation 3.1.2
    Watches or clocks with second hands

RESOURCES
Transparency Masters for Section 3.1: Toothpaste Data and Box Plot

Calculator Notes 3A, 3B, and 3C

TEACHING NOTES

There are several activities in this section that help to introduce the median, the mean, and the box-and-whisker plot. The Human Box Plot Activity (see below) is a very powerful demonstration of the box-and-whisker plot. It provides an excellent introduction to this chapter. Investigation 3.1.1 demonstrates the idea of a random sample space. Investigation 3.1.2 gives additional practice on finding the mean and median and graphing a box-and-whisker plot.

Calculator Note 3C describes how to plot a box-and-whisker plot on the calculator. However, for some calculators, graphing the box plots by hand probably will be a more efficient use of time.

If the students are not familiar with linking their calculators, this is a perfect time to teach them how to link. By linking with each other, students can share data sets and avoid the frustration caused when large data sets are entered incorrectly.

Human Box Plot Activity

Depending on the size of your class, the Human Box Plot Activity is best done outside or in a gym or hallway.

- Have the students arrange themselves in a line according to their heights. As they are arranging themselves, place index cards or mark the floor at 1-foot intervals with the numbers 56 to 75 to represent the heights of the students in inches. You may need to adjust the minimum or maximum to fit your class situation. These numbers should be in a line parallel to the student line a few feet away.

- Ask the students to find the median person and have that person stand in front of the number that is his or her height. (If the median is between two people, choose one of them—perhaps by a coin toss—to stand at the mean of their two heights.)

- Ask the students to find the median student of each half of the split group, and have each of these students stand in front of his or her height. (See the note above if the median is between two students.)

- Have the first and last person in the line (the minimum and maximum values or extremes) stand in front of their heights.

- You should have five people standing in a line away from the group, as in the diagram below.

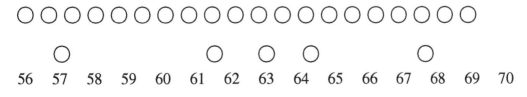

- Starting at one end, pass the clothesline from person to person among the five students who are standing on the numbers, having them hold the line as shown in the diagram below.

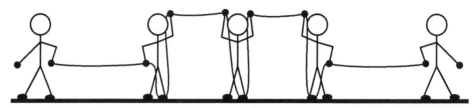

Guide a discussion on how this graph was formed. Upon returning to the classroom, the students can write their height data on the board and re-create the box plot on paper.

Extension for this activity: After the students have modeled the box plot and you have discussed all the elements, have the students form a histogram by letting everyone form a line behind their height. After the elements of a histogram have been discussed, change the interval by picking up every other index card or having the students stand on multiples of two. This is a dynamic demonstration of the meaning of the interval on a histogram.

Investigation 3.1.1: Random Samples

This investigation will help promote discussion about the need for making random sample selections. It will help to show why statistics that come from a random sample of a set provide statistical information about the whole set. It is not critical to do this investigation, but the concept should be discussed when you are analyzing a random sample of some data set. Sample results are shown below:

a. There are four cards with values 2, 3, . . . , 9 and sixteen cards with a value of 10, so the average value is $\frac{4(2 + 3 + 4 + \cdots + 9) + 16(10)}{48} = 7$.

b. Let C represent Clubs; D, Diamonds; H, Hearts; and S, Spades.

Trial #1 cards

3 C, 5 S, 6 S, 7 C, 7 S, 8 H, 9 D, 10 D, J C, K S   Average value = 7.5

c. Trial #2 cards

2 C, 4 S, 5 D, 5 S, 6 D, 6 H, 7 S, 8 D, J H, Q S   Average value = 6.3

Trial #3 cards

3 D, 3 S, 8 D, 8 S, 9 H, 10 D, 10 S, J D, Q H, K S   Average value = 8.1

Trial #4 cards

3 H, 6 D, 7 C, 7 D, 8 D, 9 C, 9 S, 10 S, J D, J H   Average value = 7.9

Trial #5 cards

2 C, 2 H, 5 C, 6 C, 9 S, 10 D, 10 H, Q H, Q S, K C   Average value = 7.4

Trial #6 cards

2 C, 3 C, 4 H, 6 C, 6 H, 7 S, 8 S, 9 S, 10 D, 10 S   Average value = 6.5

d. The average of the ten lowest-value cards is 2.6.

e. The average of the ten highest-value cards is 10.

f. Answers will vary. The average of these six trials is 7.28.
    Data will vary, but the average should be close to 7.

Investigation 3.1.2: Pulse Rates

Collecting data from the class takes time and organization, but it is far more motivating and interesting for students to analyze their own data than to consider a supplied data set. You can always save and use these collected data sets again. For example, you can use this data set when studying histograms or for comparing and contrasting various methods of representing data.

The data will vary depending on your students, their exercise choice, and their level of physical fitness. Most resting pulses should fall between 60 and 80 beats per minute. After exercise, these values will increase. Displaying both graphs simultaneously will help motivate reactions and discussion.

PROBLEM SET NOTES

Students need to do Problems 2 and 3 before doing Problem 4. Problem 4 introduces and defines interquartile range and outliers. Problems 5 and 10 refer to the toothpaste data listed at the beginning of this section in the textbook. The explanation of outliers in Problem 4 is necessary to complete Problems 6, 7, and 9.

Suggested Assignments

Individual	Group	Essential	Performance assessment	Portfolio	Journal
1–3, 8, 9	4–7, 10	4	1	Inv. 3.1.2	2

EXTENSIONS

Project: Stem-and-Leaf Plots

Section 3.2
Measures of Variability

OBJECTIVE

• To identify and use deviation, mean absolute deviation, and various deviation sums to describe variability

MATERIALS

Investigation 3.2.1

    Rulers, meter sticks, and/or tape measures

RESOURCES

Transparency Master for Section 3.2: Deviations

Calculator Notes 3D and 11E

Data and Programs Disk

TEACHING NOTES

Investigation 3.2.1 provides an excellent investigation to review mean and median. In this section, students will learn how to find the deviation and mean absolute deviation.

A data disk is available in the *Teacher's Resource Book* that contains the long data sets for this section and can be linked to the calculator. If your classroom does not have a computer link, it will be easier and more accurate for two students to enter lengthy data sets if one student reads the numbers and the other enters them. The data may be copied to other calculators through the linking process. If the calculators do not have this feature, then the students can share the one calculator with the data.

Investigation 3.2.1: A Typical Student

Collecting the data will take time, and you might want the class as a whole to choose which measurements to take. For example, have one group collect all of the nose length measurements, while another collects all of the height data. You can also use the pulse rate data from the previous section. It is important that students realize that neither the mean nor the median tells the whole story of what a typical mathematics student is like. At least one teacher extended this investigation by encouraging an artistic student to utilize the calculated statistics to create a full-size "typical student" poster.

PROBLEM SET NOTES

Problem 3 uses the information provided in Example 2 of this section. Problem 7 uses the data provided in Problem 6. Problem 10 is a journal-writing prompt.

Suggested Assignments

Individual	Group	Essential	Performance assessment	Portfolio	Journal
1, 2, 4, 5, 10	3, 6–9	1, 4	4		10

EXTENSIONS

Take Another Look 3.2

Geometer's Sketchpad Investigation: Comparing the Mean and the Mean Absolute Deviation

Project: Collecting Data

Section 3.3
Histograms and Percentiles

OBJECTIVES

- To display and organize data in a histogram
- To find, explain, and use the percentile rank of a data value

MATERIALS

None

RESOURCES

Quiz covering Sections 3.1 to 3.2

Calculator Note 3E

TEACHING NOTES

Because some students have never drawn a histogram by hand, it is important that they do this in order to have a grasp of how the calculator makes the plot. Collecting and using data that relates to your own students makes it more meaningful to them.

When creating histograms on the calculator, make sure that students understand that the x-max value must be larger than the largest data value. Otherwise, they may not see the last bar of the graph. For example, if the data values range from 12 to 80, and they group these using bar widths of 10, the 12 will be included in the bar between 10 and 20 and the 80 will be included in the bar between 80 and 90. If the x-max value is not set above 80, they will not see this final bar. The interval or the width of the bar may be determined by the x-scale.

Another caution when plotting histograms on the calculator involves the number of bars allowed. Because it takes two pixels to draw a bar of a histogram, students cannot specify more bars than one-half the number of pixels across the screen. For most calculators, this is 95 pixels, which means you cannot have more than 47 bars.

As a summary activity, have students bring graphs and data from newspapers and magazines to class. Discuss how the same data can be presented in different ways to support various hypotheses.

Note: The data in Example 2 will be used again in Problem 6, Problem Set 3.4.

Investigation 3.3.1: Fast Food
Students may also collect additional data from local fast-food restaurants to add to or replace the data in the text. Posters or other displays made from this data can be shared with health classes and other interested groups. There are many possible combinations of information that students may choose to investigate. Their reports may be short and limited or elaborate, involving prepared charts and posters, depending on how much you wish to do with the data.

PROBLEM SET NOTES
Problem 1 asks students to graph the histogram on their calculator using Calculator Note 3E for help. Problems 2 and 5 ask students to construct both box plots and histograms for a set of data. Problem 4 involves percentiles. Problem 8 has students discuss the advantages and disadvantages of histograms and box plots.

Suggested Assignments

Individual	Group	Essential	Performance assessment	Portfolio	Journal
3–6, 8	1, 2, 7	1, 6	3, 4	Inv. 3.3.1, 8	6, 8

EXTENSIONS
Take Another Look 3.3

Project: Standard Deviation (requires Calculator Note 11E)

Project: Adding Graphs (in the *Teacher's Resource Book*)

Section 3.4
Chapter Review

OBJECTIVE
• To review the mathematical terms, concepts, and problem-solving skills in Chapter 3

RESOURCES
Quiz covering Section 3.3

Test on Chapter 3 to be given following this section

TEACHING NOTES

Review the important concepts of the chapter. Assign the chapter review and allow the students to work together to solve problems while you circulate to answer questions. Students may wish to present their solutions to the class as part of the review.

PROBLEM SET NOTES

Problem 6 uses the data from Example 2 in Section 3.3. Problem 8 refers to Example 2 in Section 3.2.

Suggested Assignments

Individual	Group	Essential	Performance assessment	Portfolio	Journal
1–8				8	

Assessing What You've Learned—Performance Assessment

Students are asked to analyze their work and make sure they understand the step-by-step process in plotting histograms and box plots. They are also reminded to review their journal entries in Problem Sets 3.2 and 3.3, organize their notebooks, and update their portfolios.

Chapter 4
Data Analysis

Overview

In this chapter, students are more formally introduced to the equation of a line. Concepts of slope, intercept, and finding the equation of a line are presented in the context of real-world data analysis. Students are asked to think about the real-world meaning of numbers and equations as they work and to "make sense" of answers and predictions.

Some students may have learned about the "magic calculator regression buttons" from their work in other classes or from other students. Use of these calculator regressions, before they are introduced in the text, may hinder a student's understanding of the processes and concepts involved.

The long data sets in this chapter become very tedious for students to enter on the calculator. A disk with the data sets for this chapter, which can be used with a computer/calculator link program, is included in the *Teacher's Resource Book*.

Section 4.1
The Best-Fit Line

OBJECTIVES
- To define a mathematical model
- To consider guidelines and criteria for a best-fit line
- To draw a best-fit line that represents approximately linear data

MATERIALS
Investigation 4.1.1

    Graph paper

    Measuring tapes or yard/meter sticks

    Access to a parking lot with cars

    Clear plastic rulers

RESOURCES
Transparency Masters for Section 4.1: Best-Fit Line

Transparency/Worksheet Masters for Section 4.1: Problems 1 and 2

Data and Programs Disk

TEACHING NOTES

Before students read the four guidelines for finding a best-fit line, have them draw their own best-fit line and compare their results using some set of data, whether from Investigation 4.1.1 or a class investigation. Have students read the guidelines for constructing a new best-fit line and then have them construct one of their own. It will be beneficial for your students if you then review the guidelines with the entire class. Finding the best-fit line may be a new concept for your students. However, a thorough explanation and practice with the problems in their groups will guarantee student success.

Investigation 4.1.1: Car Data

This investigation is a good introduction to finding the best-fit line. It produces data that will show some linear correlation. If it is not possible for your students to measure cars, they can find and use similar data from recent issues of *Consumer Reports.*

PROBLEM SET NOTES

Use the Worksheet Masters for Problems 1 and 2. Graph paper will make finding the best-fit line much easier. For Problem 3, any scale that shows Pluto will make it impossible to distinguish Mercury, Venus, and Earth. Problem 5 uses the best-fit line drawn in Investigation 4.1.1. The data and information presented in Problems 3, 4, and 5 will be used again in Problem Set 4.2. The domain and range are not specified in Problem 6. Therefore, there are actually six problems here. Let each member of the group graph a different possibility. Problem 7 is a journal-writing prompt.

Ask different students or groups to share answers with the class. A good class discussion about difficulties that arise in plotting data, trying to fit data, and how to resolve these problems may be valuable.

Suggested Assignments

Individual	Group	Essential	Performance assessment	Portfolio	Journal
1, 2, 4, 7	3, 5, 6	1–3	2		7

EXTENSIONS

Take Another Look 4.1

Section 4.2
Equation of a Line

OBJECTIVES

- To find the slope of a line when given two points, the equation, or a graph

- To find the point-slope form of a linear equation given two points

- To write the equation of a line when given its graph or sufficient information about its graph

MATERIALS

Investigation 4.2.1

   Graph paper

   Calculator with recursive program or procedure

   Rulers

RESOURCES

Calculator Note 4A

Data and Programs Disk

TEACHING NOTES

The students may be curious about what is studied in trigonometry and calculus. If they have studied some right triangle trigonometry in a previous course, the "rise over run" definition of slope is the same as the tangent ratio that they learned. In some cases, a brief discussion of how this concept is related to the derivative may be appropriate.

Use class time to strengthen students' understanding of slope and intercept. Students should be able to recognize the slope of a line as being positive or negative, greater than one, or less than one. Given two lines, they should be able to identify the line with the greater slope. They should also know where to find the y-intercept on a graph and be able to sketch a line by hand. Having students verbally describe how to graph a given linear equation is also a good activity. For instance, given the equation $y - 5 = 2(x + 3)$, you should expect students to respond, "Starting at the point $(-3, 5)$, draw a line up and to the right at a slope steeper than 45°." Given the equation $y = -0.2x - 4$, you should look for a response like, "Draw a line that slopes slowly down to the right and passes through -4 on the y-axis."

The emphasis is on the point-slope form of the line because it is far more applicable to lines not near the y-axis. The slope-intercept form is introduced later as a simplification of the point-slope form.

Investigation 4.2.1: Financing a Car Loan

This investigation serves as a review of the loan-payment problems from Chapter 1. It provides an alternative method of finding the correct monthly payment.

a. The object of this investigation is to collect some random data. Have each member of the group choose a payment value and determine the balance remaining for that payment. Tell students not to try a second value and not to try to zoom in on the answer. A table of sample results is shown below.

Payment	Balance remaining
150	8,819.28
200	4,843.37
250	867.47
300	−3,108.44
350	−7,084.34

The correct payment is $260.91.

b. Graphs will vary. As students draw their graphs, each group should think about labels for the axes. The horizontal axis is monthly payment in dollars, and the vertical axis is the balance after 60 months.

c. The equations should be close to $y = -79.52x + 20,747$.

d. $260.91

e. Answers will be very close to zero.

f. $20,474. The y-intercept has no meaning for loan payments. It is the value of $12,000 *invested* at 11% for 5 years, or what you would owe if you made $0 payments.

g. $79.52. The slope indicates the decrease in the balance after 5 years per $1 increase in payment. In a sentence, "The balance at the end of 5 years will decrease by $79.52 for every $1 increase in monthly payments."

PROBLEM SET NOTES

Problems 5–7 require students to use the data and information provided in Problems 3–5 of Problem Set 4.1. The solution strategy developed in the Investigation 4.2.1 is required for Problem 8.

Suggested Assignments

Individual	Group	Essential	Performance assessment	Portfolio	Journal
1–4, 6	5, 7, 8	3, 4	1, 2, 3, 4		

EXTENSIONS

Take Another Look 4.2 (in the *Teacher's Resource Book*)

Section 4.3
Real-World Meanings

OBJECTIVES

- To analyze data pairs and determine which are independent values and which are dependent values, thus finding the domain and range values

- To interpolate and extrapolate with a linear model and to identify inherent difficulties involved

- To provide real-world meanings for values and variables of a linear model and for answers obtained with the model

MATERIALS

Investigation 4.3.1

   One to three stopwatches or digital watches with stopwatch function

RESOURCES

Data and Programs Disk

TEACHING NOTES

In this section, students examine and explore real-world meanings for answers, slopes, and intercepts. They won't be experts immediately, however. Try to encourage better dialog and communication in the classroom as groups or individuals share with classmates. Better explanations and better answers are important, but take care that some students aren't harsh or cruel to others. Ask good questions. When examining a model, trace to a point and ask for a sentence or two that describes that particular location. How meaningful are the values obtained by extrapolating with the model? Encourage explanations that are in the context of the real-world situation.

Investigation 4.3.1: The Wave

"The wave" investigation is an excellent way to collect two-variable data. This investigation is more fun when done outside or on gym bleachers. It can also be conducted effectively in the classroom if students have individual chairs and are stretched out in a line or an arc. Use some common characteristic (wearing white socks, having two vowels in the last name, and so on) to select each group to do the wave. The results are more consistent if the entire class sits and tries two or three "practice runs" first because they tend to try to beat the last group's time and become faster. Be sure to have a range of small, medium, and large size groups. Collect about ten sets of data. Below are sample data and a graph. Students will need to keep their data for use in Problem Set 4.4, Problem 9.

Number of people	2	5	6	8	9	10	15	16	16	22
Time (sec)	2.1	4.4	5.2	5.8	4.7	6.7	7.5	10.4	9.7	11.0

This is good data to use to introduce the median-median line in the next section. If you plan to do this, then you should avoid data with repeated x-values as this can make the median-median procedure more difficult.

In the example at right, the equation of the line might be $y = 0.45x + 1.9$. The slope is 0.45 sec per additional person. The y-intercept of 1.9 sec is more difficult to explain and often provides for a lively debate. The number includes the difficulty of synchronizing starts and the time for half a person to do the wave—the time person 1 stands to the time the last person sits.

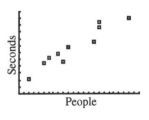

a. Answers will vary. The slope should have units like "seconds per increase of a person" meaning that the time increases m seconds if one more person is added to the group.

b. Answers will vary. If the y-intercept is positive, this is because you are timing the period between the instant the first person starts to stand and when the last person has finished sitting down.

c. Answers will vary. The x-intercept would represent the number of people in a group in which the wave would time zero seconds.

d. The domain should start at one person and increase to the number of students in the entire class.

PROBLEM SET NOTES

Problems 1–4 are review questions. Problems 9 and 10 give a range of values for a single data element. This may offer a challenge to some students. In Problem 9 ask students to defend their selections of x-values for their points. In Problem 10 find out what value they used when asked about 40-yr-old men and whether or not it was consistent with the decision they made on *x*-values. It is easy and common to use midpoints of the intervals, but this still leads to many problems with end intervals that are left open. In some cases it may even be impossible to use the first or last data point.

Suggested Assignments

Individual	Group	Essential	Performance assessment	Portfolio	Journal
1, 2, 4–8	3, 9, 10	7	1, 4	9	

EXTENSIONS
Project: Talkin' Trash

Take Another Look 4.3 (in the *Teacher's Resource Book*)

Section 4.4
The Median-Median Line

OBJECTIVES
- To learn the median-median best-fit procedure
- To find an equation of a line parallel to a given line.
- To calculate the median-median line as a model for a given data set without using the built-in calculator routine
- To begin thinking about the difference between a data value and a value predicted by the median-median model

MATERIALS
Investigation 4.4.1

    Springs

    Ring stands

    Clamps

    Mass hangers

    Masses

OR

    One-half of a metal Slinky Jr.

    Ruler

    Film canister

    String or paper clips

    M&Ms or some other small objects as the units of mass

RESOURCES

Transparency Masters for Section 4.4: Median-Median Line

Calculator Notes 4B and 4C

Data and Programs Disk

TEACHING NOTES

After your students have read and worked through the median-median procedure, provide an opportunity for sharing. It will be worth your time to do a step-by-step review of the procedure perhaps using the data collecting in Investigation 4.3.1. This is an opportunity for students to review and improve manipulative skills. They should be locating representative points, finding slopes, writing equations, finding intercepts, and thinking about what they are doing. They should be able to identify real-world meanings for each application. Discourage the use of the "magic button" built into the calculator for finding a median-median line, even though many students will already know how to use it. Later (perhaps the next day), after they have done a few problems, it is appropriate to teach and use this short cut.

Investigation 4.4.1: Spring Experiment

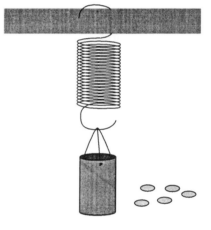

This investigation is a concrete example that applies the use of the median-median line. You may be able to borrow a set of springs, ring stands, clamps, mass hangers, and masses from your physics department. If this is not possible, then an inexpensive alternative is to use one-half of a metal Slinky Jr. as the spring and suspend this over a ruler between two tables or chairs. To the bottom of the Slinky, attach a film canister with string or paper clips through three holes along the top rim of the film can. (Usually film stores are happy to provide you with an ample supply of canisters.) Use M&Ms or some other small objects, such as beans, as the units of mass.

The sample results below were collected using springs, masses, and spring stands borrowed from the physics lab.

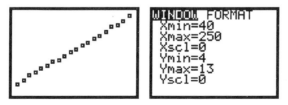

Length = 3.17 + 0.0385(mass)

a. 3.17 + 0.0385(70 g) = 5.865 cm and 6.0 − 5.865 = 0.135 cm

	Mass	Length
1.	50	5.0
2.	60	5.5
3.	70	6.0
4.	80	6.3
5.	90	6.8
6.	100	7.1
7.	110	7.5
8.	120	7.7
9.	130	8.1
10.	140	8.5
11.	150	8.8
12.	160	9.2
13.	170	9.5
14.	180	9.9
15.	190	10.3
16.	200	10.7
17.	210	11.3
18.	220	11.4
19.	230	11.9
20.	240	12.4

b. Answers will vary. For the data set at left:
(170 g, 9.5 cm) has a difference of -0.2115 cm.
(220 g, 11.4 cm) has a difference of -0.2346 cm. We might have measured incorrectly. Perhaps the spring hadn't stopped bouncing.

c. The length increases 0.0373 cm for each gram added. The slope is described in units of "centimeters per gram added."

d. The spring has a length of 3.17 cm with no mass attached. The y-intercept is the length of the unstretched spring.

e. $3.17 + 0.0385(4700 \text{ g}) = 184.12$ cm. If it is no worse than the data we have already gathered, then we expect it to be within 2.4 mm of the actual length because all measurements were within 2.4 mm of the model.

f. The spring began as a coil of wire 1.5 cm in diameter with 49 loops. This makes only $1.5(3.14)(49) = 231$ cm of wire, which will be the most it could stretch.

g. $3.17 + 0.0385(\text{mass}) = 20$, so 437 g should be about right.

Conclusions: We learned that a spring stretches an equal amount as equal amounts of weight are added and that, by measuring the length of the spring, we can find out how much weight is attached. We had difficulties getting exact measurements (see above) because of the bouncing spring, and it was difficult to hold the ruler without bumping the spring.

PROBLEM SET NOTES

Problems 3–6 ask questions about the three representative points, the slope and the equation of the line through the first and third points, the parallel slope, and the equation of the line containing the middle point. They require students to use the median-median procedure rather than get an answer directly by the built-in median-median regression. Problem 8 uses the data from Investigation 4.1.1. Problem 9 uses data from Investigation 4.3.1 and refers to Calculator Note 4C. Problem 12 is a journal-writing prompt.

Suggested Assignments

Individual	Group	Essential	Performance assessment	Portfolio	Journal
1–7, 12	8–11	1, 3, 9	1, 2, 3	11	9, 12

EXTENSIONS

Take Another Look 4.4

Take Another Look 4.4a (in the *Teacher's Resource Book*)

Project: Counting Forever

Section 4.5
The Residuals

OBJECTIVES

- To explore, find, and understand median-median models
- To find, interpret, and understand the residuals related to a model.
- To graph, interpret, and understand how residual plots relate to the model and the data plots
- To use a residual plot to help find a better model

MATERIALS

Investigation 4.5.1
    Airline schedules

RESOURCES

Transparency Masters for Section 4.5: Residuals

Worksheet Master for Investigation 4.5.1

Calculator Note 4D

Quiz covering Sections 4.1 to 4.4

Data and Programs Disk

TEACHING NOTES

This work with residuals and the median-median line procedure will be continued and extended throughout the remainder of the course. Students without list capabilities on their calculators can enter and use the residual program found in Calculator Note 4D. If necessary, set aside some class time so that they can enter and check the program before starting the section.

The procedures listed for finding residuals expect the data and the function to be in the designated location. If you use a different location, make sure the procedure reflects this alternative. The TI-81 program plots the residuals. They are not stored anywhere in the calculator's memory, but you can approximate them using the graphics screen cursor.

Students will have difficulty understanding the concept of changing the slope and y-intercept to better fit the residuals. It is best to let students explore this concept and share their results with the class. After exploration, a demonstration for the entire class may be very helpful.

Investigation 4.5.1: Airline Schedules

This investigation gives students an opportunity to model some nearly-linear data and provides wonderful discussion opportunities involving mistakes, intercepts and their real-world meanings, what is actually being timed, what happens if a flight is reversed, prevailing winds, first flight in the morning versus later flights, local daylight-savings time oddities, and so on. If done thoroughly, the investigation requires most of a class period. Students will have difficulty calculating accurate flight times because of different time zones. The schedule should contain the scheduled times and mileage from a large nearby airport to other cities. Northwest Airlines and Delta Airlines schedules contain such times and mileage.

a.–c. Answers will vary.

d. The slope of their model will be the flight speed in miles per minute.

e. The y-intercept will be the distance at time zero.

f. The x-intercept will be the time it takes for the plane to stay in the airport.

g.–h. Answers will vary.

PROBLEM SET NOTES

Problem 2 refers to the data and model in Problem 7, Problem Set 4.4. Problem 4 uses the residuals found in Problem 3. Problem 6 is a rich problem requiring time and reflection.

Suggested Assignments

Individual	Group	Essential	Performance assessment	Portfolio	Journal
1–3, 7	4, 5, 6	3, 5, 7	1, 7	Inv. 4.5.1	

Section 4.6
The Least-Squares Line

OBJECTIVES

- To explore, find, and understand a least-squares model
- To find, interpret, and understand the residuals related to a model
- To compare and contrast two best-fit linear models

MATERIALS

Investigation 4.6.1

Rulers or measuring tapes

RESOURCES

Calculator Note 4E

Data and Programs Disk

TEACHING NOTES

The examples provide an important explanation for the sum of the squares of the residuals. After working with the least-squares model for a while, provide an opportunity for students to discuss the pros and cons of using this sum as a criteria for a best-fit line. A Geometer's Sketchpad script provides a dynamic demonstration of this model.

Investigation 4.6.1: Relating Body Lengths

If time is limited, you can speed up this investigation by having the entire class collect the same information. However, groups should work independently while finding the least-squares line to fit the data. Have students present their findings and conclusions to the entire class.

PROBLEM SET NOTES

Problem 3 uses the data provided in Example 2 of this section. Problems 5 and 6 require data provided in Problems 3 and 5 of Section 4.5. Problem 8 asks students to look back at the definition of deviation in Chapter 3. Problem 9 uses data collected in Investigation 4.6.1. Problem 12 is a journal-writing prompt.

Suggested Assignments

Individual	Group	Essential	Performance assessment	Portfolio	Journal
1–5, 11, 12	6–10	1, 5		10	8, 9, 12

EXTENSIONS

Geometer's Sketchpad Investigation: Least Squares

Take Another Look 4.6 (in the *Teacher's Resource Book*)

Project: Linear Extrapolation

Section 4.7
Coefficient of Correlation

OBJECTIVES

- To introduce and describe the correlation coefficient
- To use the correlation coefficient to help determine linearity of data

MATERIALS

None

RESOURCES

Calculator Note 4F

Quiz covering Sections 4.4 to 4.6

Data and Programs Disk

TEACHING NOTES

Another way to think about the coefficient of correlation is as a measure of linear "dependency" of y to x. If $r = 0$, then y is independent of x, and if $r = \pm 1$, then there is an exact linear dependence of y on x. Problems in this section may raise more questions than answers. Be prepared to guide class discussions about what all of this means. Allow students to come to terms with the concepts without hard-and-fast rules and definitions.

Investigation 4.7.1: Analyzing Cereals

This investigation is open-ended. Each group can investigate a different linear relationship between the ten different two-variable combinations, using residual sums, mean absolute residuals, residual plots, correlation coefficients, and so on. As an alternative, it may be more meaningful if students gather their own data and try to discover interesting relationships. The class can create a list of suggestions like years they have played a musical instrument versus grade in their last math class, age of mother versus age of father, and so on. After completing the investigation, have each group make a presentation to the class discussing their findings and conclusions.

PROBLEM SET NOTES

Problem 7 uses data from Investigation 4.6.1. The long list of data in Problem 8 should be retained in some calculators so that it can be shared and used in Problem 7 in Problem Set 4.8. Problem 9 is related to Problem 8. Problem 10 is a journal writing prompt.

Suggested Assignments

Individual	Group	Essential	Performance assessment	Portfolio	Journal
1–5, 10	6–9		1, 2, 3	Inv. 4.7.1	10

EXTENSIONS

Project: Least Squares Formulas

Section 4.8
Accuracy

OBJECTIVES

- To explore and develop a common-sense understanding about prediction accuracy
- To explore models, estimate their accuracy, and determine the importance or value of accuracy for each model
- To investigate the dangers of extrapolating with models

MATERIALS

None

RESOURCES

Calculator Note 4F

Data and Programs Disk

TEACHING NOTES

The role of data analysis is important in this course, but the content of this section is not essential to the course. The material is difficult and requires a different level of thinking. A number of suggestions, without many concrete guidelines, are offered. The content requires that students have an understanding of each data set and the ability to use common sense to interpret the data. Collectively, your students may have these qualities. The mathematics is almost minor compared to the critical judgments they need to make on each problem. Almost any answer is a good answer if it is supported with sound, logical reasoning. Working through this section will help many students better understand the concepts of residuals and coefficient of correlation.

PROBLEM SET NOTES

Problem 4 uses the data in Example 1 of this section. Problem 7 requires the long list of data from Problem 8 in Problem Set 4.7.

Suggested Assignments

Individual	Group	Essential	Performance assessment	Portfolio	Journal
1–4	5–8	1			3

EXTENSIONS

Take Another Look 4.8 (in the *Teacher's Resource Book*)

Project: Linear Extrapolation (in the *Teacher's Resource Book*)

Section 4.9
Chapter Review

OBJECTIVE

• To review the mathematical terms, concepts, and problem-solving skills in Chapter 4

RESOURCES

Test on Chapter 4 to be given following this section

Data and Programs Disk

TEACHING NOTES

Review the important concepts of the chapter. Assign the chapter review and allow the students to work together to solve problems while you circulate to answer questions. Students may wish to present their solutions to the class as part of the review.

PROBLEM SET NOTES

Problems 4–27 refer to the same data set. Problem 6 refers to Problem 5. Problems 8–13 use the solution from Problem 7. Problems 15–19 use the solution from Problem 14. Problems 21–25 refer to Problem 20. Problem 26 refers to Problem 23. Problem 27 is a journal-writing prompt.

Suggested Assignments

Individual	Group	Essential	Performance assessment	Portfolio	Journal
1–27			1, 2, 3		

Assessing What You've Learned—Open-Ended Investigations
The purpose of the Take Another Look problems is discussed. Students are encouraged to make up their own open-ended investigations similar to the Take Another Look activities. It is suggested that students include their Take Another Look write-ups in their portfolios or to use one to demonstrate their understanding of a particular concept or procedure.

Students are also reminded to review their journal entries in Sections 4.1, 4.4, 4.6, and 4.7, organize their notebooks, and update their portfolios.

Chapter 5
Functions

Overview

Students begin by sketching graphs that picture personal interpretations of some relationships. They decide if a graph should be continuous or discrete, and then they justify the chosen shape. A surprising amount of information and knowledge generally emerges during small-group and entire-class discussions.

Students study a basic tool kit of functions so that they will recognize and be able to write equations for lines, parabolas, square roots, absolute values, circles, and ellipses. During the chapter, graphs of these functions are translated, flipped, stretched, and composed. In most instances, students will work with "friendly" windows and will frequently use grids to better see important features of the graphs. The notation $f(x)$ and its use are introduced. The transformation work learned in this chapter will apply to functions and relations that appear later in this text (such as exponential, trigonometric, rational, and others).

Section 5.1
Interpreting Graphs

OBJECTIVES
- To investigate dynamic relationships between graphs and real-world situations
- To interpret graphs and to create graphs that accurately describe situations

MATERIALS
None

RESOURCES
Transparency Master for Section 5.1: Soda Machine Graph

Transparency Master for Section 5.1: Examples 1 and 2 Graphs

Transparency Master for Investigation 5.1.1: Invent a Story

Transparency Master for Section 5.1: Roller Coaster (Problem 3)

TEACHING NOTES

A good introduction to this section is the soda-machine graph. Use the transparency master for the soda machine graph and Examples 1 and 2 to encourage creativity in describing graphs and to demonstrate how graphs should be labeled. Several graphing interpretation situations are presented, but you and your students might really enjoy creating some of your own. Actually, this can provide a creative opportunity for students who may not be very good at other kinds of problem solving. Investigation 5.1.1 is a good start for sparking student creativity.

*Investigation 5.1.1: Invent a Story

This investigation provides some fun, a chance for good writing, and an opportunity for students to share their work with others. Many different graphs and stories can accurately describe the given graph, as long as students explain why their graphs are correct. Students should label each change in the graph and explain what is happening at each interval. Have each group present their stories and graphs to the class. Encourage them to be creative with their presentations.

Part 1: Stories will cover a wide range of possibilities.

Part 2:

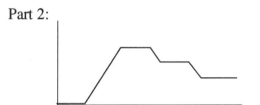

PROBLEM SET NOTES

In the problems, students are asked to invent stories to match graphs or to draw graphs to match stories and situations. Ask several students to prepare different graphs on plastic overlays and explain their solutions to the class. A transparency master is available for Problem 3. In Problems 4–20, students draw a small sketch for each problem and write one or two sentences to justify these sketches. It is not essential that each student do every problem, but the entire set should be covered by the class and shared with classmates.

Suggested Assignments

Individual	Group	Essential	Performance assessment	Portfolio	Journal
2, 12–21	1, 3–11	3	2, 4–21	Inv. 5.1.1	

EXTENSIONS
Take Another Look 5.1

Section 5.2
Connections with Sequences

OBJECTIVES

- To continue the transition from u_n or $u(n)$ sequence notation to $f(x)$ notation
- To investigate further connections between explicit formulas and graphs of arithmetic and geometric sequences
- To identify real-world meanings of slopes, intercepts, and answers

MATERIALS

Investigation 5.2.2

Graph paper

Fahrenheit and Celsius thermometers

Several different mediums in which temperature can be measured

RESOURCES

Transparency Masters for Section 5.2: Examples 1 and 2

TEACHING NOTES

Information pictured in the three graphs of Example 1 reviews familiar explicit arithmetic and geometric sequence formulas with $u(n)$ notation. Then in Example 2, continuous equations for graphs A and B of Example 1 are shown to provide the link between $u(n)$ and $f(x)$. Students will need to change from using u_n notation to $u(n)$ notation, which relates to function notation. Investigation 5.2.1 and its (*time, mileage*) questions about the odometer can lead to a very meaningful discussion on shapes of graphs. You will probably have time to complete both investigations during one class period. The Human Function Activity (later in this section guide) is fun and can be used to introduce the concept of a function.

Investigation 5.2.1: Distance from Home
In this investigation, students are asked to draw graphs picturing the distance between them and their homes from 7 a.m. to 9 p.m. These graphs will vary. The objective of the investigation is for each student to draw a graph that pictures her or his own situation. Then partners are asked to compare graphs and interpret information from the graphs of their classmates.

*Investigation 5.2.2: Temperature Scales

Students will collect Celsius and Fahrenheit temperatures from a variety of sources, plot the (*Celsius, Fahrenheit*) data, write an equation of the relationship, and interpret a variety of real-world meanings. Have students measure the temperatures of a cup of water, a bag of ice, tap water or drinking-fountain water, room temperature, outside temperature, and so on. In some situations, you may be comfortable allowing groups to collect temperatures outside the classroom. An alternative approach would be to use CBLs and temperature probes rather than thermometers. Set one CBL to record temperature in Fahrenheit and the other to record in Celsius.

a. Tables will vary.

b.–c.

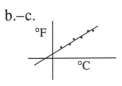

d. $F(c) = 1.8c + 32$

e. $C(f) = \dfrac{(F-32)}{1.8} = \dfrac{5}{9}(F-32)$

f. 35°C

g. 23°F

h. Answers will vary, but look for the absolute deviation from data point to best-fit line.

i. The point (0, 32) is the freezing point of water.

j. The Fahrenheit temperature increases 1.8° for each additional increase of 1° Celsius.

k. $x = 1.8x + 32$ when x is −40.

Human Function Activity

This activity is most easily done in the gym, in an empty parking lot, or on a football field. Have fifteen to twenty students, with their calculators, line up along a marked line such as a yard line or the midcourt line in the gym. The remainder of the students can observe from the sidelines or the bleachers. This line represents the y-axis. Make sure the students are evenly spaced; one arm length apart works well. Next, assign each student a different number, for example, −4, −3.5, −3, −2.5, . . . , 0, . . . , 2.5, 3, 3.5, 4. Using numbers less than −4 or greater than 4 may cause difficulty depending on the functions chosen. Have the entire group take three steps forward. If the line is not straight, ask the students to note the problem (my steps were too big or too small), return to the axis, and repeat until all students can take the same size steps. Next, hold up a piece of paper with a function written on it such as $y = 2x$. Each student then evaluates the function for his or her assigned value and takes that many steps forward if positive, or backward if negative. Have students describe what happened (they form a line). Return to the axis and repeat with another function. Use quadratics, roots, rational functions, trigonometric functions, and exponentials. In each case, ask students to describe the graph. When there are undefined values, have those students either leave the axis or just sit down. After you are finished, ask the students to consider the fact that they never moved sideways or had two different places to go at the same time. This is what a function does—it gives one and only one y-value for each x-value.

Be sure to rotate the groups of students so that all students have a chance to graph values and to observe.

PROBLEM SET NOTES

The problems help students to learn the meaning of a point $(x, f(x))$ and relate this concept to a point on a graph. Problem 1 continues the work started in Example 1. Problem 5 uses the sequence in Problem 4. Problems 4, 7, and 8 make important connections with earlier work in Chapters 1 and 2.

Suggested Assignments

Individual	Group	Essential	Performance assessment	Portfolio	Journal
3–6, 9	1, 2, 7, 8	6, 8	9		

EXTENSIONS

Take Another Look 5.2 (This investigation introduces the concept of "friendly window" and will be valuable and informative for students.)

Take Another Look 5.2a (in the *Teacher's Resource Book*)

Section 5.3
The Linear Family

OBJECTIVES

• To formally introduce the point-slope linear equation $y = m(x - x_1) + y_1$

• To experiment with and discover relationships involving midpoints, parallel lines, perpendicular lines, and slopes

MATERIALS

Graph paper

RESOURCES
Calculator Notes 5A and 5B

TEACHING NOTES
Both slope-intercept and point-slope forms of linear functions are explored in this section. Because students have already worked with $y = mx + b$ earlier in the course, this is a good opportunity to concentrate on the $y = m(x - x_1) + y_1$ form. Many students will enter and graph expressions like $y = \frac{-4x + 16}{-2}$ on their calculators. Other students will enter a simplified alternative $y = 2x - 8$. Situations in which students see, find, and compare alternative symbolic expressions will arise quite naturally throughout the course.

In Investigation 5.3.1, students discover the relationship between slopes of parallel and perpendicular lines. If students do not do this investigation, you must provide an alternative approach.

The last paragraph of the section introduces the SQUARE option for the window setting. In addition, in Calculator Note 5A students learn about the "friendly" window setting that will be used throughout the text. It may be beneficial for students to explore and compare different windows.

If you load the Lines Program into the overhead calculator, you can use this program to randomly generate graphs of lines. You can then ask students to determine the equation of the graphed lines and confirm that they are correct by graphing their equation. This activity provides a good introduction or closure to the section.

*Investigation 5.3.1: Special Slopes
Students will confirm or discover the following relationships.

i. Connecting the midpoints of the sides of a quadrilateral forms a parallelogram.

ii. Opposite sides of a parallelogram are parallel and have the same slope.

iii. The slopes of perpendicular lines are negative reciprocals of each other.

Part 1

a.–c. Answers will vary.

d. Parallelogram

e. Opposite sides are parallel.

f. The slopes should be the same.

g. Yes. The slopes are the same.

h. Parallelogram

i. Answers will vary.

Part 2

a. Answers will vary.

b. The slopes will be negative reciprocals of each other.

c. Slopes will vary. However, the perpendicular slopes should be negative reciprocals.

d. Slopes of perpendicular lines are negative reciprocals of each other.

PROBLEM SET NOTES

Problem 1 refers to Example 1 in this section. Problem 5 introduces the "friendly" window, which will be used throughout the text. This window is discussed in Calculator Note 5A. The short program in Calculator Note 5B can provide an endless number of lines, like those pictured in Problem 6. This program can be used to verify that students are comfortable with graphs and linear equations. Problem 7 introduces the concept of direct variation. Problem 11 uses the data and equation found in Problem 8.

Suggested Assignments

Individual	Group	Essential	Performance assessment	Portfolio	Journal
1–3, 6, 8, 9	4, 5, 7, 10, 11	1, 2, 5	2	Inv. 5.3.1	

EXTENSIONS

Take Another Look 5.3 (in the *Teacher's Resource Book*)

Section 5.4
The Parabola Family

OBJECTIVES

- To translate and reflect graphs of parabolas

- To discover connections between transformations of the basic parabola graph and alterations to the symbolic form of $f(x) = x^2$

- To understand the role of each number, operation, and variable in the equation $y = \pm 1(x - h)^2 + k$

- To discover what happens to the graph of $y = f(x)$ when x is replaced by $(y \pm h)$ and when y is replaced by $(y \pm k)$.

MATERIALS

Graph paper

Transparency Master for Section 5.4: The parabola $y = x_2$

Transparency Master: Grid

RESOURCES

Quiz covering Sections 5.1 to 5.3

Calculator Note 5C

TEACHING NOTES

We recommend that you do not explain the relationship between an equation and its graph. Give your students time to explore the transformations. It is crucial that your students discover and verify these connections through individual or small-group experimentation or, in some cases, logical and organized guesswork. An overhead calculator, white board, and markers allow you and your students to see a graph, predict its equation, identify the important features, and verify the results.

Load the Parabola Program (Calculator Note 5C) into the overhead calculator and use it to either introduce or bring closure to the section.

*Investigation 5.4.1: Make My Graph

This investigation gives students an opportunity to explore characteristics of transformations.

Solutions:

a. $y = x^2 - 4$ b. $y = x^2 - 2$ c. $y = x^2 + 1$ d. $y = x^2 + 3$

PROBLEM SET NOTES

Problem 5 uses the Parabola Program in Calculator Note 5C. It gives students practice finding the equation of a graphed parabola. You can also use the program to summarize the section with the entire class. Problem 9 introduces the graphing form of the parabola equation. Problem 10 provides closure to Example 1 in this section. Though not essential, Problem 12 will be useful for later problems as this is where the concept of average values is introduced.

Suggested Assignments

Individual	Group	Essential	Performance assessment	Portfolio	Journal
1–7	8–12	2–4, 6, 9, 12	5, 8		9

EXTENSIONS

Project: Even and Odd Functions

Take Another Look 5.4

Take Another Look 5.4a (in the *Teacher's Resource Book*)

Take Another Look 5.4b (in the *Teacher's Resource Book*)

Section 5.5
The Square Root Family

OBJECTIVES

- To translate and reflect square root graphs
- To discover connections between transformations of the basic square root graph and alterations to the symbolic form $y = \sqrt{x}$
- To understand the role of each number, operation, and variable in the equation $y = \pm 1\sqrt{x - h} + k$

MATERIALS

Investigation 5.5.1

Graph paper

A string about 3 meters long for each group

A weight (like a nut or washer) for each group

RESOURCES

Calculator Note 5C

TEACHING NOTES

In this section, students graph parabolas that open horizontally by writing and graphing two expressions of the form $y = \pm$ (a square root expression). For example, $(y - 2)^2 = x + 3$ can be written and graphed as $y = \pm\sqrt{x + 3} + 2$ or $y_1 = \sqrt{x + 3} + 2$ and $y_2 = -\sqrt{x + 3} + 2$

Investigation 5.5.1 provides excellent data for a square root fit.

Length (cm)	Period
100	2.0
85	1.9
75	1.8
30	1.4
15	0.9
5	0.6
43	1.4
60	1.6
89	2.0
140	2.4
180	2.6
195	2.9

*Investigation 5.5.1: Pendulum Experiment

This investigation provides data that is not linear. However, students will need to experiment with a variety of string lengths in order to see the square root curvature. This investigation can be conducted in the classroom. To get string lengths that are long enough, one students can simply hold the string, or the string can be taped securely to the ceiling. Outside the classroom, the string can be hung over a stairwell or tied to a tree branch. Over small intervals, a linear model is often a good model. At the right are experimental results from one group of students. The data collected will be used in Problem 9 to find the best-fit equation.

PROBLEM SET NOTES

Problem 9 uses the pendulum data collected in the investigation. Students should find the equation by experimenting with different coefficients in the model $y = a\sqrt{x}$. The graph of the equation $y = 0.21\sqrt{x}$ looks like a good fit.

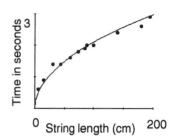

Problem 11 asks students to rewrite the program in Calculator Note 5C for square root functions.

Suggested Assignments

Individual	Group	Essential	Performance assessment	Portfolio	Journal
1–5, 8, 11	6, 7, 9, 10	1, 5–7	1, 3, 7	9	

EXTENSIONS

Take Another Look 5.5

Section 5.6
The Absolute Value Family

OBJECTIVES

- To develop understanding of transformations of all graphs by transforming the absolute value function and altering its equation to a more generic form,
  $y = a|x - h| + k$

- To develop a method for solving $y = a|x - h| + k$ for x when given the value of y

MATERIALS

Graph paper

TEACHING NOTES

Students continue to work on transformations expanding the parent functions to include the absolute value function. As an option, you or one of your students might alter the Parabola Program in Calculator Note 5C to produce an Absolute Value Program for additional practice.

PROBLEM SET NOTES

The problems provide some applications but, in general, are designed to help students make important connections with earlier work. Problem 9 has students solve absolute value equations by graphing. Problem 10 refers to the method in Problem 9. In Problem 11 students should zoom in for accuracy.

Suggested Assignments

Individual	Group	Essential	Performance assessment	Portfolio	Journal
1–7, 9–11	8, 12–14	1–4, 7, 9, 12	3, 7	13	

Section 5.7
Stretching a Curve

OBJECTIVES

- To explore translations, reflections, and stretches of the functions representing the top and bottom halves of a unit circle
- To graph a circle using the two functions $y = \pm a\sqrt{1 - x^2}$
- To graph ellipses by stretching circles

MATERIALS

Graph paper

RESOURCES

Transparency Master: Unit Circle

Calculator Notes 5D and 5G

TEACHING NOTES

Students enjoy graphing circles with their calculators, and it is likely that many of them can already graph one. In this section, they start with the top half of a unit circle and use what they have previously learned to provide the bottom half and to move the circle to different positions on the coordinate axis. To better show the vertical and horizontal stretches, we encourage you to use $y = \pm a\sqrt{1 - x^2}$ rather than $y = \pm\sqrt{r^2 - x^2}$ to generate circles.

Expect to see a variety of different-appearing equations when students write the equation of a circle that has been translated vertically and horizontally and stretched (compressed). Translations and reflections produce images that remain congruent to the original image (pre-image). However, stretches and compressions, like the vertical distortion caused by $af(x)$, mean the original shape and the new graph are not congruent.

PROBLEM SET NOTES

Students will combine translations and stretches or compressions. At times the order doesn't make any difference. However, they will always be correct if they perform any stretches *before* they translate points vertically. Problem 13 refers to Problem 13 in Problem Set 5.6. Problem 14 uses Calculator Note 5D. While not essential, Problem 14 will be useful later for problems related to average value of a function. Problem 15 is a journal-writing prompt.

Suggested Assignments

Individual	Group	Essential	Performance assessment	Portfolio	Journal
1–8, 15	9–14	1–3, 7, 9, 14	2	13	15

EXTENSIONS

Project: The Greatest Integer Function (uses Calculator Note 5G)

Geometer's Sketchpad Investigation: Transforming a Point and a Line

Section 5.8
A Summary

OBJECTIVES

- To summarize what has been learned about transformations
- To carefully develop the function relationship and related vocabulary

MATERIALS

Graph paper

RESOURCES

Calculator Note 5D

TEACHING NOTES

Students review the parent functions of the previous sections in the chapter. Function terminology is discussed in detail, and the vertical line test is introduced. Students are asked to apply their knowledge of transformations of functions to functions they have never seen before. These are skills and concepts that will be used throughout the rest of the text.

PROBLEM SET NOTES

Students will combine translations and stretches or compressions. At times the order doesn't make any difference; however, the results will always be correct if students perform any stretches *before* they translate points vertically. Problem 6 involves a manipulation skill that has not been introduced although your students may have plenty of earlier experiences to draw on. It is a good problem for encouraging students to explore and verify. In Problem 7 the average value of a function and the Average Value Program (Calculator Note 5D) introduced in Problem 14 of Section 5.7 are used to calculate areas of regions. Problem 13 is a journal-writing prompt.

Suggested Assignments

Individual	Group	Essential	Performance assessment	Portfolio	Journal
1–7, 13	8–12	1, 2, 7, 8, 10	1, 2		8, 13

EXTENSIONS

Project: Boolean Graphs

Section 5.9
Composition of Functions

OBJECTIVES

- To explore and understand compositions of functions
- To understand the meaning of expressions like $g(f(x))$
- To find $f(g(c))$ or $g(f(c))$ when given the functions $g(x)$ and $f(x)$
- To explore and explain graphs of $y = ax(1 - x)$ for various values of a

MATERIALS

Graph paper

RESOURCES

Transparency Master for Section 5.9: Web Graph

Worksheet/Transparency Master for Investigation 5.9.1: $f(f(f(f(\ldots f(x) \ldots))))$

Calculator Notes 5E and 5F

TEACHING NOTES

Transformations studied in this chapter have been examples of compositions. The graph of $y = \sqrt{x - 4}$ is the graph of $f(g(x))$ for $g(x) = x - 4$ and $f(x) = \sqrt{x}$. Students will have little difficulty finding the composition of graphs using symbolic manipulation. See Calculator Note 5F for some calculator help with compositions of graphs. One of the challenges facing you and your students throughout this text will be to recognize composition situations.

Investigation 5.9.1: $f(f(f(f(\ldots f(x) \ldots))))$

These solutions were produced using TI-82 screen dumps. The following example is used when the calculator is in sequence mode and web format with the function recursively defined. See Calculator Note 5F.

After you press [GRAPH], select [TRACE] and move through the web with the right arrow key. You can also get a table of values by pressing [2nd] [TABLE].

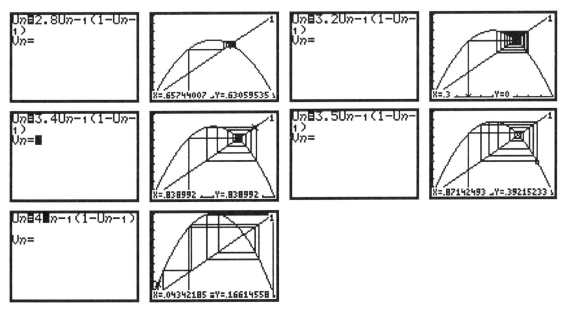

PROBLEM SET NOTES

Problem 9 is related to Investigation 5.9.1 and uses Calculator Note 5F.

Suggested Assignments

Individual	Group	Essential	Performance assessment	Portfolio	Journal
4–7	1–3, 8–10	1, 2, 4, 5, 8	4		10

EXTENSIONS

Take Another Look 5.9 (in the *Teacher's Resource Book*)

Section 5.10
Chapter Review

OBJECTIVE

• To review the transformations, concepts, and problem-solving skills in Chapter 5

RESOURCES

Quiz covering Sections 5.4 to 5.9

Test on Chapter 5 to be given following this section

TEACHING NOTES

Review the important concepts of the chapter. Assign the chapter review and allow the stud
work together to solve problems while you circulate to answer questions.
Students may wish to present their solutions to the class as part of the review.

Suggested Assignments

Individual	Group	Essential	Performance assessment	Portfolio	Journal
1–7			1, 2, 3		

Assessing What You've Learned—Constructing Test Questions

Students are asked to consider how the teacher creates test questions. In groups, students ar
instructed to write five problems that would demonstrate the concepts they have mastered i
this chapter.

Students are also reminded to review their journal entries in Problem Sets 5.8 and 5.9, organize their notebooks, and update their portfolios. They may also wish to create their own investigation pertaining to the material covered in this chapter. One challenge that you could offer to students is to develop a function that has as its graph the one pictured in Problem 3a, Problem 3b, or Problem 6 of Problem Set 5.10.

EXTENSIONS
Project: Melting Ice

Chapter 6
Parametric Equations and Trigonometry

Overview

Students will extend earlier work with transformations of graphs. As they convert between parametric and function forms, they will have the opportunity to manipulate algebraic expressions and equations. The right triangle trigonometry focuses on applications involving motion of objects. Students should be able to make strong connections between real-world motion and the mathematics involved to simulate this motion on their calculators in parametric mode. Students will also investigate geometric figures that are almost impossible to create with only two variables.

Section 6.1
Graphing Parametric Equations

OBJECTIVES

• To simulate objects in motion by writing appropriate parametric equations and setting conditions that allow control of the movement of a point across the calculator screen

• To investigate interesting geometric figures and graphs

MATERIALS
None

RESOURCES
Transparency Master for Section 6.1: Paths

Calculator Note 6A

TEACHING NOTES

As an introduction to parametric equations, sketch the floor plan of your school on the chalkboard or on a transparency. Using different colors, two students can trace their path through the school during a designated day. Are the path intersections real or not? Time, as a parameter, is not graphed, but it is an important ingredient of each point on a path.

Example 1 and Investigation 6.1.1 combined is an excellent introduction to graphing and finding the real-world meaning of parametric equations. It is important that students understand how to find the window to view the paths of the graph. Make sure calculators are set to graph equations simultaneously.

Students enjoy controlling the movement of a point across the screen of their calculator. They answer questions and investigate conjectures by tracing graphs and zooming in on points of interest.

In Example 2, Example 3, and Investigation 6.1.2, students connect parametrics with what they know about using algebraic manipulations, substituting values, and solving equations to arrive at their answers. In Example 3, students find the smallest interval for t that produces the graph pictured in the window $-9.4 \leq x \leq 9.4$ and $-6.2 \leq y \leq 6.2$. It can be found using the equations $x = t - 1$ and $y = \frac{1}{2}t + 2$. If you solve $-9.4 = t - 1$ and $9.4 = t - 1$ for t, you find the interval $-8.4 \leq t \leq 10.4$. However, the graph goes off the top of the screen before t reaches 10.4. This means the interval for t can be further restricted by solving $6.2 = \frac{1}{2}t + 2$. This occurs when $t = 8.4$. Therefore, the smallest interval is $-8.4 \leq t \leq 8.4$. As an alternative, you can use the "friendly" window values for your calculator.

Investigation 6.1.1: Simulating Motion

This investigation continues the simulations in Example 1. Students need to experiment with different expressions and values. Notice (see the screen dump) how the formula $T = \frac{D}{R}$ can be used to find that the slower tanker requires 50 hr to make the 900 mi trip. However, don't force formulas like this (and formal mathematics) too quickly. These ideas will soon be discovered and shared by your students.

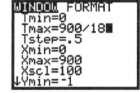

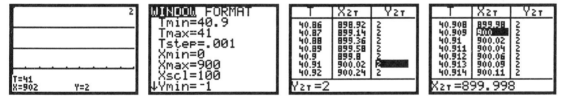

On some calculators, it is very time-consuming to zoom in on a graph or table to find the time for the faster tanker to reach St. Petersburg. The screen dumps show the kind of thinking and setups needed. You can obtain better accuracy using smaller Tsteps. A smaller interval for [Tmin, Tmax] also helps to speed up the process.

Students will create and solve some excellent questions involving the tankers. One teaching strategy is to provide groups with transparencies and overhead pens so that they can quickly share their results with the entire class.

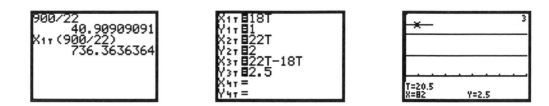

a. Some students are very patient as they search for the answer, and they are surprised (and grateful) when someone suggests $\frac{900}{22}$ is the answer they have been zooming in on.

b. The slower tanker is 736.36 mi into its trip when the faster tanker reaches its destination.

c. It can be tedious to determine when the faster tanker is exactly 82 mi in front of the slower tanker. You may have some clever students who will write and graph a function that represents the distance between the tankers (see x_{3T} in the screen dump). This occurs when $t = 20.5$ hr.

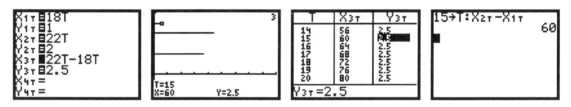

d. The tankers are less than 60 mi apart when $t < 15$. In fact, representations like $22t - 18t < 60$ are probably easier to solve by symbolic manipulation than by simulating them with the calculator.

Investigation 6.1.2: Exploring Parametrics

In this investigation, students experiment using different values in the equations $x = x_0 + at$ and $y = y_0 + bt$. When $0 \le t \le 4$, they will graph a series of line segments starting at the point (x_0, y_0) and terminating at the point $(x_0 + 4a, y_0 + 4b)$.

a. The slope of each segment is $\frac{4b}{4a} = \frac{b}{a}$. See the segment from $(3, -2)$ to $(7, 2)$ in the following example.

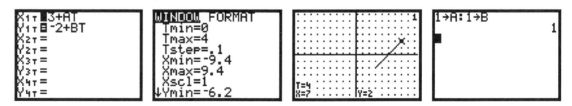

b. Group reports will vary.

c. When $-4 \le t \le 0$, the line segment starts at the point $(x_0 - 4a, y_0 - 4b)$ and terminates at the point (x_0, y_0) as t reaches 0. The slope of each segment is still $\frac{b}{a}$. In the following example, the segment starts at $(-1, -6)$ and ends at $(3, -2)$.

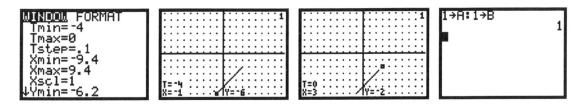

d. Group reports will vary.

e. i. Varying the values of x_0 and y_0 will change the start value of the graph.

   ii. If $m \le t \le M$, then segments will start at $(x_0 + am, y_0 + bm)$ and end at $(x_0 + aM, y_0 + bM)$.

   iii. The slope is $\frac{b}{a}$. In the example below, the slope from $(-6, -7)$ to $(4, 8)$ is $\frac{3}{2}$. If the ratio $\frac{b}{a}$ in one equation is the negative reciprocal of $\frac{b}{a}$ (or $\frac{-a}{b}$) in the other equation, the graphs will be perpendicular. (The segments might need to be extended in order to see this. Also, be sure you're using a "friendly" window.)

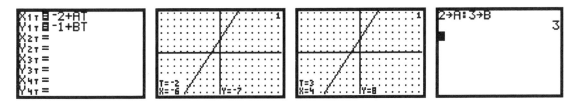

PROBLEM SET NOTES

Problems in this section give students practice with writing parametric equations and their transformations.

Suggested Assignments

Individual	Group	Essential	Performance assessment	Portfolio	Journal
3–6	1, 2	1, 2, 4, 5	1		

Section 6.2
Parametric to Nonparametric

OBJECTIVES

- To focus on the algebraic manipulations required to convert an equation between parametric and nonparametric forms

- To discover that many different parametric equations can correctly represent a graph or nonparametric equation

MATERIALS
None

RESOURCES
Calculator Note 6B

TEACHING NOTES
Provide an opportunity for group members to help bring others up to the level expected. Encourage students to think about what they are doing and to check their results on the calculator. They will make better connections between the two different equation forms if they graph both the parametric and nonparametric equation forms for each problem.

PROBLEM SET NOTES
Problem 3 is an introduction to inverses. Problem 4 requires students to use a "friendly" window. Problem 5 continues to develop transformations of graphs introduced in Section 6.1. Problem 6 asks students to experiment with the parametric equations for perpendicular lines. Problem 7 is an extension of the tanker problems in Section 6.1.

Suggested Assignments

Individual	Group	Essential	Performance assessment	Portfolio	Journal
3, 5–7	1, 2, 4	3, 4, 5, 7	2		

EXTENSIONS
Take Another Look 6.2 (requires Calculator Note 6B)

Section 6.3
Right Triangle Trigonometry

OBJECTIVES
- To discover the sine, cosine, and tangent ratios
- To use these ratios and their inverses to solve appropriate application problems

MATERIALS
Investigation 6.3.1
    Graph paper
    Protractor
    Ruler

Piece of string

Meter stick

Vertical angle measuring device: a plastic straw, protractor, string, a washer for weight, and tape

RESOURCES

Transparency Master for Section 6.3: Gulf Map

Transparency Master for Investigation 6.3.2: VAMD

Worksheet Masters for Section 6.3: Investigation 6.3.2

Quiz covering Sections 6.1 and 6.2

TEACHING NOTES

In this section, students will discover and use trigonometric ratios. Students use diagrams to relate trigonometric ratios to the position of points on coordinate axes. The concept of heading, or bearing, is introduced and will continue to be used for the remainder of the chapter. Use the transparency master of the Gulf map to demonstrate heading and the trigonometric ratios described in the opening paragraphs.

If students do not complete Investigation 6.3.1, then you will need to provide an alternative introduction to trigonometric ratios.

*Investigation 6.3.1: Trigonometric Ratios

In this investigation, students find and compare relationships of trigonometric ratios.

Part 1

a. It is important that students measure angle *A* carefully and correctly. You may need to review with them how to use a protractor. The measure of angle *A* in each triangle will be the same but will vary from group to group.

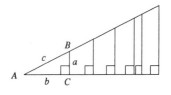

b. Values of *a*, *b*, and *c* will vary.

c.–d. Each group will discover that the entries in the columns headed $\frac{a}{c}$ and sin *A*, $\frac{b}{c}$ and cos *A*, and $\frac{a}{b}$ and tan *A* will contain equal entries.

Investigation 6.3.2: Finding the Height of a Tree

Hypsometers are available in some teacher supply catalogs. As an alternative use a plastic straw, protractor, string, a washer for weight, and tape to make a vertical angle measuring device (VAMD) similar to the one pictured. Students look through the straw to the top of a tree, note the angle of elevation, and use right triangle trigonometry to find the height of the tree. Be careful that students find the angle of elevation with the VAMD and do not read and use

students find the angle of elevation with the VAMD and do not read and use the angle's complement from the protractor.

You'll need to mark a 50 m, or alternative, distance on the ground before class and have *each* student calculate their pace length (not just the walker). Emphasize the instructions that ask students to select trees of the *same* species and measure the circumferences at the *same* height. This is an enjoyable investigation for teachers and students as they collect the data, figure out how to use the information, calculate a best-fit model, and write up their results.

PROBLEM SET NOTES

These problems help develop a strong foundation in trigonometric ratios, which is essential for the rest of the chapter. Be sure to allow enough time for students to do most of them. Problems 4–9 are quite similar. Problems 10, 11, and 12 revisit the tanker problems and prepare students for a series of motion problems that are introduced later.

Suggested Assignments

Individual	Group	Essential	Performance assessment	Portfolio	Journal
1, 2, 6, 7, 9, 10, 12	3, 4, 5, 8, 11	1, 2, 4, 10–12	1, 2	Inv. 6.3.2	

EXTENSIONS

Geometer's Sketchpad Investigation: Trigonometric Ratios

Section 6.4
Geometric Shapes

OBJECTIVE

• To create and explore geometric shapes based on parametric equations of a circle

MATERIALS

None

RESOURCES

Transparency Master: Unit Circle

Transparency Master for Section 6.4: Parametric Equations for a Circle

TEACHING NOTES

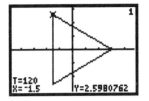

This section is pure fun. Students are generally self-motivated to write equations that replicate the figures pictured. They share different alternatives that produce similar results and try to explain what they have accomplished. In Example 1, the "3" in the equations $x = 3 \cos t$ and $y = 3 \sin t$ is the radius of the circle. Use $x = 2 \cos t$ and $y = 2 \sin t$ to graph a circle of radius 2 or $x = 1 \cos t$ and $y = 1 \sin t$ to graph a unit circle. A Tstep of 120 provides an equilateral triangle as the three points representing 0°, 120°, 240°, and 360° (360° produces the same point as 0°) are connected.

*Investigation 6.4.1: Drawing Polygons

This investigation gives students the opportunity to experiment and discover how to draw and translate polygons. Decide as a class on what window you will use for your "friendly" window.

Part 1

a. i. Answers will vary.

   ii. Tsteps of 90, 60, and 120 produce the square, hexagon, and triangle shapes, respectively. There are several different ways to produce the pictured octagon. One possibility is Tmin = 22.5, Tmax = 382.5, and Tstep = 45. The excitement occurs when students find alternative ways of producing the shapes. Some solutions involve only T-settings, others involve the equations, and some involve a combination of T-setting and equation.

   iii. The square with sides parallel to the axes can be obtained using $x = 3 \cos t$ and $y = 3 \sin t$ with a window of Tmin = 45, Tmax = 405, Tstep = 45.

   iv. Another rotation possibility is $x = 3 \cos (t + 45)$ and $y = 3 \sin (t + 45)$ with a window of Tmin = 0, Tmax = 360, and Tstep = 45.

Part 2

a. $x = 3 \cos t + 5$ and $y = 3 \sin t + 2$ translates the shape so that the center is (5, 2).

b. $x = {}^-(3 \cos t + 5)$ and $y = 3 \sin t + 2$ reflects over the y-axis.
    $x = 3 \cos t + 5$ and $y = {}^-(3 \sin t + 2)$ reflects over the x-axis.
    $x = 3 \sin t + 2$ and $y = 3 \cos t + 5$ reflects over the line $y = x$.
    $x = {}^-(3 \cos t + 5) - 2$ and $y = 3 \sin t + 2$ reflects over $x = {}^-1$.

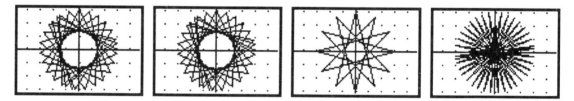

c. Explanations will vary as students produce the following pictures. Use
    Tmax = 3600 and then Tmax = 7200 to obtain the last shape. The Tsteps 125, 100,
    150, and 185 do not divide evenly into 360, so no polygons are formed. The shapes
    differ because of the way the Tsteps divide into multiples of 360°. For example, the
    graph with a Tstep of 100 is completed when T reaches 1800 because $\frac{1800}{100} = 18$ and
    the points plotted are 100° apart.

PROBLEM SET NOTES

Many of the ideas and concepts that appear in the problems will be developed more fully
in Chapters 12 and 13. In Problems 4 and 5, students will derive the standard equations
for a circle. Problem 5 uses the equations found in Problem 3e. Problem 8 uses the
equations found in Problems 7a and 7c and the procedure in Problem 5 to derive the
standard equation for an ellipse.

Suggested Assignments

Individual	Group	Essential	Performance assessment	Portfolio	Journal
1, 4, 6, 7, 9, 10	2, 3, 5, 8	2, 3, 4, 6–8	6	Inv. 6.4.1	

EXTENSIONS

Project: Viewing Angle

Project: Spirograph (in the *Teacher's Resource Book*)

Section 6.5
Wind and River Problems

OBJECTIVES

- To write parametric equations that provide a graphic simulation of real-world motion
- To discover the mathematics required to simulate this motion on a calculator
- To use these simulations and interpret the results to answer a variety of related motion, time, and position questions

MATERIALS

Investigation 6.5.1

Ruler

RESOURCES

Transparency Master for Section 6.5: Movement Diagram

Quiz covering Sections 6.3 and 6.4

TEACHING NOTES

As students work their way through the examples, they gradually develop the skills and understanding required in the problem set. Investigation 6.5.1 is a good introduction to this section. It is important that the wind and river problems are demonstrated on the graphing calculator.

Investigation 6.5.1: Modeling Motion

This investigation helps students develop an initial feel for the combined effect of motion on a moving object. Several motion situations are listed as examples.

PROBLEM SET NOTES

Students like these problems because they are able to check every conjecture and solution by simulating the motion with their calculators. There are so many good problems that the section might take two or more days. Students need the experiences from this section before they move on to the final section in the unit. Problem 10 is a journal-writing prompt. Problem 11 could be used as a journal entry or a project.

Suggested Assignments

Individual	Group	Essential	Performance assessment	Portfolio	Journal
4, 5, 7, 8, 10, 11	1–3, 6, 9	1, 4, 6		8, 11	10, 11

EXTENSIONS

Take Another Look 6.5

Take Another Look 6.5a (in the *Teacher's Resource Book*)

Project: Projectile Motion

Section 6.6
Using Trigonometry to Set a Course

OBJECTIVES

• To model motion situations using trigonometric ratios by breaking motions into vertical and horizontal components

• To use these simulations and interpret the results to answer a variety of related motion, time, and position questions

MATERIALS

None

TEACHING NOTES

Students work through a sequence of four situations (examples) to develop understanding of the objectives. They should calculate and graph their way through the sequence even though the work and explanation has been laid out for them. Your students may need a more thorough introduction to compass readings and headings.

PROBLEM SET NOTES

Some of the problems have to be solved by experimentation or guess-and-check methods. Most students will not know enough mathematics at this time to figure out explicit solutions that don't include some trials and retrials. You may prefer to assign a few problems and then tag others to be included, one at a time, in later assignments.

Problem 5 refers to Problem 4. Problem 9 is a journal-writing prompt.

Suggested Assignments

Individual	Group	Essential	Performance assessment	Portfolio	Journal
6–9	1–5	1–5		7	9

EXTENSIONS

Take Another Look 6.6

Take Another Look 6.6a (in the *Teacher's Resource Book*)

Project: Boolean Expressions

Section 6.7
Chapter Review

OBJECTIVE

• To review the mathematical terms, concepts, and problem-solving skills in Chapter 6

RESOURCES

Test on Chapter 6 to be given following this section

TEACHING NOTES

Review the important concepts of the chapter. Assign the chapter review and allow the students to work together to solve problems while you circulate to answer questions. Students may wish to present their solutions to the class as part of the review.

PROBLEM SET NOTES

Problem 12 is a journal-writing prompt.

Suggested Assignments

Individual	Group	Essential	Performance assessment	Portfolio	Journal
1–12			1, 5		12

Assessing What You've Learned—Group Presentations and Tests
Students are asked to reflect on their participation in a group. They are also reminded to review their journal entries in Problem Sets 6.5, 6.6, and 6.7, organize their notebooks, and update their portfolios. They may also wish to create their own investigations and assessment items pertaining to the material covered in this chapter.

EXTENSIONS

Project: Baseball Pitcher

Chapter 7
Exponential and Logarithmic Functions

Overview

Students will extend geometric sequences of the form $u_n = u_0 r^n$ to the continuous exponential function form $f(x) = ab^x$. Applications provide them with real-world meanings for a, b, x, and y or $f(x)$. They discover properties of exponents and roots and practice using them.

As students solve equations involving rational exponents, they construct and use inverses of functions. The logarithmic form and solution of simple exponential equations like $10^x = 47$ completes a list of different strategies (including guess-and-check and zooming) that students can use to solve similar equations. They then study properties of logarithms and use their knowledge and skills to solve growth and decay applications. Finally, they use the logarithmic function to find best-fit equations for data that are not linearly related.

Section 7.1
The Exponential Function

OBJECTIVES
- To model exponential growth and decay problems
- To explore the relationship between discrete recursive models and $f(x) = ab^x$
- To explore the notion of half-life of an amount undergoing exponential decay

MATERIALS
Investigation 7.1.1
    White board
    Dry-erase markers
    Colored transparency pens
    Blank transparencies

RESOURCES
Transparency Master for Section 7.1: Investigation 7.1.1

Calculator Note 7A

TEACHING NOTES

In this section, you can help students make important connections between recursive answer routines, the sequence formula $u_n = u_0 r^n$, and finally $f(x) = ab^x$. They work immediately with applications providing real-world meanings for a, b, x, and y or $f(x)$.

The section contains one investigation and three important examples modeling connections and applications. The investigation can consume an entire class period, but it is worthwhile. While some students are putting their results on the overhead, the remainder of the class can be busy working on other problems or projects. If you do not assign Investigation 7.1.1, consider using Take Another Look 7.2 as an introduction to the unit.

This section does not introduce how to solve exponential equations symbolically. Instead, students solve exponential equations graphically. This important concept is demonstrated in Example 2. Students will solve these equations using properties of exponents in Section 7.3 and using logarithms in Section 7.6.

Investigation 7.1.1: Radioactive Squares

In this investigation, students explore the properties of radioactive decay. Groups collect their data and record this information on acetate or the transparency master. Plan an efficient process for combining all the information from different groups. One method is for a group to tape its acetate over a plastic master of the grid on the overhead projector. Then they mark the projected colored squares that have not already been marked on the white board. Finally, the group records the total number of squares that have not yet been marked. Students will use a variety of strategies as they solve the problems. Emphasize the connection between the base b and the factor $(1 \pm r)$ that is used in recursive routines like Ans $(1 \pm r)$. Also, they will connect u_0 (the initial value in a recursive routine) with a in the expression ab^x.

Part 2

a. The uncolored squares represent unstable atoms.

b. The colored squares represent atoms that have decayed.

c. Answers for the simulation are based on random student-generated data and will vary from class to class, but here is a sample output using the Decay Program that appears below. This response simulates the investigation in a class where nine groups each colored 50 squares on a 30-by-30 grid.

Group	0	1	2	3	4	5	6	7	8
Remaining	900	851	805	761	715	682	644	609	579

The text does not introduce the ExpReg pictured in the third screen until the last section of this chapter. Instead, students can use guess-and-check methods to write an equation in the form $f(x) = ab^x$. For example, $u(n) = 900(1 - 0.053)^n$. They can use a recursive model for this data:

900 Enter

Ans $(1 - 0.053)$

It is a good idea for them to do both. They should realize that the base b is an approximation for the common ratio of the y-values.

d. $(x) = 900(1 - 0.053)^x$

e. 12.7 trials (for this example). Students should find this graphically, recursively, or by using guess-and-check.

When the investigation is finished, you can simulate the same investigation using the calculator program listed below. This TI-82 program will simulate the results for Investigation 7.1.1. It was written by Adam Kropp, a student at Redwood High School in San Rafael, California.

```
PlotsOff :GridOff              0→L1(1)
Input "GRID SIZE =",N          T→L2(1)
min(max(1,N),60)→N             For(I,1,Z)
Input "DECAY NUM =",D          For(J,1,D)
Input "NUMBER OF TRIES =",Z    iPart Nrand+1→X
N²→T                           iPart Nrand+1→Y
0→Xmin                         If not Pxl-Test(Y,X)
95→Xmax                        Then
0→Ymin                         Pxl-On(Y,X)
63→Ymax                        T-1→T
AxesOff                        End
FnOff                          End
ClrDraw                        Text(15,62,I)
Line(0,63,N+1,63)              Text(35,62,T)
Line(0,63,0,61-N)              I→L1(I+1)
Line(0,61-N,N+1,61-N)          T→L2(I+1)
Line(N+1,63,N+1,61-N)          End
Text(5,62,"TIME=")             Pause
Text(25,62,"REMAIN.="          ClrDraw
Text(15,62,0)                  PlotsOn 1
Text(35,62,T)                  Plot1(Scatter,L1,L2,+)
0→dim L1                       ZoomStat
0→dim L2
```

PROBLEM SET NOTES

Student develop creative and interesting solutions for this problem set. Ask students to share their solutions. Problem 2 is referred to in the introductory paragraph of the next section. Problem 5 refers to Example 3.

Suggested Assignments

Individual	Group	Essential	Performance assessment	Portfolio	Journal
1, 5–7	2–4	3		Inv. 7.1.1	

EXTENSIONS

Project: Baseball for Bucks

Take Another Look 7.1 (in the *Teacher's Resource Book*)

Section 7.2
Rational Exponents and Roots

OBJECTIVE

- To review or discover a connection between fractional exponents and roots:
  $$a^{m/n} = \left(\sqrt[n]{a}\right)^m \text{ or } \sqrt[n]{a^m} \text{ for } a \geq 0$$

MATERIALS

None

RESOURCES

Calculator Notes 7A, 7B, 7C, 7D, and 8A

TEACHING NOTES

Encourage students to work their way through the investigation and examples. The content of the section, or much of it, may be quite familiar to them. Within their groups they will have the opportunity to communicate with others as they work, asking questions for the help needed. The concept of solving equations graphically is again demonstrated in Examples 3 and 4.

*Investigation 7.2.1: Fractional Exponents
In this investigation, students will discover the definition of fractional exponents. Have them work in pairs.

a. Use Calculator Note 7B.

b.–d. Students will discover $\sqrt{x} = x^{0.5}$.

e. Tables will vary.

f. The first screen shows missing table values for part e. Answers will vary for part f, but they should read something like $25^{3/2} = \left(25^{1/2}\right)^3 = \left(\sqrt{25}\right)^3$.

g. The second screen indicates $x^{3/2} = \left(\sqrt{x}\right)^3$.

h. An equation that fits the requirement is $x^{5/3} = \left(\sqrt[3]{x}\right)^5$. The nth power of the cube root of 27 is equivalent to $27^{n/3}$. The third screen confirms the fact that some calculators do not define $x^{5/3}$ for values $x \leq 0$ (however, on some calculators an imaginary number may be the output).

PROBLEM SET NOTES

Problem 5 provokes interesting responses from different students. Even though many think it is corny, they do invent creative (though also corny) Bolombo messages to share with others. The table feature available on some calculators can help students explore and check answers to Problems 3 and 6. They should enter the original $y_1 = \sqrt[4]{x}$ and their solution $y_2 = x^{1/4}$, and check table values for a match. Problem 11 uses parametric equations.

Suggested Assignments

Individual	Group	Essential	Performance assessment	Portfolio	Journal
3–7, 10	1, 2, 8, 9, 11	3, 4, 9	3, 4, 6		9

EXTENSIONS

Take Another Look 7.2 (uses Calculator Notes 8A and 7A)

Section 7.3
Properties of Exponents

OBJECTIVE

- To review or discover several properties: $a^m a^n = a^{(m+n)}$, $(a^n)^m = a^{(mn)}$, $\frac{a^m}{a^n} = a^{(m-n)}$, $a^{-n} = \frac{1}{a^n}$ or $\left(\frac{a}{b}\right)^{-n} = \left(\frac{b}{a}\right)^n$, $a^0 = 1$, and $(ab)^n = a^n b^n$ for $a > 0$, $b > 0$

MATERIALS

None

TEACHING NOTES

Students discover the properties and have the opportunity to use and apply them as they work through examples and investigations of the section. It is important that the investigations be assigned unless all students are extremely familiar with these properties. The introductory paragraph makes a connection between Investigation 1.6.1 and exponents. Examples 4 and 5 demonstrate how to use the properties of exponents to solve exponential equations.

*Investigation 7.3.1: Ratios and Exponents
In this investigation, students discover the division property of exponents.

a. i. $\frac{2^{63}}{2^9}$ or 2^{54}

   ii. $\frac{1(1.08)^{20}}{1(1.08)^6} = (1.08)^{14}$

   iii. $\frac{300(0.65)^2}{300(0.65)^5} = (0.65)^{-3}$

   iv. $\frac{25 \cdot 2^{15}}{25 \cdot 2^7} = 2^8$

b. See the table for some possibilities; m and n must sum to 20.

m	18	15	10	5	3	1
n	2	5	10	15	17	19

c. $\frac{4^5}{4^2}$ or 4^3

d. i. 8^3 ii. $x^{2.5}$ iii. $(0.94)^{10}$ iv. Not possible

e. This will be true for all values of m, n, and $a > 0$.

*Investigation 7.3.2: Negative Exponents
Students will discover the definition of negative and zero exponents in this investigation. Part a refers to the population growth of India examined in Section 7.1.

a. i. 774.44   ii. 789.16   iii. 804.15   iv. 819.43

b. Explanations will vary. One way to show this is by dividing out common factors: $\frac{x^3}{x^5} = \frac{xxx}{xxxxx} = \frac{xxx}{xxx} \cdot \frac{1}{xx} = \frac{1}{x^2}$, but it also equals x^{-2} because $\frac{x^3}{x^5} = x^{(3-5)}$.

c. Answers will vary, but in each instance the number of times x appears as a factor in the denominator should be one more than the number of times it appears in the numerator, $\left(\frac{xxx}{xxxx}\right)$.

d. i. $y = \frac{1}{x^3}$ ii. $y = 2^{-x}$ iii. $y = \frac{10.5}{(1 + 0.035)^{4x}}$ iv. $y = x^2$

e. i. $\frac{3}{2}$ ii. $\frac{2}{3}$ iii. $\frac{9}{4}$ iv. $\frac{b}{a}$

f. $\frac{300(0.65)^5}{300(0.65)^2} = (0.65)^3$

g. This will be true for all values of n and for $a > 0$, $b > 0$.

h. This is true when $x = 0$. Explanations will vary.

i. $x^3 \cdot x^{-3} = x^0$ Multiplication property of exponents.

   $x^3 \cdot x^{-3} = x^3 \cdot \frac{1}{x^3}$ Definition of negative exponents.

   $x^3 \cdot \frac{1}{x^3} = 1$ A number times its multiplicative inverse.

   $x^0 = 1$ Substitution.

j. $2^0 = 1$

PROBLEM SET NOTES

Your students might enjoy creating messages similar to that in Problem 3. Problem 8 refers to Problems 6 and 7. Problem 9 introduces the concept of increasing and decreasing functions.

Suggested Assignments

Individual	Group	Essential	Performance assessment	Portfolio	Journal
1–5	6–11	5, 6, 9, 11	1, 2, 5		

EXTENSIONS

Take Another Look 7.3 (in the *Teacher's Resource Book*)

Section 7.4
Building Inverses of Functions

OBJECTIVES

- To develop a rationale for the inverse of a function
- To investigate symbolic, graphic, and tabular connections between a function and its inverse
- To write an inverse of a function when the function is given as an equation, a graph, or tabular data

MATERIALS

None

RESOURCES

Calculator Notes 7E, 7F, 7G, and 5F

Quiz covering Sections 7.1 to 7.3

TEACHING NOTES

In this section, students develop many important ideas and concepts. The section contains two examples, an investigation, and many problems. It requires careful reading and study. Students discover that the equations of a graph and its inverse are reflections of each other over the line $y = x$. They also discover that these reflections can be produced by switching point coordinates from (x, y) to (y, x), by switching the variables x and y in an equation, and by switching the x- and y-equations in the parametric forms of a relation and its inverse. They learn that the inverses of some functions are not themselves functions. Example 1 demonstrates three methods to find an inverse. Example 2 shows how to find the inverse of parametric equations.

*Investigation 7.4.1: Compositions of Inverse Functions
This investigation works best if students work in pairs. They will explore what happens when you take the composition of a function and its inverse.

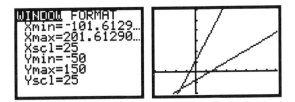

a. Answers will vary for different calculators.

b. Choices of x-values will vary but $f^{-1}(f(x)) = x$ for all choices of x.

c. On some calculators (like the TI-82), $y^3 = y_2(y_1(x))$ will produce the graph of $f^{-1}(f(x))$ or $y = x$.

d. $y_3 = y_1(y_2(x))$ provides the graph of $f(f^{-1}(x))$. Again this is the same as $y = x$.

e. Graphs and values of both $f(f^{-1}(x))$ and $f^{-1}(f(x))$ provide the line $y = x$.

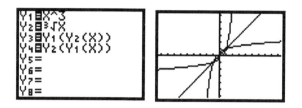

PROBLEM SET NOTES

Problems 1, 3, 4, 5, 6, and 7 use parametric equations. Problems 3 and 4 are similar. Problems 5 and 6 are similar. Problem 10 asks students to write best-fit equations and refers to Investigation 7.4.1.

Suggested Assignments

Individual	Group	Essential	Performance assessment	Portfolio	Journal
1, 2, 4, 6, 8, 9, 12, 13	3, 5, 7, 10, 11	2, 5, 8, 9	1, 8		13

EXTENSIONS

Take Another Look 7.4 (uses Calculator Note 5F)

Geometer's Sketchpad Investigation: Inverse Functions

Section 7.5
Equations with Rational Exponents

OBJECTIVES

- To solve equations of the form $x^{a/b} = c$ by raising both sides to an appropriate power; $(x^{a/b})^{b/a} = c^{b/a}$

- To investigate the graphs of $f(x), f^{-1}(x), f(f^{-1}(x))$ and $f^{-1}(f(x))$ and consequences involving domain and range limitations

MATERIALS
None

RESOURCES
Calculator Note 7G

TEACHING NOTES
In this section, students discover another technique for solving equations. Some probably have been asking for this addition to their repertoire because they are tired of zooming in on table values or points on a screen.

Investigation 7.5.1: Bacterium in a Bottle
This investigation provides a realistic look at exponential growth as regularly faced by decision makers. For example, at a compounded growth rate of 7%, a community will double in population in approximately 10 yr. This means the community can be very comfortable and yet be only one doubling period from chaotic overcrowded conditions. At 11:59 most bacteria may be of the opinion that they still have plenty of room for growth because the bottle is only half full.

Year	Tons consumed	Tons remaining
1974		$4.34 \cdot 10^{11}$
1975	$5.58 \cdot 10^8$	$4.33 \cdot 10^{11}$
1988	$1.116 \cdot 10^9$	$4.33 \cdot 10^{11}$
2002	$2.232 \cdot 10^9$	$4.32 \cdot 10^{11}$
2016	$4.464 \cdot 10^9$	

If the amount consumed doubles every 14 yr, then the consumption growth rate is about 5.076% per year. You can find this by solving $2 = (1 + r)^{14}$ for r. Therefore, the amount remaining after x years is $4.34 \cdot 10^{11} - 5.58 \cdot 10^8(1.05076)^{(x - 1)}$. This amount seems to decrease slowly but becomes negative after 136 yr (the year 2110). The assumptions are probably questionable because the difficulty in matching the consumption need will increase as the amount of coal reserves decreases.

PROBLEM SET NOTES
Problem 1 provides practice directly related to Examples 1 and 2. Problem 7 refers to Calculator Note 7G. Problem 9 uses results from Problem 8. Problem 10 is a journal-writing prompt.

Suggested Assignments

Individual	Group	Essential	Performance assessment	Portfolio	Journal
1, 2, 4–6, 10	3, 7–9	7	1, 2	Inv. 7.5.1	10

EXTENSIONS

Take Another Look 7.5

Take Another Look 7.5a (in the *Teacher's Resource Book*)

Project: Finding *e*

Section 7.6
The Logarithmic Function

OBJECTIVES

- To focus on the function $y = b^x$ and its inverse
- To discover that the inverse of $y = b^x$ is the logarithm function
- To solve the equation $a = b^x$ (with $a, b > 0$) for x using the logarithm definition $\log_b a = x$
- To recognize and identify asymptotes

MATERIALS

None

RESOURCES

Transparency Master: Log Paper

Quiz covering Sections 7.4 and 7.5

TEACHING NOTES

First, students are reminded that the intersection of the graphs of both sides of an equation like $10^x = 47$ will provide the solution for x. This means 47 can be written as a power of 10. This same notion (writing numbers as powers of 10) is extended to solve equations involving other bases. In Example 3, both sides of the equation $4^x = 128$ are rewritten as powers of 10, and the equation involving exponents provides the solution for x.

Several examples are presented to provide conceptual understanding. Students discover and learn to use the identity $10^{\log n} = n$. The ideas presented in this section are formalized in the next section.

PROBLEM SET NOTES

Problem 4 involves transformations of the functions $y = 10^x$ or $y = \log x$. Problems 5–9 offer a variety of applications involving $y = b^x$. Problem 10 is a journal-writing prompt.

Suggested Assignments

Individual	Group	Essential	Performance assessment	Portfolio	Journal
1–6, 10	7–9	1, 2	1		10

EXTENSIONS

Take Another Look 7.6 (in the *Teacher's Resource Book*)

Section 7.7
Properties of Logarithms

OBJECTIVES

- To understand the relationship between a base, an exponent, and a logarithm

- To use this understanding to solve exponential equations with bases other than 10

- To discover the logarithm change of base property and to learn how and when it can be used

MATERIALS

Investigation 7.7.2

    Strips of card stock

    Graph paper

RESOURCES

Transparency/Worksheet Master for Section 7.7: Investigation 7.7.1

Calculator Note 7H

TEACHING NOTES

Most class time will be spent working through the two investigations. Both are important and will be used throughout the remainder of the chapter. There are good alternatives for developing the logarithm product, quotient, and power properties. Making and using the log ruler takes time. However, the log ruler will be used again in Section 7.9 as a manipulative to help students make sense of curve-straightening strategies. If you do not assign Investigation 7.7.1, then you will need to devise another approach for the development of the logarithmic properties. Guided exploration with the calculator works well.

Investigation 7.7.1: The Log Function

In this investigation, students will explore the relationship between a base, an exponent, and a logarithm. As students complete the investigation and examples, they make the connection between $a = b^x$ and $\log_b a = x$ to solve equations and exponential applications. They discover and then use the logarithm change of base property, $\log_b x = \frac{\log x}{\log b}$, when the base b is not 10.

a. The table for $x = 4^y$.

x	0.0625	0.125	0.25	0.5	1	2	4	8	16
y	−2	−1.5	−1	−0.5	0	0.5	1	1.5	2

b. The "best" a is $\frac{1}{\log 4}$.

```
WINDOW FORMAT
 Xmin=-2
 Xmax=20
 Xscl=2
 Ymin=-2.5
 Ymax=2.5
 Yscl=.5
```

Base	4	7	10	0.2
a	1.661	1.183	1	−1.431
Log of base	0.602	0.845	1	−0.699

c.–d. Students will discover the relationship $a = \frac{1}{\log b}$ as they complete the table.

e. i. $\left(\frac{1}{\log 4}\right) \log 8 = 1.5$ ii. 1.4307   iii. 1.2323   iv. 2.2619

Investigation 7.7.2: Making a Logarithmic Ruler

Students use their log rulers to discover the logarithm product, quotient, and power properties. If the rulers are carefully made, and construction directions are carefully followed, the discoveries will occur quickly. Students could also learn the properties with their calculators given a list of expressions that lead to the conclusions desired.

PROBLEM SET NOTES

As written, Problems 1–3 require the use of the log ruler made in Investigation 7.7.2. As an alternative, students could use their calculators. Students can use their calculators for Problem 4. Problem 5 refers to the results of Problems 1–3. Problem 11 uses Calculator Note 7H. Problem 13 is a journal-writing prompt.

Suggested Assignments

Individual	Group	Essential	Performance assessment	Portfolio	Journal
4–10, 13	1–3, 11, 12	1–3	1, 2		5, 13

Section 7.8
Applications of Logarithms

OBJECTIVES

• To focus on modeling and applications that involve logarithms

• To discover and learn strategies and techniques for solving application problems involving logarithms

MATERIALS

Investigation 7.8.1

One or more containers of hot water

Thermometers or data probes that measure in °C or °F.

TEACHING NOTES

The section begins with a summary list comparing the properties of exponents and logarithms. Time, discussion, and good interactions will be required as students try to understand and work their way through the examples. Perhaps students who are knowledgeable about the Richter scale, acid concentrations, pH, star magnitude, and chemical reaction rates could be prepared to expand on the information presented.

Investigation 7.8.1: A Cup of Hot Water

In this investigation, students will explore the relationship between time and temperature of water as it cools. The data can be collected as a lab for all groups, during a class session by one student who can do two things simultaneously or by one or more students before the class session. If you don't have the time for everyone to collect hot-water data, assign one or two students to collect a set of data for the entire class. They can collect it throughout the class period, or they might come to class with the data. The information and data collected will be used in Problem 6 of Problem Set 7.9.

a. Graphs will vary.

b. The temperatures in this sample are in °C and elapsed time is in minutes. The water temperature was actually taken at one-minute intervals.

Time	1	6	11	16	21	26	...	46	51	56
Temp	64.51	57.99	53.20	49.5	46.43	43.75	...	35.86	34.12	32.65

c.

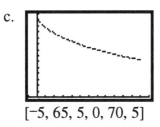

[−5, 65, 5, 0, 70, 5]

PROBLEM SET NOTES

Problem 10 can be assigned as a project.

Suggested Assignments

Individual	Group	Essential	Performance assessment	Portfolio	Journal
1–4	5–10	2	3	10	

EXTENSIONS

Take Another Look 7.8 (in the *Teacher's Resource Book*)

Section 7.9
Curve Straightening and More Data Analysis

OBJECTIVES

• To explore combinations of (*x*, log *y*), (log *x*, log *y*), (log *x*, *y*) to find a plot that is linear

• To find best-fit models for nonlinear data

• To introduce nonlinear regression functions on the calculator

MATERIALS

Problem 3

    M&Ms

    Shallow boxes

RESOURCES

Transparency/Worksheet Master: Semilog Paper

Transparency/Worksheet Master: Log-log Paper

Calculator Notes 7I and 7J

TEACHING NOTES

This section could require up to three days of class time. Until now the power, exponential, and logarithmic regression models that are available in the calculator have not been introduced in the text. However, you may have already introduced them, or your students may have learned about them from other students, from another course, or because they "knew" there must be an easy way to do the regressions on the calculator. Be sure to keep the domain of log x in mind. You will not be able to take the log of a list that contains zero or any negative numbers.

The development of a strategy to linearize data can often be accomplished by choosing from possible combinations of $(x, \log y)$, $(\log x, \log y)$, $(\log x, y)$ to find a plot that is linear. The calculator alters (x, y) to $(x, \log y)$ for an exponential best fit, to $(\log x, \log y)$ for a power fit, and to $(\log x, y)$ for a logarithmic fit. The investigation, examples, and early problems allow students to learn what the calculator is doing before they use the built-in regressions.

Investigation 7.9.1: Linearizing Data

In Part 1, students learn how to linearize or straighten exponential data.

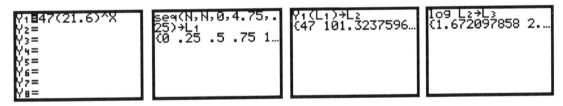

a. The table (list) created in the fourth screen above will indicate that $0 < y < 10$ can be used to create an appropriate window.

The graph of $y_2 = \log y_1$ is a straight line that contains the points (L1, L3).

b. Students will choose their own points, but for this solution we will use (1, 3.0065516) and (3, 5.6754591).

c. $y = \dfrac{5.6754591 - 3.0065516}{3 - 1}(x - 1) + 3.0065516$ is a point-slope form of one equation that works. (Or $y = 1.672097849 + 1.33445375x$.)

d. The slope of the line is 1.33445375, and log 21.6 = 1.33445375.

e. The y-intercept is 1.672097849, which is the same as log 47.

f. Explanations will vary. However, the curve $y = ab^x$ can be linearized by graphing $(x, \log y)$ or $y = \log ab^x$. The slope of the linear equation is log b and the y-intercept is log a.

Part 2: Consider the graph of $y^1 = \pi x^2$ on the domain $0 \le x \le 4.75$.

a. You will have to ignore the point (0, 0) because log 0 isn't defined. Remove the point from the data lists.

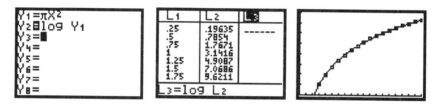

b. The nonlinear graph pictured above is in the window $0 \le x \le 4.75$ and $0 < y \le 2$.

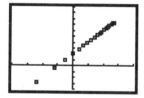

c. The linear scatter plot of (log x, log y) pictured is in the window $-1 \le x \le 1$ and $-1 \le y \le 2.5$.

d. $y = \dfrac{1.8036 - 0.4971}{0.6532 - 0}(x - 0) + 0.4971$ or $y = 2.0001x + 0.4971$

x	$y = \pi \cdot x^2$	log x	log y
0.5	$0.5^2\pi$	−0.3010	−0.1049
1.0	π	0	0.4971
1.5	$1.5^2\pi$	0.1761	0.8493
. . .	. . .	. . .	. . .
4.5	$4.5^2\pi$	0.6532	1.8036

e. The slope of the line is the exponent of the original function.

f. The y-intercept of the line is the logarithm of the coefficient π.

g. The power curve, $y_1 = ax^b$, is linearized by an equation with slope b and y-intercept of log a.

PROBLEM SET NOTES

Students are encouraged to work on all of these problems with their group. They are officially introduced to the calculator regression models in Problems 3 and 4. Problem 4 uses Calculator Note 7I. Problem 5 uses Calculator Note 7J. Problem 6 uses the data collected in Investigation 7.8.1.

Suggested Assignments

Individual	Group	Essential	Performance assessment	Portfolio	Journal
	1–8	4–6			

EXTENSIONS

Take Another Look 7.9 (in the *Teacher's Resource Book*)

Project: Fractal Dimensions (in the *Teacher's Resource Book*)
(need worksheet master)

Project: Income by Gender

Section 7.10
Chapter Review

OBJECTIVE

• To review the mathematical terms, concepts, and problem-solving skills in Chapter 7

RESOURCES

Test on Chapter 7 to be given following this section

TEACHING NOTES

Review the important concepts of the chapter. Assign the chapter review and allow the students to work together to solve problems while you circulate to answer questions. Students may wish to present their solutions to the class as a review.

PROBLEM SET NOTES

Problem 7 is a journal-writing prompt.

Suggested Assignments

Individual	Group	Essential	Performance assessment	Portfolio	Journal
1–7			1, 2, 3		7

Assessing What You've Learned—Self-Assessment Overview
Students are asked to assess their own work. Students may be assigned to think about different ways they would like to be assessed.

Students are also reminded to review their journal entries in Problem Sets 7.5, 7.6, and 7.7, organize their notebooks, and update their portfolios. They may also wish to create their own investigations and assessment items pertaining to the material covered in this chapter.

EXTENSIONS
Take Another Look 7.10

Chapter 8
Topics in Discrete Mathematics

Overview

This chapter introduces a wide variety of topics, each of which could be an entire unit. The initial emphasis is on randomness and the meaning of probability. Students find probabilities by constructing and interpreting tree diagrams, devising simulations, and using simulation programs. They use matrices and network graphs to help organize and present information. They derive transition matrices from transition graphs, and vice versa. Section 8.7 introduces matrix multiplication in the context of a meaningful and familiar problem. Because some students take quite naturally to programming, reorganizing your groups so that at least one programmer is in each group might be helpful.

Section 8.1
Using Random Numbers

OBJECTIVES
- To explore the meaning of randomness
- To use simulations and experimental evidence to develop initial probability concepts

MATERIALS
Spinners, coins, cards, and dice may be useful in this section and throughout the chapter.

Investigation 8.1.1
  Sets of ten numbered chips
  Containers to hold chips (a lunch sack works well)

RESOURCES
Transparency/Worksheet Master for Section 8.1: Random Number Table

Calculator Notes 8A, 8B, and 8C

TEACHING NOTES
The first investigation helps students to begin to understand the concept of randomness. They will know the word, but probably have never thought about what it means. The second investigation demonstrates that results can be surprising even when you know the probabilities. It also makes a case for constructing simulations to test hypotheses.

There are many ways to explore randomness. The use of chips, coins, cards, dice, spinners, and a random number table (provided in the *Teacher's Resource Book* and as a transparency master) is encouraged throughout this chapter. Class discussion is valuable as students try to understand this difficult concept. The calculator **rand** function is not very intuitive to students. Spend some time "playing with" this function and with the **int** function (especially with problems like Problem 7).

*Investigation 8.1.1: Random Selection

In this investigation, students will explore the concept of random selection. This investigation helps them make a connection between single events and long-run averages. As students complete this investigation, they will decide that replacing the chip each time provides a more random order. Help students understand that, although nothing is cetain, probability can take some of the uncertainty out of decisions.

*Investigation 8.1.2: Medical Testing

Students will apply their knowledge of probability and use a random generator to explore the accuracy of medical test results. The directions for this investigation may be confusing to students. A successful or accurate test on a healthy person is a negative test result. But a successful or accurate test on a sick person is a positive test result. To make certain that students collect the right data, you may wish to go through a few trials and ask students where they would put tally marks. The end results will vary, but the distribution should be close to the table below.

a.–c.

Patient's condition	Test results	
	Accurate	Inaccurate
Doesn't have the disease	36	4
Has the disease	9	1

d.

Patient's condition	Test results	
	Accurate	Inaccurate
Doesn't have the disease	Negative	Positive
Has the disease	Positive	Negative

e. If the result is positive, the probability is $\frac{9}{4+9} = 69.2\%$ that the person tested has the disease. A negative result implies that there is a $\frac{36}{36+1} = 97.3\%$ probability that the person tested does not have the disease. Therefore, the probability that Hi has the disease is 69.2% and the probability that Pocon does not have the disease is 97.3%.

PROBLEM SET NOTES

Encourage the use of a variety of simulation models. Remember to provide students with the random number tables copied from the blackline master. Problem 6 refers to Calculator Note 8B, and Problem 7 refers to Calculator Note 8C. Using parametric equations offers an alternative to or an extension for Problem 7. The number of plotted points can be controlled by Tmax. For example, while in Dot Mode, try graphing the equations $x = 6$ rand $- 2$ and $y = 3$ in the window $[-6, 6, 1, 0, 6, 1]$ with $0 \leq t \leq 100$ and a Tstep of 1. You actually see the interval $-2 \leq x \leq 4$ being formed. Tracing a function involving rand is also interesting, because a trace provides different (random) points every time.

Suggested Assignments

Individual	Group	Essential	Performance assessment	Portfolio	Journal
6, 7	1–5, 8	4, 6, 7		Inv. 8.1.2	

Section 8.2
Random Numbers in Two Dimensions

OBJECTIVES

- To simulate random situations and solve problems using computer (calculator) simulation routines and programs

- To understand and use geometric probability as a model for solving appropriate probability problems

MATERIALS

Demonstration

    Transparency with large triangle drawn on it

    A small amount of rice

RESOURCES

Calculator Notes 8D and 8E

TEACHING NOTES

If students are using linkable calculators, you may wish to have the program entered into your calculator so that it can be quickly shared. It is not necessary for students to be programmers, but they should be able to make small changes as they use these programs. They can explore problems more completely if they understand some of the structure involved in a program.

Students should understand that computer simulations can be used to understand, explore, and solve complex probability problems. Care must be taken in setting up any routine to ensure that the results are meaningful.

Geometric probability is a useful visual tool that helps students to solve some problems. It can change the way they look at and think about problems. As a demonstration, draw a triangle within a square on an overhead transparency, and then drop a tablespoon of rice on the square. Find the ratio of the number of grains in the triangle to the number of grains in the square and the ratio of the triangle's area to the area of the square. As the amount of rice is increased, these ratios should get closer to each other.

The investigation, Calculator Note 8D, and geometric probability involve important concepts. Provide the time required so that your students will be able to apply what they learn here to their next encounter with these concepts.

*Investigation 8.2.1: Calculator Candy Simulation

In this investigation, students work with the concept of geometric probability. Rather than actually using candy for the investigation, they will use a calculator program to gather information.

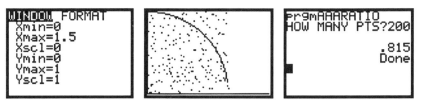

a. Results are random. As shown here, about 81.5% of the random points are under the curve. This represents (0.815 • 200) or 163 of the 200 tested.

b. Again, the results will vary, but they should be very close to 0.25π or about 0.785.

c. If n points are plotted, then $\left(n \cdot \frac{0.25\pi(1)^2}{1} \right)$ or $0.25\,\pi n$ of them should land under the curve.

PROBLEM SET NOTES

Problems 1–3 are related to Example 1 using dice sums. Problems 2 and 3 ask different questions about the same events. In Problem 6, the y-values range between 0 and 4. There is no real reason to use an integer as Ymax except to make calculations easier. The number 4 was selected because it is the first integer greater than $\sqrt{10}$. Numbers less than $\sqrt{10}$ will provide incorrect results, and numbers much greater than 4 reduce the accuracy. Every problem dictates some of the values used in the routine. Problem 6 refers to Problem 14 in Problem Set 5.7 and Calculator Note 8E.

Suggested Assignments

Individual	Group	Essential	Performance assessment	Portfolio	Journal
1–4, 7	5, 6, 8, 9	6			

EXTENSIONS

Take Another Look 8.2

Take Another Look 8.2a (in the *Teacher's Resource Book*)

Geometer's Sketchpad Investigation: Random Points and Objects

Section 8.3
Some Counting Techniques

OBJECTIVES

• To further develop strategies for counting and calculating random selection outcomes

• To examine the differences between experimental and theoretical probability

MATERIALS

Investigation 8.3.1

   18-in. to 24-in. long pieces of string

TEACHING NOTES

Provide some time for discussion of the examples before students start the investigation. You may wish to use data from local news issues or surveys to examine experimental and theoretical probability. You could also gather and use data from your classes for the questions asked in Example 1.

Investigation 8.3.1: Loops

Students should work on this investigation in groups of four. Make certain that your students understand the directions. They are to take hold of string ends on their left with their left hands and string ends on their right with their right hands. They should not be concerned about completely untangling loops. The loops need only to be untangled enough so that they can count how many loops are formed. There are three possibilities: one large loop, two loops (one medium and one small), or three small loops. It may be surprising to students that the possibilities are not equally likely. Theoretical values are 1/2 for two loops, 1/3 for one loop, 1/6 for three loops.

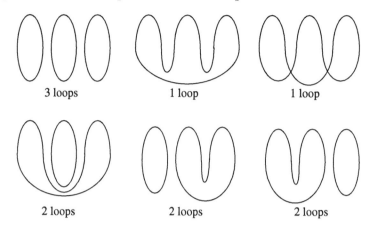

3 loops   1 loop   1 loop

2 loops   2 loops   2 loops

PROBLEM SET NOTES

Students should be reminded to draw probability tree diagrams that correctly interpret the situations. The visual representations they use should make sense to them and to others in the class.

Suggested Assignments

Individual	Group	Essential	Performance assessment	Portfolio	Journal
1–6	7–11	6–8	2, 3		

EXTENSIONS

Take Another Look 8.3 (in the *Teacher's Resource Book*)

Project: Permutations and Combinations

Section 8.4
Waiting and Expected Value

OBJECTIVES

• To find the wait-time-for-success probabilities using tree diagrams and calculator lists

• To find expected values of appropriate events

MATERIALS

Money Bags Simulation

    Play money (five-, ten-, and hundred-dollar bills)

Investigation 8.4.1

    Lots of pennies (about 25 per group)

    Graph paper ruled in fractions of an inch

Example 2

    A small gumball machine (or a plastic container)

    2 purple gumballs

    6 nonpurple gumballs

RESOURCES

Transparency Master for Section 8.4: Tree Diagram

Transparency Master for Section 8.4: Example 2

Transparency/Worksheet Master for Section 8.4: Investigation 8.4.1

Quiz covering Sections 8.1 to 8.3

Calculator Notes 8F, 8G, and 8H

TEACHING NOTES

A "money bags" simulation offers a good introduction of expected value before students start Investigation 8.4.1. Put 10 five-dollar bills and 10 ten-dollar bills of play money in one bag, and then put 18 five-dollar bills and 2 hundred-dollar bills in a second bag. Now ask for the expected value of "pulling one random bill from each bag." Discussion should lead to a value of 0.5(5) + 0.5(10) or $7.50 for bag 1 and 0.9(5) + 0.1(100) or $14.00 for bag 2.

Revisit Example 2 after some initial work with expected-value concepts. Help students find the theoretical expected number of gumballs that it takes before selecting a purple gumball. Make sure that students understand the tree as drawn.

Number selected	1	2	3	4	5	6	7
Probability it is purple	$\frac{2}{8}$	$\frac{6}{8} \cdot \frac{2}{7}$	$\frac{6}{8} \cdot \frac{5}{7} \cdot \frac{2}{6}$	$\cdots$			

$$\text{EV} = (1) \cdot \frac{2}{8} + (2) \cdot \frac{6}{8} \cdot \frac{2}{7} + (3) \cdot \frac{6}{8} \cdot \frac{5}{7} \cdot \frac{2}{6} + (4) \cdot \frac{6}{8} \cdot \frac{5}{7} \cdot \frac{4}{6} \cdot \frac{2}{5} + \cdots = 3$$

Make sure that students understand the meaning of every number in this equation.

Investigation 8.4.1: Pennies on a Grid

The theoretical value for the first part of the investigation is about 6.25% because the center of the penny must land in a 0.25 in. × 0.25 in. square if the penny is to stay within the 1-in. square. This means that the center of the penny

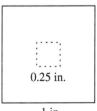

0.25 in.

1 in.

will land in the 0.0625-square-inch region about 6.25% of the time. The theoretical expected value comes from an infinite sum:

$0.0625 (1) + 0.9375 \cdot 0.0625 (2) + 0.9375^2 \cdot 0.0625 (3) + 0.9375^3 \cdot 0.0625 (4)$
$+ \cdots = 16$ (also $\frac{1}{0.0625} = 16$).

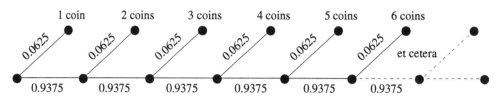

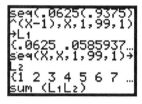

Some calculators can find the first 99 of these events if you use the sequence command and lists. First store the probabilities in list 1 with Seq(0.0625(0.9375)^(X – 1), X, 1, 99, 1)→L1. Then store the value of each branch in list 2 with Seq(X, X, 1, 99, 1)→L2. Now ask for the sum of the products of these two lists by entering the command sum (L1L2).

It might be useful to have some students add up the first 10, the first 25, the first 50, the first 99, or even the second 99 terms simply by changing the limits after the X in the sequence command. For example, Seq(X, X, 1, 25, 1)→L2 will provide the first 25 terms.

PROBLEM SET NOTES

Problem 1 refers to Calculator Note 8G. Problem 2c requires the use of Calculator Note 8H. Problem 6 uses the data collected in Investigation 8.1.2. Problem 8 is a journal-writing prompt.

Suggested Assignments

Individual	Group	Essential	Performance assessment	Portfolio	Journal
3, 5, 7, 8, 9	1, 2, 4, 6	1, 2		Inv. 8.4.1	8

EXTENSIONS

Project: Coin Toss Game

Section 8.5
Chromatic Numbering

OBJECTIVES

- To explore and examine applications of network graphs, edges, and vertices

- To analyze, construct, and apply network graphs to solve application problems

MATERIALS
Investigation 8.5.1

    Colored pencils or pens

    Colored chips

    Transparent colored chips (optional)

RESOURCES
Transparency Master for Section 8.5: Investigation 8.5.1

Transparency/Worksheet Master for Section 8.5: Problem 4

TEACHING NOTES
This section serves as a bridge from probability trees or graphs to more general network graphs. Two investigations demonstrate that network graphs are useful for understanding and solving some types of problems. The chromatic number of a graph is explained in Problem 3.

Investigation 8.5.1: Conflict Resolution
In this investigation, students create a large network graph from a classroom setting that all students will relate to. Students may be very frustrated at first by the large amount of information. However, with help from their group members, they will be able to tackle this investigation. Students will enjoy finding a strategy for solving Part 1 of the investigation. They might be so proud of their own strategy that you will have to encourage them to consider the strategy proposed in Part 2. Plastic sheets and colored pens, colored pencils, or transparent colored chips are good tools for graph coloring. The transparent colored chips are very effective for overhead presentations.

Investigation 8.5.2: Visiting Colleges
Students apply their knowledge of drawing network graphs to this college problem. There are two solutions: from *home* to *Yale* to *U of M* to *Oberlin* to *SMU* to *USC* to *home,* or the reverse. The cost for this trip is $904. With some 120 possible trips to consider, how do you select the minimum? One method is to begin with the

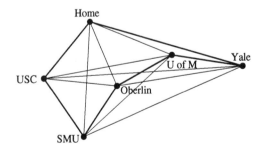

cheapest fare on the graph and continue by adding the next-lowest cost, without closing a loop, until all the colleges have been included.

PROBLEM SET NOTES
Problem 3 introduces chromatic numbering. There is a worksheet master for Problem 4.

Suggested Assignments

Individual	Group	Essential	Performance assessment	Portfolio	Journal
1–3	4, 5	2, 3		Inv. 8.5.2	

EXTENSIONS
Take Another Look 8.5

Section 8.6
The Transition Matrix

OBJECTIVES

- To use matrices for organizing and presenting information and as a tabular interpretation of a network graph

- To produce an adjacency matrix when given a network graph

- To produce a network graph when given an adjacency matrix

- To produce a transition matrix and transition diagram representing now-next transitions

MATERIALS
None

TEACHING NOTES

This section provides the transition from networks to matrices. The problem in Example 1 was first introduced in Chapter 1. It will be revisited again in the problem set and then in Section 8.7 to show a real-world application of multiplying matrices. Investigation 8.6.2 should be assigned after some initial classroom discussion about graphs and matrices. Before beginning on the problem set, students must understand how to draw a directed graph and transfer that information to a transition matrix. Students will learn how to solve these matrix equations in the next section.

Another example of a transition matrix can be made from a house floor plan. Draw a simple floor plan indicating all doors. Make sure there are multiple exits from some rooms. Then create a matrix to show the probabilities of moving from one room to

another. One example is shown below. Using a student's house or your own will make
this activity more interesting.

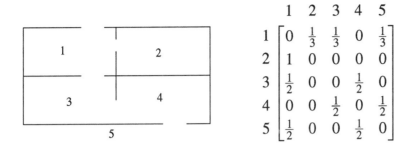

$$\begin{array}{c} \\ 1 \\ 2 \\ 3 \\ 4 \\ 5 \end{array} \begin{array}{ccccc} 1 & 2 & 3 & 4 & 5 \\ \left[\begin{array}{ccccc} 0 & \frac{1}{3} & \frac{1}{3} & 0 & \frac{1}{3} \\ 1 & 0 & 0 & 0 & 0 \\ \frac{1}{2} & 0 & 0 & \frac{1}{2} & 0 \\ 0 & 0 & \frac{1}{2} & 0 & \frac{1}{2} \\ \frac{1}{2} & 0 & 0 & \frac{1}{2} & 0 \end{array}\right] \end{array}$$

Investigation 8.6.1: Sprouts

The Sprouts game is an excellent way to review networks and develop problem-solving
strategies. Students enjoy playing this game. Allow them time to play and analyze the
game. At first it seems that the game will never end, but because of the rules that no
edges can intersect and a vertex can have no more than three edges, a winner will appear
quite soon. Consider extending solution presentations for a few days until most students
are ready to demonstrate and explain their strategy.

a. The game will end after 6, 7, or 8 edges are drawn. The second player will win only
    when there are seven moves.

b. Sprouts is not a fair game. If the second player understands the game, she can
    always win.

A possible strategy for the game of Sprouts: The game must end in at most
eight moves and can end in six or seven moves. Player 1 will win if there are
six or eight moves. Player 2 will win only if there are seven moves. For the
game to end with seven moves, one vertex must be isolated from another. In
the example below, point 2 cannot be connected to point 3.

As Player 2, you can always win because you can force the result above quite
easily. As Player 1, you can win only if Player 2 is unaware of the strategy.
The six-move version is almost impossible to orchestrate.

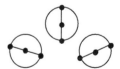

In the eight-move game, you need to keep points from being isolated.

Investigation 8.6.2: Graphs and Matrices

In Part 1 of this investigation, students practice drawing graphs and adjacency matrices.
In Part 2, the adjacency graph is given and students must describe a situation that would
match this matrix and draw a graph.

Part 1

	A	B	C	D	E	F
A	0	1	0	0	0	1
B	1	0	0	1	0	1
C	0	0	0	0	1	0
D	0	1	0	0	1	1
E	0	0	1	1	0	1
F	1	1	0	1	1	0

Part 1

Part 2

PROBLEM SET NOTES

Problem 1 refers to the matrix at the top of page 410. Problem 4 extends the solution offered in Example 1. The problem was originally presented in Chapter 1 and will be used again in the next section to motivate matrix multiplication. Another extension for your stronger students is to suggest that the United States population not be a constant 240 million, but grow at some fixed yearly rate. Problem 5 is similar to Problem 4. Encourage a tree solution for Problem 6.

Suggested Assignments

Individual	Group	Essential	Performance assessment	Portfolio	Journal
1–4	5, 6	1, 3, 4			

EXTENSIONS

Project: Sensitive Survey

Project: Pizza Conflicts (in the *Teacher's Resource Book*)

Section 8.7
Matrix Operations

OBJECTIVES

• To find the meaning of matrix multiplication and to discover how to multiply two matrices

• To use matrix multiplication as a strategy for solving problems

MATERIALS

None

RESOURCES

Quiz covering Sections 8.4 to 8.6

Transparency Master for Section 8.7: Investigation 8.7.1

Transparency Master: Markov Chain Activity

Calculator Note 8I

TEACHING NOTES

In this section, students use Markov chains as the first application of matrices. Several problems, including the California problem, are investigated using this new tool. Connecting recursion and matrices helps students understand why matrices are multiplied in the strange way that they are. Other applications for matrices appear in later chapters. It is essential that students learn how to multiply matrices by hand and later learn how to do it on the calculator. Some students will figure out how to multiply on the calculator right away, but you need to encourage students to make sure they understand the process before using their calculators.

Investigation 8.7.1: Word to Word

This investigation uses the adjacency matrix created in Part 1 of Investigation 8.6.2 to demonstrate the significance of matrix multiplication. A transparency/worksheet master is available for this investigation. The initial matrix [1 0 0 0 0 0] means that the document is in format A. After multiplying by the transition matrix, the new matrix [0 1 0 0 0 1] indicates that the document can be changed to format B or F in one conversion. Multiplying again gives the matrix [2 1 **0** 2 1 1], which shows the conversion to all but format C after two conversions. The fourth matrix, [2 5 **1** 3 3 6] shows that it takes three conversions to get from format A to format C.

Markov Chain Activity

You can use this activity as an alternative to Investigation 8.7.1. In this simulation, students represent chemicals in a reaction that is moving toward equilibrium. The various states of the chemicals in reaction are the vertices in the model. For best results you need to start with an average of ten students per vertex. If you have fewer than fifteen students, see if you can "borrow" some from elsewhere. It takes about 10–15 minutes to collect the data.

Next you need to set up the probabilities for movement or change of state. These can be anything and are not critical. You can use the models provided below for two, three, and four vertices. These models are also provided as transparency masters in the *Teacher's Resource Book.*

Two-vertex model		Three-vertex model		Four-vertex model	
State A rand ≤ 0.3 → rand > 0.3 stay	State B rand ≤ 0.2 ← rand > 0.2 stay	State A rand ≤ 0.2 → 0.2 < rand ≤ 0.7↓ rand > 0.7 stay	State B rand ≤ 0.5 ← rand > 0.5 stay	State A rand ≤ 0.2 → 0.2 < rand ≤ 0.6↓ rand > 0.6 ↘	State B rand ≤ 0.3 ← 0.3 < rand ≤ 0.8↓ rand > 0.8 stay
		State C rand ≤ 0.1 0.1 < rand ≤ 0.3↗↑ rand > 0.3 stay		State C rand ≤ 0.2 0.2 < rand ≤ 0.5↗↑ rand > 0.5 stay	State D rand ≤ 0.1 ← 0.1 < rand ≤ 0.4↑ rand > 0.4 stay

First, students must recall how to generate a random number on their calculator. Display the appropriate transparency and make sure students understand how to interpret it. For example, if a student in State C of the three-vertex model has generated a .352 . . . , he or she will move to State A. You can check students' ability to read the diagram by asking some of the weaker students "what they would do if they were in State X and got a Y on the calculator." Designate corners of the room as the different states. Hanging a large letter in each corner will help eliminate confusion.

Randomly assign students to each corner (vertex). You can have them go to a corner alphabetically (i.e., A through J to State A, K through S to State B, and so on, and then readjust the numbers, if necessary). For better results, start with a distribution opposite of the final outcome. In the models provided above, the long run will have small values in the low letters and high values in the high letters. So you should begin with more students assigned to A and B and fewer students at corners C and D.

A sample result is given below.

Record the initial conditions:	State A	State B	State C	State D
	16	14	7	3

Now have everyone generate a random number and think about where they are going. On a signal have everyone move (or stay) according to their number. Record the new numbers.

Record the initial conditions:	State A	State B	State C	State D
	16	14	7	3
	12	8	8	12

Repeat this 8 to 10 times. It goes pretty quickly after the first time. Have students return to their groups and do the following tasks.

• Draw a transition diagram.

• Create a transition matrix.

• Give theoretical values for the first few moves based on the initial conditions.

• Compare these to the experimental values.

• Predict the long run values to the nearest integers.

The transition matrices and the long-run values for the three given models are provided below.

Two-vertex model: $\begin{bmatrix} 0.7 & 0.3 \\ 0.2 & 0.8 \end{bmatrix}$ long run: State A – 40%, State B – 60%

Three-vertex model: $\begin{bmatrix} 0.3 & 0.2 & 0.5 \\ 0.5 & 0.5 & 0 \\ 0.2 & 0.1 & 0.7 \end{bmatrix}$ State A ~ 29%, State B ~ 22%, State C ~ 49%

Four-vertex model: $\begin{bmatrix} 0 & 0.2 & 0.4 & 0.4 \\ 0.3 & 0.2 & 0 & 0.5 \\ 0.3 & 0.2 & 0.5 & 0 \\ 0 & 0.3 & 0.1 & 0.6 \end{bmatrix}$ A ~ 13%, B ~ 24%, C ~ 19%, D ~ 43%

PROBLEM SET NOTES

Matrix calculations in Problems 1–4 should be done without calculators. Problem 5 extends the California problem and introduces students to matrix multiplication on the calculator, which is explained in Calculator Note 8I. Problem 10 is a journal-writing prompt.

Suggested Assignments

Individual	Group	Essential	Performance assessment	Portfolio	Journal
1, 3–6, 9, 10	2, 7, 8	1, 4, 9	1, 4, 6		10

EXTENSIONS

Take Another Look 8.7

Section 8.8
Chapter Review

OBJECTIVES

• To review the mathematical terms, concepts, and problem-solving skills in Chapter 8

RESOURCES

Test on Chapter 8 to be given following this section

TEACHING NOTES

Review the important concepts of the chapter. Assign the chapter review and allow the students to work together to solve problems while you circulate to answer questions. Students may wish to present their solutions to the class as part of the review.

PROBLEM SET NOTES

Problem 11 may be used as a journal-writing prompt or an alternative assessment activity. Problem 12 is a journal-writing prompt.

Suggested Assignments

Individual	Group	Essential	Performance assessment	Portfolio	Journal
1–12					11, 12

Assessing What You've Learned

Students are reminded to review their journal entries in Problem Sets 8.4, 8.7, and 8.8, organize their notebooks, and update their portfolios. There are also several suggestions for alternative assessment for students to complete.

Chapter 9
Systems of Equations

Overview

Students have explored and solved systems of equations throughout the text by zooming in on intersection points or by comparing table values of two or more functions. This chapter introduces techniques—substitution, elimination, and matrices—that have traditionally been used with systems. Their utility in mathematics extends far beyond this particular application.

Systems of linear inequations, feasible regions, and linear programming are presented in the context of applications that can be examined in a two-dimensional setting. Linear programming is an important tool that provides maximum and minimum solutions of real-world problems that can be represented with linear inequations. A recent survey of Fortune 500 companies lists linear programming, vertex edge models, and regression data analysis as the three most useful applications of mathematics.

For Investigation 9.6.1, you will need prices and nutrition labels from a variety of prepared foods. You may wish to have your colleagues save and provide empty packages from foods like macaroni and cheese, frozen pizza, instant oatmeal, soups, tuna, and so on.

Section 9.1
Zooming In on Systems

OBJECTIVES
- To locate and examine the intersection points of curves, using graphing and zooming techniques or tables (if tables are available on your calculators)
- To write and solve systems of equations that model the information provided

MATERIALS
None

RESOURCES
Calculator Note 9A

TEACHING NOTES

The concepts in this section are not difficult, and most have been introduced previously. The examples are real-world applications of simple 2-by-2 systems, and students are expected to solve them graphically. During the investigation, and in Problems 1–3, students are encouraged to find the x-intercept of $f(x) = y_1 - y_2$ rather than locate the intersection of y_1 and y_2 on their calculator screens.

Investigation 9.1.1: Intersecting Graphs

In this investigation, students explore the solutions and relationships of graphs in the form of $y = a^x$ and $y = x^a$.

a. Students can either locate the actual point (x, y) or find the x-intercept of $f(x) = y_1 - y_2$. The three x-intercepts are 2, 4, and -0.767. Therefore, $y = 2^x$ and $y = x^2$ intersect at $(2, 4)$, $(4, 16)$, and $(-0.767, 0.588)$. One possible window is $-2.5 \leq x \leq 4.5$ and $0 \leq y \leq 20$, but there isn't a good window to picture all three intersections.

x	2	4	-0.767
y	0	0	0

b. If $y_3 = 0$, this means $y = 2^x$ and $y = x^2$ intersect. If $y_3 > 0$, this means 2^x is greater than x^2. If $y_3 < 0$, then 2^x is less than x^2. A reasonable window for y_3 is $-2.5 \leq x \leq 4.5$ and $-2 \leq y \leq 2$.

c. i. The curves $y = 3^x$ and $y = x^3$ intersect at the two points $(3, 27)$ and $(2.478, 15.217)$.

   ii. The curves $y = 4^x$ and $y = x^4$ intersect at the three points $(2, 4)$, $(4, 256)$, and $(-0.767, 0.345)$.

   iii. The curves $y = 5^x$ and $y = x^5$ intersect at the two points $(5, 3125)$ and $(1.765, 17.125)$.

   iv. The curves $y = 6^x$ and $y = x^6$ intersect at the three points $(-0.790, 0.243)$, $(1.624, 18.361)$, and $(6, 46656)$.

   The pattern suggests two intersections when b is odd, and three intersections when b is even, in $y = b^x$ and $y = x^b$.

d. The graphs of $y = 10^x$ and $y = x^{10}$ intersect at $(10, 10^{10})$, $(1.371, 23.512)$, and $(-0.827, 0.149)$.

PROBLEM SET NOTES

The **int** function in Problem 8 is introduced more formally in Section 9.3. You and your students may already have used this function in attempts to create more accurate models of situations.

Suggested Assignments

Individual	Group	Essential	Performance assessment	Portfolio	Journal
3–6	1, 2, 7, 8	2, 8		8	8

EXTENSIONS
Take Another Look 9.1

Section 9.2
Substitution and Elimination

OBJECTIVES
- To solve simple two-variable systems using substitution and elimination methods
- To understand the meaning of a solution in the context of graphs, tables, and symbolic expressions

MATERIALS
Investigation 9.2.1
    Graph paper
    Straightedge

TEACHING NOTES
Most of this section will be familiar to your students. However, this is an important opportunity to connect graphs, tables, and meaningful symbolic expressions. One appropriate focus here is for students to write equations that will model the situations presented, and then use substitution and elimination techniques to find the solutions of the resulting systems of equations. The techniques and concepts should be meaningful. Students need to know why they are doing something and whether or not it worked. Investigation 9.2.1 gives students an opportunity to discover the elimination method.

*Investigation 9.2.1: Pick a Number—Get the Point
In this investigation, students explore multiples of equations and their relationship to the original system. Students are asked to continue this investigation until they "get the point" or until they understand the elimination process.

Step 1:   The two lines $7x + 2y = -3$ and $3x + 4y = 5$ intersect at $(-1, 2)$.

Step 2:   Equation Three will intersect the first two lines at the same point (a linear combination of two equations will contain the same solution point).

Step 3: The factors are chosen so that one of the variables is eliminated.

Equation One: $7x + 2y = {}^-3$ multiply by $^-3$ $-21x - 6y = 9$

Equation Two: $3x + 4y = 5$ multiply by 7 $21x + 28y = 35$

Adding the results gives Equation Four: $22y = 44$, or $y = 2$.

Step 4: The point of this investigation is to select multiplication factors so that one of the variables will be eliminated when the equations are combined by addition. The point $(^-7, {}^-1)$ is the solution of the system $9y - 5x = 26$ and $4y - 3x = 17$.

PROBLEM SET NOTES

Problem 2 provides an early look at a nonlinear system. Problem 11 involves the solution of a system of two sequences.

Suggested Assignments

Individual	Group	Essential	Performance assessment	Portfolio	Journal
3, 4, 6–10	1, 2, 5, 11				

EXTENSIONS

Take Another Look 9.2

Section 9.3
Number of Solutions

OBJECTIVES

- To discover the meanings of consistent, inconsistent, and dependent systems
- To predict solution possibilities for a system
- To explore the meaning of a system solution in the context of parametric equations
- To write equations that will model several real-world application problems

MATERIALS

None

TEACHING NOTES

Inconsistent and dependent systems are introduced in the Investigation 9.3.1. This investigation will not take much time, but it must be completed. Investigation 9.3.2 and

Example 1 feature the intersection of parametric equations. Consider revisiting some of the parametric problems from Problem Set 6.6. At that time, students were asked to use guess-and-check methods to find angle adjustments to keep a plane or boat on the required heading. Those problems can now be solved by substitution.

*Investigation 9.3.1: Intersecting Lines
In this investigation, students will find that an inconsistent system is a pair of parallel lines. They will also discover that dependent equations have the same graph (because they represent the same solution points).

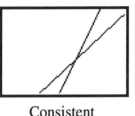 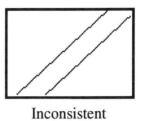 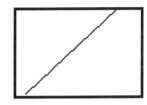

    Consistent   Inconsistent   Consistent and dependent

Investigation 9.3.2: Systems of Parametric Equations
In this investigation, students confirm that there must be an instance when the values of (t, x, y) are identical in order for two parametric equations to intersect. The marbles do hit each other when $(t, x, y) = (1.195, 3.586, 0)$.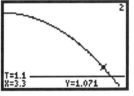
Students can extend their solution techniques beyondzooming and tables by solving $0 = 7 - 4.9t^2$ for t where $t = \sqrt{\frac{7}{4.9}} \approx 1.195$. Then they substitute this result into the equation $x_1 = x_2 = 3t$ to find the horizontal distance traveled at the time themarbles hit. If the ledge is 5 m high, the marbles intersect at $(1.010, 3.030, 0)$. They intersect at $(0.639, 1.917, 0)$ when the ledge is 2 m high.

PROBLEM SET NOTES
Problem 8 is the only application in the problem set related to the discussion of the **int x** function. However, this function can be used to refine models for many problems found earlier in the book.

Suggested Assignments

Individual	Group	Essential	Performance assessment	Portfolio	Journal
1–5	6–11	1, 3	1, 2, 3,	8	11

EXTENSIONS
Project: Bifurcation and Systems

Take Another Look 9.3 (in the *Teacher's Resource Book*)

Section 9.4
Matrix Solutions of Systems

OBJECTIVES

- To solve matrix equations using the inverse of a matrix
- To write and solve matrix equations representing a system of linear equations
- To understand matrix, inverse, and identity matrix connections

MATERIALS

None

RESOURCES

Quiz covering Sections 9.1 to 9.3

Calculator Note 9B

TEACHING NOTES

The methods introduced in this section, and the results derived, are used throughout the remainder of the text. Students must understand what is going on when they use $X = A^{-1} B$. Working together might be the best way for them to read and understand the discussion and examples presented.

Students are asked to find and use identity and inverse matrices to solve systems of equations by rewriting the linear system equations as a matrix equation and then solving the matrix equation. Calculator Note 9B explains calculator matrix operations needed for this process. The use of calculators with limited accuracy and awkward matrix capabilities requires that answers be interpreted carefully.

PROBLEM SET NOTES

Problems 1–6 focus on matrix operations, matrix equations, inverses, and solving systems with matrices. Problems 7–11 provide opportunities for writing and then solving appropriate systems.

Suggested Assignments

Individual	Group	Essential	Performance assessment	Portfolio	Journal
1–7	8–11	4	1, 2, 6	8–11	

EXTENSIONS

Take Another Look 9.4 (in the *Teacher's Resource Book*)

Project: Nonlinear Systems with Three Variables

Project: Inverse by Hand (in the *Teacher's Resource Book*)

Section 9.5
Linear Inequations and Systems

OBJECTIVES

- To identify two-variable inequalities with specific regions of the coordinate plane
- To identify and write inequalities representing conditions or constraints that must be met simultaneously
- To understand the meaning of and locate points of feasible regions
- To find boundary intersection points of feasible regions

MATERIALS

None

RESOURCES

Transparency Master for Section 9.5: Math Time versus Chem Time

Transparency Master for Section 9.5: Graham Crackers and Blueberry Yogurt

TEACHING NOTES

Students should work their way through the investigation and the two related examples. An extension of the second example is considered in the next section. The feasible region is formed by the boundary equations for a system of inequations. The region itself contains the solution points of the system of inequations. This section provides an opportunity for students to graph equations, identify the feasible regions, and locate vertex points of the feasible regions. These skills are vital to the next section.

Traditionally, the feasible region is shaded. But, if you shade the feasible region on a calculator screen, then the solution points are not visible. A better choice is to shade the nonfeasible region. In fact, some calculator shading routines are so primitive that you may prefer to use graph paper and shade the regions by hand. A transparency master is available for Example 2.

*Investigation 9.5.1: Math Time versus Chemistry Time

This investigation is a real-world example of systems of linear inequations.

Part 1

Negative values of x and y don't make sense in this activity. However, fractions will work.

Part 2

The transparency master for this investigation provides an excellent visual. The points above the line $x + y = 3$ solve the inequation $x + y > 3$. The points on or below the line solve the inequation $x + y \leq 3$.

PROBLEM SET NOTES

Problems 1–7 are directly related to the new content of this section. Problem 9 is a journal-writing prompt.

Suggested Assignments

Individual	Group	Essential	Performance assessment	Portfolio	Journal
1, 2, 4, 6, 8, 9	3, 5, 7	8	2		9

Section 9.6
Linear Programming

OBJECTIVES

- To graph inequations and locate the feasible region
- To determine an optimum solution choice for the function provided

MATERIALS

Investigation 9.6.1

   Several canned or packaged food items (labeled with prices, calories, fat, protein, iron)

RESOURCES

Transparency Master for Section 9.5: Graham Crackers

TEACHING NOTES

The solution choices for the function to be optimized (maximized or minimized) come from the feasible region. The best choice is usually at a vertex. This is why students are asked to evaluate this function at each vertex of the feasible region.

One visual option is to graph the function to be optimized. In the graham cracker/yogurt discussion at the beginning of the section, you can invent a *cost* function and graph where the *cost* = 0.06x + 0.30y. Different cost values produce a series of parallel lines that probably will identify a vertex as the optimal solution. However, all points on a boundary line are "best choices" if the function to be optimized is parallel to a boundary line. Some applications restrict solutions to integer values of *x* and *y*. If this is the case, choose the best solution with integer values for coordinates. A transparency master is available for the graham cracker/yogurt problem.

Investigation 9.6.1: Nutritional Elements
Each group will select two food items and then describe and solve a problem similar to the graham cracker/yogurt problem at the beginning of the section. Provide enough food packages so that each group can select and work with two items as they complete this investigation.

PROBLEM SET NOTES
Problem 4 may be used for an assessment item.

Suggested Assignments

Individual	Group	Essential	Performance assessment	Portfolio	Journal
4	1–3	1			

EXTENSIONS
Geometer's Sketchpad Investigation: Linear Programming

Section 9.7
Applications of Linear Programming

OBJECTIVE
• To write constraint equations and inequations, graph the feasible region, and find the optimum value of a corresponding function

MATERIALS
For solutions presentations
  Blank transparencies
  Colored transparency pens

RESOURCES
Quiz covering Sections 9.3 to 9.6

TEACHING NOTES
This section continues graphic solutions of linear programming applications. You can save class time if students prepare carefully graphed solutions on transparencies for overhead projector presentations. A closed-circuit color video camera display of neat solutions on paper may be an available option for some classrooms. Though not part of this course, computer programs and Simplex methods can provide solutions for systems involving several variables and linear inequations.

Investigation 9.7.1: Paying for College
This investigation gives students an opportunity to practice setting up linear programming problems.

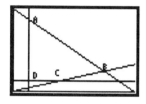

    a. Let x represent the amount invested in stocks and y represent the amount invested in bonds.

    b. $x + y \leq 40{,}000$, $x \geq 5000$, $y \geq 5000$, $x \leq 3y$

    c. The feasible region is outlined by the polygon $ABCD$. The points are $A(5000, 35{,}000)$, $B(30{,}000, 10{,}000)$, $C(15{,}000, 5000)$, and $D(5000, 5000)$.

d. $profit = 0.10x + 0.08y$

e. $profit = 0.10(5000) + 0.08(35{,}000) = 3300$

    $profit = 0.10(30{,}000) + 0.08(10{,}000) = \mathbf{3800}$ The best choice

    $profit = 0.10(15{,}000) + 0.08(5000) = 1900$

    $profit = 0.10(5000) + 0.08(5000) = 900$

Marti's parents should invest $30,000 in stocks and $10,000 in bonds for a profit of $3,800.

PROBLEM SET NOTES
Consider assigning Problems 4 and 5 later on. They could be included, one at a time, within the next few assignments.

Suggested Assignments

Individual	Group	Essential	Performance assessment	Portfolio	Journal
4, 5	1–3			4, 5	

EXTENSIONS

Take Another Look 9.7

Project: Nonlinear Programming

Section 9.8
Determinants and System Classification

OBJECTIVES

- To explore systems and their determinants
- To find a unique solution for a system or determine that the system is inconsistent or dependent

MATERIALS

None

RESOURCES

Transparency Master for Section 9.8: Intersecting Planes

Calculator Note 9B

TEACHING NOTES

This section is optional and is not crucial to the remainder of the course. Students may encounter an error message as they attempt to solve the associated matrix equation when using A^{-1}. The determinant of matrix A, det A, will be zero if the coefficient matrix, A, has no inverse. If $A \cdot x = c$ is an inconsistent system or a dependent system, then det $A = 0$ and A has no inverse. If students find that this is the situation in a two-variable system, they need to identify a point that satisfies one of the equations. If this point does not satisfy the other equation, then the system is inconsistent (graphs are parallel). If this point does satisfy the other equation, then the system is dependent (identical graphs).

The three-dimensional discussion of the difference between an inconsistent system and a dependent system is difficult. You may have, and be prepared to use, software and technology that will provide visual help. Be sure that the students can identify the different situations that occur when three planes intersect. If students cannot identify them in the photo following Example 2, you may wish to have your students build models using poster board.

Investigation 9.8.1: A Matrix Without an Inverse

Part 1

a. $\det A \neq 0$; A has an inverse.   b. $\det A \neq 0$; A has an inverse.

c. $\det A \neq 0$; A has an inverse.   d. $\det A = 0$; A has no inverse.

e. $\det A \neq 0$; A has an inverse.   f. $\det A = 0$; A has no inverse.

g. $\det A \neq 0$; A has an inverse.   h. $\det A = 0$; A has no inverse.

Part 2

a. The matrix $\begin{bmatrix} 2 & 6 \\ c & d \end{bmatrix}$ has no inverse if $2d = 6c$.

b. Answers will vary.

c. The matrix $\begin{bmatrix} 8 & ^{-}3.5 \\ c & d \end{bmatrix}$ will have no inverse if $8d = ^{-}3.5c$. Several choices of c and d can be used, such as $c = 4$ and $d = ^{-}1.75$.

d. The $\det A$ for $A = \begin{bmatrix} a & b \\ c & d \end{bmatrix}$ is the number $ad - bc$.

PROBLEM SET NOTES

Problems 2 uses the solutions from Problem 1. Problems 5 and 6 can be used as journal-writing prompts.

Suggested Assignments

Individual	Group	Essential	Performance assessment	Portfolio	Journal
4–6	1–3		1		5, 6

EXTENSIONS

Take Another Look 9.8

Project: Inverse by Hand

Section 9.9
Chapter Review

OBJECTIVE

• To review the mathematical terms, concepts, and problem-solving skills in Chapter 9

RESOURCES
Test on Chapter 9 to be given following this section

TEACHING NOTES
Review the important concepts of the chapter. Assign the chapter review and allow the students to work together to solve the problems while you circulate to answer questions. Students may wish to present their solutions to the class as a review.

PROBLEM SET NOTES
Problems 11 and 12 are journal-writing prompts.

Suggested Assignments

Individual	Group	Essential	Performance assessment	Portfolio	Journal
1–12			1, 3, 4		11, 12

Assessing What You've Learned
Students are reminded to review their journal entries in Problem Sets 9.5, 9.8, and 9.9, organize their notebooks, and update their portfolios. There are also several suggestions of alternative assessment for students to complete.

Chapter 10
Polynomials

Overview

Students model polynomials as they consider an assortment of problems and activities. Finite differences are used to determine if a polynomial model is applicable and to find the degree of the polynomial. They study three different forms of polynomials—polynomial, vertex, and factored—and learn how to convert from one form to another as they make connections between x-intercepts, polynomial zeros, and factors. In this chapter, students derive the quadratic formula and then use it to find zeros. Finally, complex numbers and synthetic division are introduced.

Section 10.1
Finite Differences

OBJECTIVES

- To find the polynomial model that fits a set of data exhibiting a regular finite-difference pattern

- To use finite differences to predict the degree of a polynomial that fits a set of data

MATERIALS

For alternative to Investigation 10.1.1

    CBL and sonic probe

RESOURCES

Transparency Master for Section 10.1: Investigation 10.1.1

Transparency Master for Section 10.1: Finite Differences Grid

TEACHING NOTES

In this section, students are introduced to polynomials and finite differences as they complete the two investigations. With measured data, the finite differences may be *nearly* equal, and students will have to be content with *approximately* equal nonzero numbers in D_n.

Below are the steps used to predict the degree of a polynomial that fits a set of data when the x-values are in an arithmetic sequence. These are also listed in the text.

1. Find the finite differences of the y-values by subtracting consecutive values.
2. Check to see if the first differences, D_1, are all equal nonzero numbers. If this is so, then the polynomial that fits the data is linear.
3. If you find the polynomial isn't first degree, find D_2, the finite differences of the D_1 values.
4. Check the second differences, D_2. If they are all equal nonzero numbers, then the polynomial that fits the data points is second degree.
5. If not, continue. The polynomial has the degree n which matches the first D_n with equal nonzero numbers.

*Investigation 10.1.1: Falling Objects

In this investigation, students complete a table by reading heights from the picture. It is important that the table entries be accurate to the nearest hundredth of a meter. In Section 10.2, students will use these results to generate the equation for the height of an object falling from an initial height of 10 m, $h(t) = 10 - 4.9t^2$.

Time	0.0	0.2	0.4	0.6	0.8	1.0	1.2	1.4
Height	10.00	9.81	9.22	8.24	6.86	5.10	2.94	0.40
D_1		−0.19	−0.59	−0.98	−1.38	−1.76	−2.16	−2.54
D_2			−0.40	−0.39	−0.40	−0.38	−0.40	−0.38

An alternative method of collecting data for this investigation is to use a CBL with a sonic probe.

*Investigation 10.1.2: Diagonals of Polygons

In this investigation, students draw polygons and complete a chart to determine a relationship between (*number of sides, number of diagonals*).

a.

Side (s)	4	5	6	7	8	9	20	23
Diagonals (d)	2	5	9	14	20	27	170	230
D_1		3	4	5	6	7		
D_2			1	1	1	1		

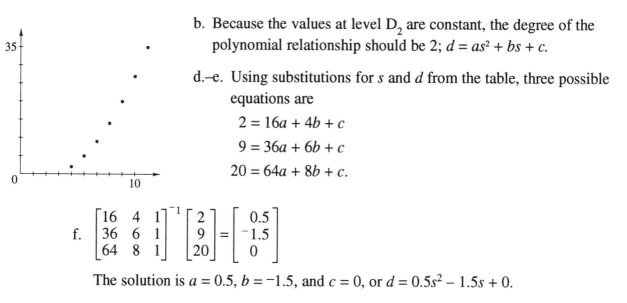

b. Because the values at level D_2 are constant, the degree of the polynomial relationship should be 2; $d = as^2 + bs + c$.

d.–e. Using substitutions for s and d from the table, three possible equations are

$$2 = 16a + 4b + c$$
$$9 = 36a + 6b + c$$
$$20 = 64a + 8b + c.$$

f. $\begin{bmatrix} 16 & 4 & 1 \\ 36 & 6 & 1 \\ 64 & 8 & 1 \end{bmatrix}^{-1} \begin{bmatrix} 2 \\ 9 \\ 20 \end{bmatrix} = \begin{bmatrix} 0.5 \\ -1.5 \\ 0 \end{bmatrix}$

The solution is $a = 0.5$, $b = -1.5$, and $c = 0$, or $d = 0.5s^2 - 1.5s + 0$.

g. $d = 0.5(8)^2 - 1.5(8) = 20$ and $d = 0.5(20)^2 - 1.5(20) = 170$ means that an octagon should have 20 diagonals and a 20-sided polygon should have 170 diagonals.

h. A 23-sided polygon will have 230 diagonals.

It doesn't matter which three points (s, d) are selected to build the model when using exact data (as in this investigation). However, when using measured data, the points should be widely separated to better represent the entire data set.

PROBLEM SET NOTES

Problems 1–3 continue and extend the opening discussion and Example 1. Problems 4–6 provide more work with finite differences. Do Problems 1 and 4 during class.

Suggested Assignments

Individual	Group	Essential	Performance assessment	Portfolio	Journal
3, 5, 6	1, 2, 4	1, 2		Inv. 10.1.2, 6	

Section 10.2
Different Quadratic Forms

OBJECTIVE

• To make important connections between vertex form and polynomial form, and convert between the forms

MATERIALS
None

TEACHING NOTES
This section introduces three equivalent forms for quadratics:

$y = ax^2 + bx + c$ Polynomial form

$y = A(x - H)^2 + K$ Vertex form

$y = A(x - R_1)(x - R_2)$ Factored form

Most of the time spent can be allocated to the problems. The important and straightforward Investigation 10.2.1 will not require much time.

Investigation 10.2.1: Patterns of Squares
In this investigation, students discover constant values at level D_2, so the equation is of the form $t = an^2 + bn + c$. The equation $t = 2n^2 + 2n + 0$ is a model for the data.

Side length (n)	1	2	3	4	5
Total segments (t)	4	12	24	40	60

D_1	8	12	16	20

D_2	4	4	4

PROBLEM SET NOTES
Problems 1, 4, and 5 will be extended in Section 10.4 to find one form of the quadratic formula. Problem 5 uses the answer to Problem 2c. Problem 6 uses the results from Problem 5. Problem 10 uses the data collected in Investigation 10.1.1.

Suggested Assignments

Individual	Group	Essential	Performance assessment	Portfolio	Journal
5–8	1–4, 9, 10	1, 2, 4, 5	1, 2	9, 10	

Section 10.3
Factored Polynomials

OBJECTIVES
- To convert functions written in polynomial form to an equivalent factored form
- To discover important connections between the roots and the factored form of polynomial equations

MATERIALS

Investigation 10.3.1

    Graph paper

    Scissors

    Tape

TEACHING NOTES

Students need to complete the investigation and understand concepts involved in the examples. In this section, students convert functions written in polynomial form to an equivalent factored form by graphing the polynomial and locating its x-intercepts. Each x-intercept, r_i, has a corresponding factor $(x - r_i)$. The product of the factors associated with each intercept multiplied by a constant A provides a factored form of the polynomial over the real numbers. Using the zero-factor property, students will be able to find the x-intercepts.

Investigation 10.3.1: Open-Top Boxes

In this investigation, students cut out and then fold several open-top boxes and determine an equation fitting their (*length of x, volume of box*) data.

a.–c.

x	1		2		3		4		5		6		7
Volume	252		384		420		384		300		192		84
D_1		132		36		−36		−84		−108		−108	
D_2			−96		−72		−48		−24		0		
D_3				24		24		24		24			

d. Because the x-values form an arithmetic sequence, finite differences can be used to determine if the model is a polynomial. Constant values at the D_3 level imply a cubic polynomial model $y = ax^3 + bx^2 + cx + d$. Students can use substitution and solve a system of equations to find the values of a, b, c, and d to get $y = 4x^3 - 72x^2 + 320x$.

e. The values 0, 8, and 10 would each cause one of the three dimensions to be zero, and therefore, the volume would be zero. The realistic domain for x lies in $0 < x < 8$.

f.

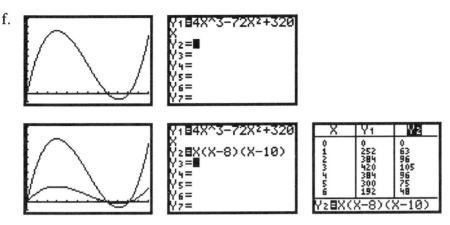

Students can use the three x-intercepts $r_1 = 0$, $r_2 = 8$, and $r_3 = 10$ to build the equation $y = A(x - 0)(x - 8)(x - 10)$, and then find A by substituting in one of the points from the table. For example, $420 = A(3 - 0)(3 - 8)(3 - 10)$ means $A = 4$.

The table confirms that the two equations are the same, that is, $y = A(x - 0)(x - 8)(x - 10) = 4x^3 - 72x^2 + 320x$ when $A = 4$.

g. Length $= 20 - 2x$; Width $= 16 - 2x$; Height $= x$

Volume $= x(20 - 2x)(16 - 2x)$

If you expand the volume equation, it will be the same as the equation found in part d.

PROBLEM SET NOTES

Most problems aren't difficult, but they will require some time and careful thought. Your students can use their factoring skills, or they will use the fact that an x-intercept, r_i, has a corresponding factor $(x - r_i)$ of the polynomial. This means that they can factor by graphing and locating roots by zooming in on the x-intercept or by zooming in within a table of values.

Suggested Assignments

Individual	Group	Essential	Performance assessment	Portfolio	Journal
1, 2, 8–11	3–7	1, 2, 7–9	1, 4		

Section 10.4
The Quadratic Formula

OBJECTIVES

- To derive the quadratic formula and use it to find x-intercepts or zeros of polynomial equations
- To model projectile motions with parametric equations

MATERIALS

For Alternative Investigations

    Stopwatch or CBL light probe and laser pointer

RESOURCES

Quiz covering Sections 10.1 to 10.3

TEACHING NOTES

In this section, students derive the quadratic formula and then use two different forms of this formula to find x-intercepts or zeros of polynomial equations.

The Quadratic Formula

Vertex form

If $A(x - H)^2 + K = 0$,

then the solutions are $x = H \pm \sqrt{\frac{-K}{A}}$.

Polynomial form

If $ax^2 + bx + c = 0$, then the solutions are

$$x = \frac{-b \pm \sqrt{b^2 - 4ac}}{2a} .$$

They model projectile motions with appropriate functions or parametric equations. In each new situation, encourage your students *to derive the parametric equations* (similar to the solution strategy used in Example 5) rather than just substituting values into the generic equations $x = v_0 t \cos A + x_0$ and $y = at^2 + v_0 t \sin A + y_0$. Students should describe or explain the meaning of every number and variable in the parametric equations.

Six important examples, the formula derivation, an investigation, and twelve problems make this a long section that may take two days.

Investigation 10.4.1: Getting Sunburned

This investigation gives students a real-world application of quadratics. When students plot the data, the elapsed hours should be used as the domain rather than the actual time of day.

Time	9 a.m.	10 a.m.	11 a.m.	Noon	1 p.m.	2 p.m.	3 p.m.	4 p.m.
Elapsed hours	0	1	2	3	4	5	6	7
Minutes to redden	34	20	15	13	14	18	32	60

Students will probably see a parabola or quadratic polynomial (approximately $y = 2.8x^2 - 16.8x + 35$) as the appropriate model. Domain and data values will vary, depending on geographic location, altitude, angle of the sun, humidity, cloud cover, and so on.

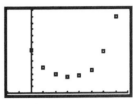

Alternative 1 for Investigation 10.4.1:

Take the students outside. Have them throw a ball as high as they can. Time the interval between the release of the ball and when it hits the ground. Calculate the maximum height.

Alternative 2 for Investigation 10.4.1:

Set up a light beam at ground level and use the CBL to time a student's jump. Calculate the height of the jump.

PROBLEM SET NOTES

Problem 8 refers to Example 4 of this section. Problem 10 asks students to create a quadratic formula program. At this point, the program should display real roots and recognize nonreal situations. Some students will jump at this opportunity to write a program. Problem 12 is a journal-writing prompt.

Suggested Assignments

Individual	Group	Essential	Performance assessment	Portfolio	Journal
5, 8, 11, 12	1–4, 6, 7, 9, 10	3, 5	1, 2	Inv. 10.4.1	12

EXTENSIONS

Take Another Look 10.4

Project: Air Drag (in the *Teacher's Resource Book*)

Section 10.5
Applications and Algebraic Solutions

OBJECTIVES
- To find polynomial models using finite differences
- To use polynomial equation factors and x-intercepts of graphs to answer related application questions

MATERIALS
Investigation 10.5.1

    Graph paper

    Scissors

    Tape

TEACHING NOTES
The section contains one quick (provided that students did Investigation 10.3.1) and enjoyable investigation, as well as examples that review and extend previous work. Most class time can be spent working on the problem set.

Investigation 10.5.1: Making a Suitcase
In this investigation, students will construct a box (with a top) by cutting paper using the pattern pictured in the text. All students should start with standard-size pieces of paper.

a. Constructed boxes will have different volumes because each individual or group can freely choose the length of x.

b. The value of A in the equation, *volume* $= A(x - 0)(x - 0.5W)(x - 0.25L)$, can be determined after substituting the paper dimensions, the x-value, and the box volume.

c. Everyone should arrive at the same three values ($x = 0$, $x = \frac{\text{width}}{2}$, or $x = \frac{\text{length}}{2}$) that will produce a box with no volume.

d. The graph (or table values) of $y = A(x - 0)(x - 0.5W)(x - 0.25L)$ can be used to determine the choice for x that produces the maximum value of y. If the sheet of paper is 8.5 in. by 11 in., a value of $x \approx 1.09$ provides a maximum $V \approx 91.48$. In this situation, $A = 16$.

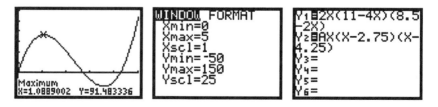

PROBLEM SET NOTES

For problems like 3, 4, 5, 6, 8, and 9, students can use (or create) tables of information, find finite differences, and then write the appropriate equations. Alternative strategies could be shared by students who find and use them.

Suggested Assignments

Individual	Group	Essential	Performance assessment	Portfolio	Journal
1, 2, 4, 6, 9	3, 5, 7, 8		1		

Section 10.6
Higher-Degree Polynomials

OBJECTIVES

- To predict graph features: y-intercept, one or more x-intercepts, and local maxima or minima points

- To identify and predict multiple roots when given a graph or factored form of the polynomial equation

MATERIALS

Investigation 10.6.1

    Graph paper

    Rulers

RESOURCES

Calculator Note 10A

TEACHING NOTES

Students are formally introduced to higher-degree polynomials. A definition ($y = a_n x^n + a_{n-1} x^{n-1} + a_{n-2} x^{n-2} + \cdots + a_2 x^2 + a_1 x + a_0$ where $a_n \neq 0$ and the exponents, $n, n-1$, and so on, are positive integers) is provided, but students are not asked to use subscripted variables. Students examine features of graphs and equations for higher-degree polynomials. The investigation is loaded with surprises and should be assigned.

Investigation 10.6.1: The Largest Triangle

In this investigation, students are asked to find the largest triangle. There are many different strategies students can use to find the requested area. As written, the investigation is rich and open to a variety of approaches. Students might collect (*x, area*) data, use the Pythagorean theorem, use trigonometric relationships, or just use guess-and-check. We encourage you to avoid offering suggestions on this investigation. Generally, students come up with surprisingly strong approaches.

x	Area	x	Area
0	0	12	42.6
2	10.4	14	40.6
4	20.2	16	35.2
6	28.8	18	25.2
8	36.0	20	10.0
10	40.5	21	0

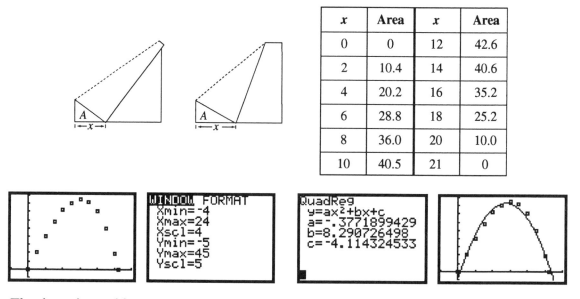

The data pictured here were collected by plotting (*x, area*) after folding a sheet of paper with height or width of 21 cm. The paper length is unimportant, provided it is longer than 21 cm. One of the biggest surprises to students is that the polynomial fit is not quadratic. If quadratic, with *x*-intercepts at $x = 0$ and $x = 21$ (these are values that provide an area of 0), the maximum point would be on the line $x = 10.5$. The maximum for this set of points is not on this line of symmetry.

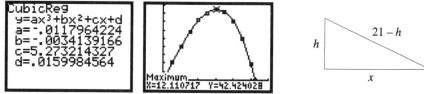

In fact, the best-fit polynomial for (*x, area*) is cubic. Another solution uses the Pythagorean theorem to write *h* in terms of *x*. If the equation $h^2 + x^2 = (21 - h)^2$ is expanded, then $h = \frac{441 - x^2}{42}$. The area of the triangle is $\frac{1}{2}bh$, or

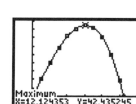

$$A = \frac{1}{2}x\frac{441 - x^2}{42} \text{ or } \frac{x(21 - x)(21 + x)}{84}.$$

The approximate maximum area of 42.44 occurs when $x = 12.12$.

PROBLEM SET NOTES

Problem 8 offers a particular solution strategy for Investigation 10.6.1. Most of the other problems extend the multiple-root connections.

Suggested Assignments

Individual	Group	Essential	Performance assessment	Portfolio	Journal
1, 4, 7, 8	2, 3, 5, 6	1, 2, 4	1	Inv. 10.6.1, 8	

EXTENSIONS

Take Another Look 10.6 (in the *Teacher's Resource Book*)

Geometer's Sketchpad Investigation: The Largest Triangle

Project: Coefficient of Fit (uses Calculator Note 10A)

Section 10.7
No Real Solutions

OBJECTIVES

- To find roots, which may include nonreal roots, of polynomials

- To determine and write the equation of a polynomial when provided with its real and nonreal roots

- To understand definitions, operations, and number hierarchy of imaginary and complex numbers

MATERIALS

None

RESOURCES

Transparency Master for Section 10.7: Complex Number Chart

Calculator Notes 10B and 10C

TEACHING NOTES

Students work with imaginary and complex numbers after they learn that imaginary numbers come from square roots of negative numbers and that $\sqrt{-1} = i$ or $i^2 = -1$.

This relationship between sets of numbers is diagrammed in the text. In the problem set, students write the polynomial equation corresponding to a given set of zeros, and vice versa. In Problem 1, they learn that nonreal answers always occur in conjugate pairs $a + bi$ and $a - bi$. This is an important, though short, section. More work with complex numbers is in Section 10.8, and further interesting applications are in Chapter 13.

PROBLEM SET NOTES

Problems 1–5 and 9 are directly related to the material covered in the section.

Suggested Assignments

Individual	Group	Essential	Performance assessment	Portfolio	Journal
1, 2, 4, 8, 9	3, 5–7	1, 2, 5	1, 4		

EXTENSIONS

Take Another Look 10.7 (uses Calculator Note 10B)

Project: Least-Squares Polynomial Fit (uses Calculator Note 10C)

Section 10.8
More About Finding Solutions

OBJECTIVES

- To find a second factor when given one factor or root of a polynomial
- To use synthetic division to find roots of polynomials
- To find approximate roots using a bisection algorithm

MATERIALS

Investigation 10.8.1

    Water container with a hole in the bottom (a 2-liter bottle works well)

    Ruler

    Timing device

    Tape

RESOURCES

Calculator Notes 10D, 10E, and 10F

TEACHING NOTES

In this section, students will use the relationship between the zeros of a polynomial and its factors to find missing factors. An algorithm for dividing a polynomial by a polynomial is briefly described. Students then discover the algorithm for synthetic division and the relationship between synthetic division, the zeros (or roots) of the polynomial, and the linear factors of the polynomial.

Root finding and synthetic division programs are listed in Calculator Notes 10D and 10E.

Investigation 10.8.1: A Leaky Bottle Experiment

This investigation can be conducted outside, over a sink, or over a larger water container. The data (*time, water height*) will be approximately quadratic when the experiment is conducted carefully. Students should not start collecting data until the water has emptied to the vertical part of the container and should quit before the water level reaches the rounded portion of the bottom. Depending on the size of the hole, students may wish to record data at smaller or larger time intervals. Students have several options available to write a best-fit quadratic model. If they use the method of finite differences to predict a second degree polynomial, they should not expect the D_2 values to be exactly the same.

PROBLEM SET NOTES

Problem 2e uses Calculator Note 10D. Problem 4 uses Calculator Note 10E. Problems 1–4 and 7 are directly related to the section. Problems 6 and 7 are journal-writing prompts.

Suggested Assignments

Individual	Group	Essential	Performance assessment	Portfolio	Journal
3, 5–7	1, 2, 4	2	3	Inv. 10.8.1	6, 7

EXTENSIONS

Take Another Look 10.8

Take Another Look 10.8a (in the *Teacher's Resource Book*)

Take Another Look 10.8b (in the *Teacher's Resource Book*)

Project: Mandelbrot Set (uses Calculator Note 10F)

Section 10.9
Chapter Review

OBJECTIVES

• To review the mathematical terms, concepts, and problem-solving skills in Chapter 10

RESOURCES

Quiz covering Sections 10.4 to 10.8

Test on Chapter 10 to be given following this section

TEACHING NOTES

Review the important concepts of the chapter. Assign the chapter review and allow the students to work together to solve problems while you circulate to answer questions. Students may wish to present their solutions to the class as part of the review.

PROBLEM SET NOTES

Problems 6 and 7 are journal-writing prompts.

Suggested Assignments

Individual	Group	Essential	Performance assessment	Portfolio	Journal
1–7			2, 4		6, 7

Assessing What You've Learned

Students are reminded to review their journal entries, organize their notebooks, and update their portfolios. There are also several suggestions for alternative assessment for students to complete.

Chapter 11
Probability and Statistics

Overview

Initial sections extend earlier notions about probability, counting processes, and tree representations. Permutations, combinations, combination numbers, and binomial expansions lead to binomial distribution investigations. Students study and discover connections between the standard deviation measure and normal distribution applications. They explore and model normal distributions and normal curves. Finally, they use the normal curve and a series of programs to find probabilities associated with normally distributed events.

Section 11.1
Permutations and Probability

OBJECTIVES

- To review and extend earlier notions about probability

- To make a connection between the use of a tree diagram and the counting principle as organizational strategies for counting

- To discover and apply strategies involving permutations

MATERIALS
None

RESOURCES
Calculator Note 11A

TEACHING NOTES
Students need to spend time with the examples and the investigation, but they don't have to become permutation experts. Concentrate on the language so that everyone is considering the same problem. Time spent laying out a visual solution strategy, sketching a tree, or reducing the problem to a simpler case is not wasted time. Most students will gain conceptual insight when they manipulate, sort, and arrange a set of books or a line-up of students. The section does not focus on any formulas; rather, students have the opportunity to discover formulas when working on the investigation and the problems.

*Investigation 11.1.1: The Factorial Function

Students explore the properties of the factorial function in this investigation.

a.

n	1	2	3	4	5	6	7
$n!$	1	2	6	24	120	720	5040

b. i. Multiply by 7   ii. Divide by 6   iii. $8 \cdot 7 \cdot 6 \cdot 5 \cdot 4 \cdot 3 \cdot 2 \cdot 1$

c. i. You can't   ii. You can't

   iii. Limited by largest exponent display such as $9.9999^{\wedge}10^{99}$. This display limit depends on your calculator model.

   iv. 0

d. $n! = n(n-1)(n-2) \ldots (3)(2)(1)$, except $0! = 1$

e. $n! = \begin{cases} 1 & n = 0 \\ n(n-1)! & n \geq 1 \end{cases}$

f. If the cursor traces on integer values for x, then you will see a discrete graph. The graph appears to be exponential.

PROBLEM SET NOTES

Problems 1, 4, and 7 require a lot of thought. Problem 6 should provide insight about the size of $N!$ and its rate of growth.

Suggested Assignments

Individual	Group	Essential	Performance assessment	Portfolio	Journal
2, 3, 5	1, 4, 6, 7	2, 3	1a, 2, 5	7	

EXTENSIONS

Take Another Look 11.1 (in the *Teacher's Resource Book*)

Section 11.2
Combinations and Probability

OBJECTIVES

- To recognize counting situations involving combinations
- To discover the relationship between $_nC_r$ and $_nP_r$ and to be able to calculate each

MATERIALS
None

TEACHING NOTES
This is an important section because many of the concepts introduced will be developed in the remainder of the chapter. Spend extra time with Example 3. The ideas involved are important to later sections and to Problems 8 and 9. You may wish to do the investigation on the second day, after your students have gained more experience recognizing and calculating combinations. Consider asking each group to complete the investigation questions and turn in a group write-up for a possible assessment item.

Investigation 11.2.1: Winning the Lottery
Students explore their chances of winning the lottery in this investigation. You may wish to alter the investigation or use your own state lottery and have available a supply of blank lottery forms that include the lottery rules. The following answers are for the Lotto 47 game and may be different if you use your own state lottery. To make this investigation more interesting, consider offering a prize. Have the students calculate the expected value if the prize were $4 million. Your students should learn something about the probability of winning the lottery during this investigation. Remember, if someone knows the seed value for the rand routine, they can predict the sequence. How does the probability change if you alter the set by selecting from 46 or 48 numbers?

a. The person left standing won the lottery, by getting all six numbers correct.

b. $\frac{1}{47}C_6 = \frac{1}{10,737,573} = 0.00000009313$

c. Answers will vary.

d. Answers will vary.

e.–f. $1 - (1 - 0.00000009313)^{ng}$

g. 169.5 mi

PROBLEM SET NOTES
Problem 10 is a writing question that will demonstrate understanding of permutations and combinations. Problems 1–5 develop the relationship between permutations and combinations.

Suggested Assignments

Individual	Group	Essential	Performance assessment	Portfolio	Journal
1–4, 7, 10	5, 6, 8–9	1, 5	2, 3	Inv. 11.2.1, 5	8, 10

Section 11.3
Binomial Theorem

OBJECTIVES

- To make connections among combination numbers, expanding binomials, and Pascal's triangle

- To explore graphs of binomial distributions

MATERIALS

Investigation 11.3.2

    Basketball

    Basketball hoop

Preparation for Investigation 11.4.1

    Heavy cord, with only a little stretch, that is slightly longer than 1.5 m

    Meterstick

    Envelope

    Slips of paper

RESOURCES

Calculator Notes 11B, 11C, and 11D

TEACHING NOTES

Provide time so that students understand how to expand a binomial term by term. Students will discover many connections between combination numbers and binomial coefficients as they complete Investigation 11.3.1. This investigation should be completed on the first day, and students could prepare for Investigation 11.3.2 by entering the program in Calculator Note 11B. Following Investigation 11.3.1, students should solve Example 1. The completed chart is given below. The percentages may vary because of the rounding factor involved when students use the numbers they found in the "Exactly" row rather than the original equation from the binomial expansion.

Survival	0 birds	1 bird	2 birds	3 birds	4 birds	5 birds	6 birds
Exactly	0.5%	4.5%	15.7%	28.9%	29.9%	16.5%	3.8%
At most	0.5%	5%	20.7%	49.6%	79.7%	96.2%	100%
At least	100%	99.5%	95%	79.1%	50.2%	20.3%	3.8%

Conduct and complete Investigation 11.3.2 after students have had the opportunity to explore the examples and some problems. The histograms created will differ because the probabilities are different. But after looking at a few of them, students should begin to see a common "bell" shape. Encourage class discussion about similarities and differences in the graphs.

Prepare for Investigation 11.4.1 by collecting the needed data. You will need between 75 and 100 points, so it is a good idea to start collecting this data several days before doing the investigation. You probably will want to collect the data in several classes. Be sure to remind students to measure to the nearest millimeter.

*Investigation 11.3.1: The Binomial Expansion
Students will make the connection between the binomial expansion and combination numbers.

a. $(H + T)^4 = 1H^4 + 4H^3T + 6H^2T^2 + 4H^1T^3 + 1T^4$
   $(H + T)^5 = 1H^5 + 5H^4T^1 + 10H^3T^2 + 10H^2T^3 + 5H^1T^4 + 1T^5$

b. 1; 5; 10; 10; 5; 1

c. i. 1; 2; 4; 8; 16; 32   ii. 64   iii. 128   iv. 2^n

d.

```
                          1
                       1     1
                    1     2     1
                 1     3     3     1
              1     4     6     4     1
           1     5    10    10     5     1
        1     6    15    20    15     6     1
     1     7    21    35    35    21     7     1
  1     8    28    56    70    56    28     8     1
1     9    36    84   126   126    84    36     9     1
1    10    45   120   210   252   210   120    45    10    1
1   11    55   165   330   462   462   330   165    55    11    1
1  12    66   220   495   792   924   792   495   220    66    12    1
```

e. $1a^{10} + 10a^9b^1 + 45a^8b^2 + 120a^7b^3 + 210a^6b^4 + 252a^5b^5 + 210a^4b^6 + 120a^3b^7$
   $+ 45a^2b^8 + 10a^1b^9 + 1b^{10}$

f. $1p^{12} + 12p^{11}q^1 + 66p^{10}q^2 + 220p^9q^3 + 495p^8q^4 + \cdots$

g. $_nC_0a^n + {}_nC_1a^{n-1}b^1 + {}_nC_2a^{n-2}b^2 + \cdots$; 6th term $= {}_nC_6a^{n-6}b^6$; General term $= {}_nC_xa^{n-x}b^x$
   Last three terms $= {}_nC_{x-2}a^{n-(x-2)}b^{x-2} + {}_nC_{x-1}a^{n-(x-1)}b^{x-1} + {}_nC_xb^x$

Investigation 11.3.2: Free Throw

Students will discover graphs that are "bell-shaped." Graphs will be less symmetric as the probability of success moves away from 0.5.

PROBLEM SET NOTES

Problem 5 asks students to enter and use a simulation program from Calculator Note 11C. This simple program can be used on any problem involving the sum of binomial terms. You may wish to demonstrate the program on Example 1. Problem 8 is extended in Problem 8, Problem Set 11.4. You may wish to provide class time for discussion of student approaches and results on this problem. The window given in Calculator Note 11D is selected for Problem 8 because the equation has value only for integer values of x. The calculator tests function values based on the number of pixels on the graphing window; an incorrect window will result in a partial or completely missing graph. For a value of $P = 0.645$, $y = 0.08757B^{(x-32)^2}$ with $B = 0.97355$.

Suggested Assignments

Individual	Group	Essential	Performance assessment	Portfolio	Journal
1, 2, 4, 8	3, 5–7	1, 8	2		7

EXTENSIONS

Take Another Look 11.3

Project: Trinomial Distribution

Section 11.4
Standard Deviation

OBJECTIVES

- To discover the concepts involved and how to calculate the standard deviation

- To begin to understand what standard deviation measures

MATERIALS

Investigation 11.4.1

See Section 11.3

RESOURCES

Quiz covering Sections 11.1 to 11.3

Calculator Notes 11D, 11E, 11F, and 11G

Data and Programs Disk

TEACHING NOTES

During the investigation, students will calculate the standard deviation step by step. When this is completed, you may explain to students how to use the calculator function to find the standard deviation value. A connection between standard deviation and normally distributed data is suggested several times during the section.

Investigation 11.4.1: Measuring a Cord Length

The instructions for collecting data for the investigation are in the section guide for Section 11.3.

In this investigation, students will find the deviation from the mean and define the variance. Ask a student to enter the collected measurements into a data list on his or her calculator and then share the data by linking calculators. The more data, the better the results will be.

PROBLEM SET NOTES

Problem 4 can be done without the program described in Calculator Note 11F, but the number of dice rolls involved will be easier if data are gathered by a group rather than individually. The data set in Problem 6 can be found on the Data and Programs Disk. Problem 8 is connected to Investigation 11.5.1 and to Problem 8, Problem Set 11.3. Students should have the time and assistance to find a solution to this problem even if they have to play with it for a while. Problem 8 uses Calculator Notes 11D and 11G.

Suggested Assignments

Individual	Group	Essential	Performance assessment	Portfolio	Journal
1–3	4–8	7, 8		Inv. 11.4.1	

EXTENSIONS

Take Another Look 11.4

Project: Helping Out

Section 11.5
Normal Distributions

OBJECTIVES

- To work with the area between the x-axis and a curve
- To find equation values for $y = ab^{x^2}$ modeling normal distributions
- To alter these equations to create a normal curve with an area of 1 between itself and the x-axis

MATERIALS

None

RESOURCES

Calculator Notes 11H and 11I
Data and Programs Disk

TEACHING NOTES

The normal distribution is compared to a large binomial distribution. A binomial distribution is discrete. The normal distribution is continuous and can be graphed without being extremely careful of the window values. The model given is an approximation for the normal curve. If your class has been introduced to the number e, then you may wish to alter the normal distribution equation in this section and in the next section.

The area program in Calculator Note 11H uses the rectangle method for approximating the area under a curve. In most problems, only one endpoint will be given and students will use their own judgment for the other endpoint and the number of divisions. They may wish to run the program with a small number of divisions, say 100, for a quick approximate answer and then again with larger values for more accurate answers.

Investigation 11.5.1: Areas and Distributions
During this investigation, students explore the area under a normal distribution and its relationship to probabilities.

PROBLEM SET NOTES

The data for Problem 8 are available on the Data and Programs Disk. Students can collect data for Problem 8 instead of using the data provided. They can collect pulse rates of family members and neighbors (five to ten people) as part of the first night's assignment, and then share this data in class. The shared data could be used to complete the problem during the second assignment.

In Problems 5–8, the equations are based on the model $y = ab^{x^2}$. The most difficult part of this section may be entering the complicated equations needed to graph the normal curves and finding a window to see the function. The window used will normally be $\bar{x} \pm 3s$ for x and at least 0 to $\frac{1}{\sigma\sqrt{2\pi}}$ for y. The equation in y_2 suggests that if $y = ab^{x^2}$, then $a = \frac{1}{\sigma\sqrt{2\pi}}$ and $b = 1 - \frac{1}{2(\sigma)^2}$. These equations will be introduced in the next section.

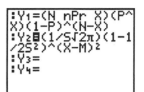

Suggested Assignments

Individual	Group	Essential	Performance assessment	Portfolio	Journal
2–5, 9	1, 6–8	5, 6			

EXTENSIONS

Take Another Look 11.5

Geometer's Sketchpad Investigation: Normal Curves

Project: Skewed Data (in the *Teacher's Resource Book*)

Section 11.6
Using the Normal Curve

OBJECTIVES

• To use $y = ab^{x^2}$, with $a = \frac{1}{\sigma\sqrt{2\pi}}$ and $b = 1 - \frac{1}{2(\sigma)^2}$ to model a normal curve

• To use programs to find the probability of an event and to match a distribution interval with a given probability

MATERIALS

None

RESOURCES

Quiz covering Sections 11.4 and 11.5

Calculator Notes 11F, 11H, and 11J

TEACHING NOTES

Using and understanding the programs in Calculator Notes 11H and 11J is vital. Students use these programs as a replacement for looking up numbers on a Z-score table and doing all the conversions that result from using the table.

As indicated in Example 2, a standard deviation greater than 2 is needed for the program in Calculator Note 11J. If the standard deviation needs to be greater than 2, multiply the mean and standard deviation by a factor and then compensate, as when interpreting final results.

If students are familiar with e, then ask them to find an equation in the form of $y = ae^{k(x - m)^2}$, which is the exact form of the normal curve. The value for a is the same and the value for k is $-\frac{1}{2\sigma^{-2}}$.

*Investigation 11.6.1: The Normal Curve Equation

In this investigation, students explore the normal curve equation in the context of the unemployment program discussed in the beginning of this section.

PROBLEM SET NOTES

Don't hurry through this problem set. Curve sketches are valuable, as students must decide what is given and which program they will use. Problem 6 uses Calculator Note 11F.

Suggested Assignments

Individual	Group	Essential	Performance assessment	Portfolio	Journal
1–4	5–7	7		5, 6	

EXTENSIONS

Take Another Look 11.6

Take Another Look 11.6a (in the *Teacher's Resource Book*)

Project: Normal Curves and e (uses Calculator Note 11J)

Section 11.7
Chapter Review

OBJECTIVES

• To review the mathematical terms, concepts, and problem-solving skills in Chapter 11

RESOURCES

Test on Chapter 11 to be given following this section

TEACHING NOTES

Review the important concepts of the chapter. Assign the chapter review and allow the students to work together to solve the problems while you circulate to answer questions. Students may wish to present their solutions to the class as part of the review.

Suggested Assignments

Individual	Group	Essential	Performance assessment	Portfolio	Journal
1–10			1, 4, 9		2

Assessing What You've Learned

Students are reminded to review their journal entries, organize their notebooks, and update their portfolios. There are also several suggestions for alternative assessment that students can complete.

Chapter 12
Functions and Relations

Overview

In this chapter, students study a variety of functions and relations. In the initial sections, they consider rational functions and some related applications. Then the focus changes to an extended growth model with varying growth rates dependent on population sizes and carrying capacities. Students write distance-time functions and explore their graphs to determine the optimal values. The last few sections provide connections between equations, table data, and graphs of the conics—circles, ellipses, parabolas, and hyperbolas. Completing the square and rotations are covered at the end of the chapter.

Section 12.1
The Inverse Variation Function

OBJECTIVES
- To write an appropriate equation when given a graph involving asymptotes
- To determine the graph and locate asymptotes when given a rational equation

MATERIALS
Investigation 12.1.1

    Several pieces of sturdy spaghetti

    Small film canister

    String or thread

    M&Ms or other objects with small but uniform mass

    Tape

    Ruler

Investigation 12.1.2

    200 tokens in two colors (light-colored and dark-colored beans work nicely)

RESOURCES
Transparency/Worksheet Master for Section 12.1: Investigation 12.1.2

TEACHING NOTES

The development, investigations, and problems concentrate on functions with horizontal or vertical asymptotes. Students study and connect table values, equations, and graphs. Encourage a discussion on asymptotes and the end behavior of rational functions.

Table values below for $y = \frac{1}{x}$ should indicate the following observations:

As x nears 0 from the left, y approaches $-\infty$.

As x nears 0 from the right, y approaches ∞.

The variable x is undefined at 0. All of this means $y = \frac{1}{x}$ has a vertical asymptote at $x = 0$.

-1	-0.1	-0.01	-0.001	x	0.001	0.01	0.1	1
-1	-10	-100	-1000	y	1000	100	10	1

As x approaches $-\infty$, y approaches 0 from below. (See the table values below.)

As x approaches ∞, y approaches 0 from above.

The end behavior of $y = \frac{1}{x}$ is that the graph approaches the line $y = 0$.

(The function has a horizontal asymptote at $y = 0$.)

$-10,000$	-1000	-100	-10	x	10	100	1000	10,000
-0.0001	-0.001	-0.01	-0.1	y	0.1	0.01	0.001	0.0001

Investigation 12.1.1: The Breaking-Point Experiment

In this investigation, students collect (*length, number of mass weights*) data that display an inverse variation. As students collect data, each data pair compares the number of M&Ms required to break a length of spaghetti. This is an inverse relationship, $y = \frac{k}{x}$ or kx^{-1}. Another group, using an alternative brand or type of spaghetti, might find a different k-value. Care and cooperation during this investigation helps avoid a mess with M&Ms scattered about the floor. Taping the threads to the spaghetti helps to keep the container and thread from slipping off. Part of the write-up should be a discussion of the experimental procedure used for the investigation.

Investigation 12.1.2: Increase the Percentage

This investigation provides a real-world meaning for an asymptote. Students must find several data points by adding small and large amounts of beans. If students only use the three data points in the chart, the graph will look linear.

Part 1

a.

Number of light beans added (x)	0	10	20	30	. . .	x
Total number of light beans	30	40	50	60	. . .	$30 + x$
Total number of beans	100	110	120	130	. . .	$100 + x$
Percentage of the total that are light (y)	30%	36.36	41.67	46.15	. . .	$\frac{30 + x}{100 + x} \cdot 100$

b. Groups will find that 75 light-colored beans must be added before the percentage reaches 60%. The percentage reaches 75% when 180 light-colored beans have been added and 90% when 600 have been added. The percentage cannot reach 100% because 70 dark-colored beans are always included in the total. However, 100% serves as a horizontal asymptote, and, if you have the patience, the percentage can be as close as you want.

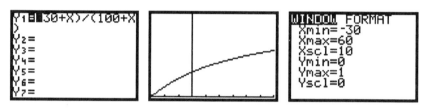

Part 2

a.

Number of light beans removed (x)	0	5	10	15	. . .	x
Total number of light beans	30	25	20	15	. . .	$30 - x$
Total number of beans	100	95	90	85	. . .	$100 - x$
Percentage of the total that are light (y)	30%	26.32	22.22	17.65	. . .	$\frac{30 - x}{100 - x} \cdot 100$

b. Graphs will vary.

c. $y = \frac{30 - x}{100 - x}$

PROBLEM SET NOTES

Problems 1–3 and 8 offer practice with transformations and asymptotes.
Problems 4–7 provide applications.

Suggested Assignments

Individual	Group	Essential	Performance assessment	Portfolio	Journal
1–3, 5, 6	4, 7, 8	2	1	Inv. 12.1.2, 8	

Section 12.2
Rational Functions

OBJECTIVES

- To investigate rational equations and determine the subtle differences that produce either a vertical asymptote or a hole

- To study and analyze slant asymptotes

MATERIALS

Investigation 12.2.2

    Several cylindrical containers that offer a variety of radii—a collection of tin cans works well

    Sand, salt, sugar, or liquid

TEACHING NOTES

Students learn to identify slant asymptotes and holes in graphs in the investigations, examples, and problems. Investigation 12.2.1 is quick and straightforward. During the investigation, students will extend their understanding of asymptotes.

*Investigation 12.2.1: Predicting Asymptotes and Holes

This investigation gives students the opportunity to explore and discover the properties of the equations that have asymptotes and holes.

Part 1

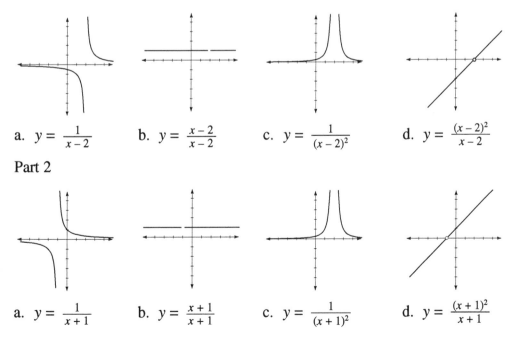

a. $y = \dfrac{1}{x-2}$ b. $y = \dfrac{x-2}{x-2}$ c. $y = \dfrac{1}{(x-2)^2}$ d. $y = \dfrac{(x-2)^2}{x-2}$

Part 2

a. $y = \dfrac{1}{x+1}$ b. $y = \dfrac{x+1}{x+1}$ c. $y = \dfrac{1}{(x+1)^2}$ d. $y = \dfrac{(x+1)^2}{x+1}$

Part 3

The first graph in each list has a horizontal asymptote at the x-axis and a vertical asymptote at the x-value that makes the denominator zero (and the function undefined).

In the second graph in each list, both the numerator and denominator contain the same function. This means the quotient is 1 for all x-values that satisfy the defined function values. The quotient is undefined (a hole) at values of x that make the quotient $\frac{0}{0}$. The third graph in each list always displays positive values because each quotient is $\frac{1}{\text{a positive expression}}$. Each graph shows a horizontal asymptote at $y = 0$ and vertical asymptotes when the denominators are zero.

In the fourth graph in each list, each quotient simplifies to a linear function unless the x-value makes the quotient $\frac{0}{0}$.

Investigation 12.2.2: Constant Volume
In this investigation, students find the radius and height measurements of the contents of several different cylinders that are each filled with the same amount of material. They plot the data and find a regression model that is a good fit for their data. The correlation coefficients, residual plots, and sums of squares of residuals should help them decide that a power regression model fits the (*radius, height*) data. This power equation can be converted to an inverse square or $y = \frac{k}{x^2}$ relationship.

PROBLEM SET NOTES
Problems 1–3 and 8 offer practice with transformations and asymptotes.
Problems 4–7 and 9 are applications.

Suggested Assignments

Individual	Group	Essential	Performance assessment	Portfolio	Journal
2, 5–8	1, 3, 4, 9	1, 2, 4	1, 3	9	

EXTENSIONS
Project: Going Downhill Fast

Section 12.3
Refining the Growth Model

OBJECTIVE
- To study recursively defined growth models that depend on both the population size and carrying capacity of the ecosystems

MATERIALS
None

RESOURCES
Transparency/Worksheet Master for Section 12.3: Population Graphs

TEACHING NOTES
Students have been introduced to sequences and functions that approach a particular value (or limit) over the long run. Again in this section, recursive growth expressions are used to model the changing populations. This offers an extension of earlier work and provides interesting contemporary applications. Students should be able to make sense of all the numbers and symbols in the equation

new population = old population + net growth rate • old population

$$\text{or } u_n = u_{(n-1)} + r\left(1 - \frac{u_{(n-1)}}{L}\right) \cdot u_{(n-1)}.$$

Until now, growth rates have been fixed over time. Here the rates change because they are dependent on populations and carrying capacities of the ecosystems.

The concept of variable growth rates should not be particularly difficult for students even though they probably haven't been introduced to it previously. However, this is also a topic that many teachers have not formally studied. Technology makes these applications accessible. Reading, discussing, working examples, and doing the investigation and the problems in small groups are appropriate approaches to this section.

Investigation 12.3.1: Variable Rates
Students explore the various growth rates of different rabbit populations. They take this information and extend it to finding rates according to a given limit.

Part 1
1. When the population is less than 500, the growth rate should be greater than zero and less than 0.2.

2. When the population is more than 500, the growth rate should be less than zero.

3. When the population is very small, the rate should have a value near the maximum unrestricted rate, 0.20.

4. When the population is 500, the rate should have a value of zero.

Part 2

1. An unrestricted rate of 0.20 and a population limit of 1000.

$y = -\frac{0.20}{1000}x + 0.2$

2. An unrestricted rate of 0.30 and a population limit of 500.

$y = -\frac{0.30}{500}x + 0.3$

3. An unrestricted rate of 0.20 and a population limit of L.

$y = -\frac{0.20}{L}x + 0.2$

4. An unrestricted rate of r and a population limit of L.

$y = -\frac{r}{L}x + r$ or $y = r\left(1 - \frac{x}{L}\right)$

Population	Rate
x	$y = -0.0004x + 0.20$
	$y = -\frac{0.20}{500}(x - 0) + 0.2$
100	0.16
700	−0.08

PROBLEM SET NOTES

The early problems offer practice using the population model explored in this section. Problem complexity increases in the problem set. Students could share results of their work, especially the results of Problem 8.

Suggested Assignments

Individual	Group	Essential	Performance assessment	Portfolio	Journal
1–3, 6	4, 5, 7, 8	1		8	

EXTENSIONS

Take Another Look 12.3

Section 12.4
Functions Involving Distance

OBJECTIVES

- To learn and use the distance formula

- To write and interpret distance and rate functions

- To write and interpret parametric representations of objects moving or rotating about a circle at a constant rate

MATERIALS

Investigation 12.4.1

    Ruler

    Graph paper

RESOURCES

Transparency Master for Section 12.4: Functions Involving Distances

Transparency Master: Unit Circle

Quiz covering Sections 12.1 to 12.3

TEACHING NOTES

Before the availability of graphing calculators, most of the problems in this section first appeared in calculus courses. They are now entirely appropriate and can be solved with graphs and tables. Investigation 12.4.1 sets up the early problems in the problem set. It is an important investigation for students to complete. Example 1 introduces applications where cos Bt and sin Bt provide a circular motion. The parameter t is measured in time (seconds in this example). Because the sines and cosines operate on degree measures, Bt must represent a degree measure. Students will think of B as a rotation rate, like degrees per second.

In the last paragraph of the example, the starting point of a circular motion is adjusted or rotated. This information provides a significant hint for the Ferris wheel problem in the problem set because it allows the ride to start one-fourth of the way up.

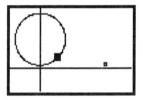

Investigation 12.4.1: Water Bucket

This investigation continues the problem introduced in the first paragraph of this section. The shortest possible path can be found (approximated) by drawing each line segment to scale and measuring to find the combined length of the segments. Another alternative is to use the Pythagorean theorem to write a distance function to represent the length of the combined segments. The best (shortest) distance shows up on a graph or in a table.

Part 1

a. Scale drawing (see diagram in the text)

b.

x	$AC + CB$
5	23.624
7	23.367
20	27.616

c.–d. In the first screen, y_1 = length of $AC + CB$. Each is the hypotenuse of a right triangle, so the total distance is $\sqrt{5^2 + x^2} + \sqrt{7^2 + (20 - x)^2}$. The graph display indicates the shortest total length for $AC + CB$ is 23.3234 m when $x = 8.33$ m.

e. Scale drawing (see diagram in the text)

Part 2

a. Because time = $\frac{\text{distance}}{\text{rate}}$, the first screen below shows y_1 = time to travel the length ($AC + CB$).

b. The shortest time, 33.747 sec, to travel this distance is displayed in the related graph below. It occurs when $x = 17.63$ m.

x	$AC + CB$	Time
5	23.624	47.275
7	23.367	44.081
20	27.616	34.680

PROBLEM SET NOTES

Problem 5 involves an application of the distance formula to the graphs of two equations. The rest of the problems are application problems. You could assign different problems to different groups, and then ask students to present and share their solutions with classmates.

Suggested Assignments

Individual	Group	Essential	Performance assessment	Portfolio	Journal
2, 4, 5	1, 3, 6, 7	3		3, 6	

EXTENSIONS

Take Another Look 12.4

Take Another Look 12.4a (in the *Teacher's Resource Book*)

Project: Basketball (See additional suggestions in the *Teacher's Resource Book*)

Project: Jeep in the Desert (in the *Teacher's Resource Book*)

Section 12.5
The Circle and the Ellipse

OBJECTIVE

- To investigate and discover properties, relationships, equations, and applications involving circles and ellipses

MATERIALS

Investigation 12.5.1
    Two rulers

Investigation 12.5.2
    Flashlights
    Graph paper
    Ring stands and clamps (to hold the flashlights steady)

Problem 6
    String
    Ruler
    Two tacks
    Graph paper

TEACHING NOTES

The section, containing two important investigations and examples, will require adequate time to explore and discover the aspects of the circle and the ellipse. Investigation 12.5.1 is important for students to discover properties of circles and ellipses. You could use the Geometer's Sketchpad to demonstrate the properties of the circle and ellipse, or you may prefer to use paper-folding explorations.

*Investigation 12.5.1: Constructing a Circle and an Ellipse
Students will discover the properties of a circle and an ellipse in this investigation. Some teachers might substitute a paper-folding investigation or perhaps a dynamic software investigation as an alternative. Students construct a circle and an ellipse by plotting points P that fit the definitions $|(P - C)| = r$ and $F_1 P + F_2 P = d$, and then draw smooth curves through the constructed points. (C, F_1, and F_2 are fixed points; r and d are fixed distances.) Stretching a circle so that the vertical stretch is different from the horizontal stretch produces an ellipse. These transformations also provide a review of function and parametric equations based on the unit circle.

Investigation 12.5.2: Shine On
In this investigation, students make an ellipse with a flashlight and then find the best-fit equation. Data and equations will vary from group to group. Students will need to use some intelligent guess-and-check methods and the special points located at the ends of the major and minor axes to write the equations.

PROBLEM SET NOTES
Several problems contain multiple parts, and you may need to select and assign parts rather than the entire problem. Problem 6 requires students to construct an ellipse using an alternative method to Investigation 12.5.1. Students investigate, identify, and locate the foci of ellipses in Problems 6–9. They will discover the relationships between the center, foci, and lengths of the major and minor axes.

Suggested Assignments

Individual	Group	Essential	Performance assessment	Portfolio	Journal
1–3, 7	4–6, 8, 9	3, 6	1, 3		

Section 12.6
The Parabola

OBJECTIVE
- To graph a parabola and locate its vertex, focus, and directrix when given an equation, and vice versa

MATERIALS
Investigation 12.6.1
  Two rulers

Investigation 12.6.2
  Graph paper
  Tape
  Smooth clipboard
  Carbon paper
  Large ball bearing
  Two books

TEACHING NOTES

In this section, students construct a parabola using the definition, and then they derive the equation based on the construction and definition. In Investigation 12.6.2, they collect data and find a parabolic equation that models the results. You may wish to use the Geometer's Sketchpad to demonstrate the properties of the parabola, or you may prefer to have students discover these properties using paper-folding activities.

Investigation 12.6.1: Constructing the Parabola

In this investigation, students construct a parabola by measuring and placing points P that are equidistant from a fixed point and a fixed line, the focus and the directrix. Distance relationships and some analytic development produces the equations $y^2 = 4fx$ and $x^2 = 4fy$.

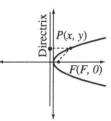

This parabola is horizontal with vertex at the origin. The focus is point $(f, 0)$. The vertex is on the curve, so it should be as far from the focus as it is from the directrix. The equation of the directrix is $x = {}^-f$. The reasons for each step in the derivation follow:

$\sqrt{(x - f)^2 + (y - 0)^2} = \sqrt{(x + f)^2 + (y - y)^2}$ Definition of a parabola.

$\sqrt{(x - f)^2 + y^2} = \sqrt{(x + f)^2 + (0)^2}$ Simplification.

$(x - f)^2 + y^2 = (x + f)^2$ Square both sides of equation.

$x^2 - 2fx + f^2 + y^2 = x^2 + 2fx + f^2$ Expand each binomial.

$y^2 = 4fx$ Add $2fx - x^2 - f^2$ to each side.

Investigation 12.6.2: A Rolling Ball

Students create a parabolic path using a heavy ball, carbon paper, and a ramp. You may need to test your ball and carbon paper combination before the students do this investigation because some carbon paper will require a very heavy ball. One possibility is to borrow the shot put from the P.E. instructor. It is important that students practice rolling the ball up and down the board. After the path is recorded with the carbon paper, students will find a best-fit equation for the curve and then use residuals to verify the equation.

PROBLEM SET NOTES

Students may need guidance with Problems 4 and 5 to handle this degree of complex algebraic manipulation. Use of finite differences and matrices is one possible approach for Problems 6 and 7.

Individual	Group	Essential	Performance assessment	Portfolio	Journal
1–3	4–6		1, 2	Inv. 12.6.2	

Section 12.7
The Hyperbola

OBJECTIVE
• To graph a hyperbola and locate its vertices, asymptotes, and foci when given an equation, and vice versa

MATERIALS
Investigation 12.7.1
   Two rulers

Piston Pressure Project
   Set of masses
   60 cc medical syringe with one end closed

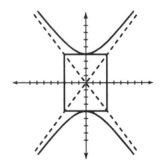

TEACHING NOTES
As indicated in the examples, graphs of hyperbolas are generated bytransformations of the unit hyperbola $x^2 - y^2 = 1$. In parametric form,equations are generated by transforming the equations $x(t) = \frac{1}{\cos t}$ or $x(t) = \sec t$ and $y(t) = \tan t$.

In this section, students will sketch graphs (on paper) of the hyperbolas defined by $\left(\frac{x-h}{a}\right)^2 - \left(\frac{y-k}{b}\right)^2 = 1$ or $\left(\frac{y-k}{b}\right)^2 - \left(\frac{x-h}{a}\right)^2 = 1$.

Hand-drawn curves are bounded by drawing asymptotes and the related rectangle as pictured.

You may wish to use the Geometer's Sketchpad to demonstrate the properties of the hyperbola, or you could use a paper-folding investigation.

*Investigation 12.7.1: Constructing a Hyperbola
Students construct hyperbolas by locating points P so that the difference of the distances from P to two fixed points F_1 and F_2 remain constant.

PROBLEM SET NOTES

Problem 7 has students find a best-fit equation for a hyperbola. Problem 8 is a journal-writing prompt.

Suggested Assignments

Individual	Group	Essential	Performance assessment	Portfolio	Journal
2–5, 8	1, 6, 7	3	1	7	8

EXTENSIONS

Take Another Look 12.7

Project: Piston Pressure

Section 12.8
The General Quadratic

OBJECTIVES

- To convert between several different forms of two-variable quadratic equations
- To discover and use the completing-the-square process

MATERIALS

None

TEACHING NOTES

Students will need time to work their way through the four examples. There is a substantial amount of symbolic-manipulation work in this section. Given the general form of a quadratic, $Ax^2 + Bxy + Cy^2 + Dx + Ey + F = 0$, they are asked to rewrite it in center-vertex form. This rewrite may involve completing the square for x, for y, or for both variables, which is introduced and then practiced in Examples 2, 3, and 4.

Students are also required to change the equation to function form so that they can graph the functions on their calculators. One appropriate method involves the quadratic formula, so this formula is reintroduced. Derivations and algebraic manipulations make the section lengthy.

PROBLEM SET NOTES

Problem 2 offers an extension of the completing-the-square process. The Example 3 revisit process is continued in Problem 6 and extended again in the next section. Problem 8 is a journal-writing prompt.

Individual	Group	Essential	Performance assessment	Portfolio	Journal
1, 3, 4, 8	2, 5–7	2, 6	1		8

EXTENSIONS

Take Another Look 12.8

Geometer's Sketchpad Investigation: Constructing an Ellipse

Section 12.9
The Rotation Matrix

OBJECTIVE

• To discover a rotation matrix and learn how to use and apply it

MATERIALS

Investigation 12.9.1

  Graph paper

  Ruler

  Protractor

  Compass

TEACHING NOTES

Students solve for y using the quadratic formula in some very complicated equations. In the first example, the coefficients a, b, and c in the equation $ay^2 + by + c = 0$ are identified as $\boxed{25}\, y^2 + \boxed{(-8 - 24x)}\, y + \boxed{16x^2 - 60x + 100} = 0$.

Provide time for students to read and work the examples and to discover the rotation matrix. They will discover appropriate and powerful uses of their calculator in this section.

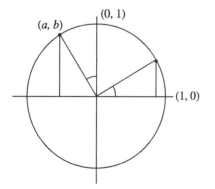

The drawing at left shows the images after rotating points $(1, 0)$ and $(0, 1)$ $\theta°$ counterclockwise about the origin. The point $(1, 0)$ rotates into $(\cos \theta, \sin \theta)$ because of the unit circle definition of cosine and sine. The point $(0, 1)$ rotates into (a, b). Because the two triangles in this drawing are congruent, $a = {}^-\sin \theta$ and $b = \cos \theta$. Therefore, $[\text{Rotation matrix}] \bullet \begin{bmatrix} \cos \theta & {}^-\sin \theta \\ \sin \theta & \cos \theta \end{bmatrix}$.

This means $\begin{bmatrix} \cos\theta & ^-\sin\theta \\ \sin\theta & \cos\theta \end{bmatrix} \cdot \begin{bmatrix} x_1 \\ y_1 \end{bmatrix}$ provides a transformed set of points $\begin{bmatrix} x_2 \\ y_2 \end{bmatrix}$ that has

been rotated $\theta°$. If parametric equations of a set of points are given in x_1 and y_1, then x_2

$= x_1 \cos\theta - y_1 \sin\theta$ and $y_2 = x_1 \sin\theta + y_1 \cos\theta$ provide the graph after a rotation of $\theta°$.

Investigation 12.9.1: Transformations and Matrices

This investigation develops the matrix $\begin{bmatrix} e & f \\ g & h \end{bmatrix} = \begin{bmatrix} \cos\theta & ^-\sin\theta \\ \sin\theta & \cos\theta \end{bmatrix}$ that rotates a figure

counterclockwise through an angle of $\theta°$. Vertices of the geometric figures are identified

with the matrix form $\begin{bmatrix} A_x & B_x & \cdots \\ A_y & B_y & \cdots \end{bmatrix}$. During the investigation, students must measure

and locate points very carefully if they are to discover this relationship.

a.

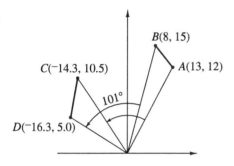

b. Suppose the segment from $A(13, 12)$ to $B(8, 15)$ is rotated $101°$ into segment CD.

The coordinates for C and D can be measured approximately as $C(-14.3, 10.5)$ and

$D(-16.3, 5.0)$. Solving the matrix equation $\begin{bmatrix} e & f \\ g & h \end{bmatrix} \begin{bmatrix} 13 & 8 \\ 12 & 15 \end{bmatrix} = \begin{bmatrix} ^-14.3 & ^-16.3 \\ 10.5 & 5 \end{bmatrix}$

using an inverse matrix gives $\begin{bmatrix} e & f \\ g & h \end{bmatrix} = \begin{bmatrix} ^-0.191 & ^-0.985 \\ 0.985 & ^-0.192 \end{bmatrix}$.

c. Sin $101° = 0.982$ and cos $101° = -0.1908$. The connection expected is that because

$\begin{bmatrix} \cos 101° & ^-\sin 101° \\ \sin 101° & \cos 101° \end{bmatrix} = \begin{bmatrix} ^-0.191 & ^-0.982 \\ 0.982 & ^-0.192 \end{bmatrix}$, this is the rotation matrix for a rotation

of $101°$.

PROBLEM SET NOTES
Problem 3 provides an important check for understanding.

Suggested Assignments

Individual	Group	Essential	Performance assessment	Portfolio	Journal
1, 2, 4, 8	3, 5–7				

Section 12.10
Chapter Review

OBJECTIVE

• To review the mathematical terms, concepts, and problem-solving skills in Chapter 12

RESOURCES

Quiz covering Sections 12.4 to 12.9

Test on Chapter 12 to be given following this section

TEACHING NOTES

Review the important concepts of the chapter. Assign the chapter review and allow the students to work together to solve the problems while you circulate to answer questions. Students may wish to present their solutions to the class as part of the review.

PROBLEM SET NOTES

Problem 9 is a journal-writing prompt.

Suggested Assignments

Individual	Group	Essential	Performance assessment	Portfolio	Journal
1–9			1	8	2, 9

Assessing What You've Learned

Students are reminded to review their journal entries, organize their notebooks, and update their portfolios. There are also several suggestions for alternative assessment for students to complete.

Chapter 13
Trigonometric Functions

Overview

In this chapter previous definitions of trigonometric functions are extended, and the cosecant, secant, and cotangent functions are introduced. Musical instrument overtones and sounds provide one of the applications involving combinations of trigonometric functions. Students apply the law of sines and the law of cosines in real-world problem settings, and they use inverse trigonometric relations and functions to solve for the variable in periodic and pendulum-type application problems. Polar coordinates and curves, polar form, graphing powers of complex numbers, and iterations of complex numbers are extensively involved in the activities and explorations of the chapter.

Section 13.1
Defining the Circular Functions

OBJECTIVES

- To extend right triangle definitions of sine, cosine, and tangent and apply them to angles greater than 90° and to negative angles

- To apply simple transformations to the graphs of these circular functions

MATERIALS

Investigation 13.1.1

    Card stock

    Ruler

    Protractor

    Compass

    CBL Alternative for Investigation 13.1.1

    CBL

    Sonic probe

    Turntable

RESOURCES

    Transparency Master: Trigonometric Graph

TEACHING NOTES

In this section, a rationale is provided for why the right triangle definitions for trigonometric functions need to be extended. The circular definitions for sine and cosine are developed in Investigation 13.1.1. Students are introduced to the term *reference angle,* and they discover that the sine is the *x*-coordinate and the cosine is the *y*-coordinate of a point on the coordinate plane. The examples show the calculator results when finding the sines and cosines of angles and explain how these results are related to the reference angle and the coordinates of a point. Students should be comfortable with the definitions and examples before starting the problems.

Have students explain the connection between transformations on the trigonometric function graphs and the other function transformations that they have studied previously. This can be either in writing or during a follow-up class discussion.

Throughout this chapter, remind students to have their calculators in degree mode. This will alleviate much of the confusion when students get incorrect answers.

*Investigation 13.1.1: Anne Fibian and the Paddle Wheel

While working in groups, students will discover the values for sine and cosine by measuring the *x*- and *y*-values for the position of the frog on the paddle wheel. It is important that they complete this investigation carefully because the results are the basis for the extended definitions of the trigonometric functions. The time required for the investigation can be shortened if the circles are cut out ahead of time. Students need to write a report to summarize their findings before going on to the problems.

As an alternative to this investigation, you can mount an object vertically on a turntable. Using a CBL, adjust the sampling to 24 samples per revolution. Collect data with the sonic probe, and replace the time list with multiples of 15.

Following are sample table results.

Time (sec)	0	30	45	60	90	120	135	150	180	240	270
Height (m)	0	2.5	3.5	4.3	5	4.3	3.5	2.5	0	−4.3	−5

Time (sec)	300	360	420	480	540	600	660	720	780	840	900
Height (m)	−4.3	0	4.3	4.3	0	−4.3	−4.3	0	4.3	4.3	0

The equation $y = 5 \sin x$ should fit the points quite nicely. After 315 sec, Anne should be 3.5 m underwater. Anne is 4 m underwater after about 233 sec, 307 sec, 593 sec, and again at 667 sec.

PROBLEM SET NOTES

Problem 1 is related to Investigation 13.1.1. The tangent function is explored in Problem 3. The periodic concept is introduced between Problems 4 and 5 and should be read carefully. Problem 7 uses the results of Problem 6.

Suggested Assignments

Individual	Group	Essential	Performance assessment	Portfolio	Journal
1, 2, 4, 5, 8	3, 6, 7, 9	3, 5	1	Inv. 13.1.1	

EXTENSIONS

Project: Design a Picnic Table

Section 13.2
Other Periodic Functions

OBJECTIVES

- To introduce the reciprocal functions secant, cosecant, and cotangent
- To develop an understanding of the relationship between the graphs of the reciprocal functions and the graphs of the primary functions

MATERIALS

None

RESOURCES

Transparency Master: Trigonometric Graph

TEACHING NOTES

Because calculators do not have keys labeled with these reciprocal functions, students will need to spend some time discovering how to enter the functions in their calculators. For many calculators there is an advantage in entering the cotangent as cos x/sin x rather than as 1/tan x (the latter will not give a value for cot 90°, whereas the former will give the proper value of 0). This quirk should be discussed, though not necessarily at the beginning of the lesson. When the investigation is completed, a class exploration to find several possible equations for any given graph is a good way to reinforce the relationships between the trigonometric functions.

Investigation 13.2.1: Reciprocal Function Graphs
In this investigation, students will explore the graphs of reciprocal trigonometric functions and their relationships to other trigonometric functions. When students sketch the graphs, make sure they identify the scale and important points on the graph.

Part 1

a. Sketch of $y = \sin x$ and $y = \csc x$.

b. The range of $y = \sin x$ is $^-1 \leq y \leq 1$ and of $y = \csc x$ is $1 \leq y < \infty$ and $^-\infty \leq y < ^-1$. The period of the cosecant is $360°$.

c. The asymptotes are located at multiples of $180°$ and correspond to the x-values where the sine function is zero. With reference to the ramp-building example, they indicate ramps that are flat.

Part 2

a. Sketch of $y = \cos x$ and $y = \sec x$.

b. The range of $y = \cos x$ is $^-1 \leq y \leq 1$ and of $y = \sec x$ is $1 \leq y \leq \infty$ and $^-\infty \leq y \leq ^-1$. The period of the secant is $360°$.

c. The vertical asymptotes are at $90° \pm 180n°$.

Part 3

a. Sketch of $y = \tan x$ and $y = \cot x$.

b. The range of these two functions is all real numbers. The period of the cotangent is $180°$.

c. The vertical asymptotes are at multiples of $180°$.

Part 4

a. Students share findings with other group members.

b. The secant graph is a cosecant graph that has been translated $90°$ to the right (or $270°$ to the left).

c. It is a tangent graph that has been reflected over the y-axis and translated $90°$ to the left (or right). Alternatively, it may be thought of as a tangent graph that has been reflected over the x-axis and translated $90°$ to the left (or right).

PROBLEM SET NOTES

You may need to remind students how to change dates into numbers before they do Problem 6. All dates are five days apart. You can fill the x list with a sequence command. The sine curve appears to be a good model for Problem 7 until the residuals are examined. Residuals will show that the tangent curve provides a much better model. Use this problem to reinforce the need to evaluate the appropriateness of a model.

Suggested Assignments

Individual	Group	Essential	Performance assessment	Portfolio	Journal
1–5	6–9	1, 3, 9	2	Inv. 13.2.1	

EXTENSIONS

Take Another Look 13.2

Geometer's Sketchpad Investigation: Constructing Trigonometric Curves

Section 13.3
Combinations of Functions

OBJECTIVES

- To discover the relationship between the periods of individual trigonometric functions and the period of a function created by adding these functions

- To discover some fundamental identities by examining the graphs of function combinations

MATERIALS

None

RESOURCES

Transparency Master: Trigonometric Graph

Quiz covering Sections 13.1 and 13.2

TEACHING NOTES

Much of the written material in this section is informational and is not necessary for the problem set. The investigation will help students discover the relationship between individual trigonometric functions and the sum of the functions. Using an oscilloscope and microphone as students play various musical instruments to see the resulting wave forms is an interesting extension and application of this section.

Please note that in Take Another Look 13.3, the dates for the equinox are not exact because the time and day varies slightly from year to year.

Investigation 13.3.1: Period Search
Students will discover that the period of a function depends on the period of each part of the equation.

a.

a	b	Period
1	2	360°
2	3	360°
3	6	120°
2	4	180°
4	12	90°

b. The period is 360° divided by the greatest common factor of a and b.

c.

a	b	Period
$\frac{1}{2}$	$\frac{1}{4}$	1440°
$\frac{1}{2}$	$\frac{1}{3}$	2160°
$\frac{1}{2}$	$\frac{1}{5}$	3600°
$\frac{5}{6}$	$\frac{3}{4}$	4320°
$\frac{5}{8}$	$\frac{3}{10}$	14,400°

d. The period is 360° multiplied by the least common denominator of a and b.

e. 8640°, which is 360° • 24, which is the least common denominator for $\frac{2}{3}$ and $\frac{1}{8}$. Because the period of sin $4x$ is 90° and 90 is a factor of 8640, the period of sin $4x$ does not affect the period of this sum of functions.

PROBLEM SET NOTES

Problem 2, the biorhythm cycles, is lengthy and may be used as a second investigation or as an extended assignment. The technique of adding ordinates of the addend functions to determine the sum function discussed in Problem 2 is useful when students try to analyze more complex functions in later classes. It provides understanding of why the graph looks the way it does. Encourage students to actually graph these points by hand to see how the two curves sum to make a straight line. The identities explored in Problems 5–8 are used later in the chapter. Beat frequency is introduced and explored in Problem 9.

Suggested Assignments

Individual	Group	Essential	Performance assessment	Portfolio	Journal
1, 3, 5–7	2, 4, 8, 9	1, 3, 5, 6		2	

EXTENSIONS
Take Another Look 13.3

Section 13.4
The Law of Sines and the Law of Cosines

OBJECTIVE
- To discover and learn how to use the Law of Sines and the Law of Cosines to solve for unknown parts of oblique triangles

MATERIALS
Investigation 13.4.1
    Ruler
    Protractor

TEACHING NOTES
There is a great deal of material in this section. Investigation 13.4.1 is a discovery approach to finding the Law of Sines. Some students may be familiar with the Law of Sines and the Law of Cosines from previous courses, but the laws may be entirely new to others. Students must know which formula to use in different situations before they begin the problem set. Two days may be needed to fully cover both the laws and their use.

*Investigation 13.4.1: Oblique Triangles
In this investigation, students will discover the Law of Sines. Encourage them to use rulers as they draw their triangles and to measure as carefully as possible.

a. $\frac{\sin B}{b} = \frac{\sin C}{c}$ b. $\frac{\sin C}{c} = \frac{\sin A}{a}$ c. $\frac{\sin A}{a} = \frac{\sin B}{b} = \frac{\sin C}{c}$

PROBLEM SET NOTES
Problem 2 is an extension of Problem 1 and is an opportunity for students to summarize and clarify applications of the laws. It can be assigned as a journal-writing prompt or within a special writing assignment. Problem 4 is a difficult problem and may require additional time.

Suggested Assignments

Individual	Group	Essential	Performance assessment	Portfolio	Journal
1–3	4–8	1, 2	1	2	2

EXTENSIONS

Project: Sum and Difference Identities

Section 13.5
Trigonometric Equations and Inverse Functions

OBJECTIVE

- To solve problems and applications requiring the use of inverse trigonometric functions and to obtain answers that make sense in the problem setting

MATERIALS

None

RESOURCES

Transparency Master: Trigonometric Graph

Calculator Note 13A

TEACHING NOTES

Students will learn how to solve for unknown variables using inverse functions and then apply this knowledge to several situations. They may be able to describe other periodic motions not listed in this section. Class discussions about these situations and problems designed by the students can provide better motivation for the topics of the section.

The spring situations described here are somewhat idealized because the amplitude of the oscillation actually decreases. The spring problems can be demonstrated or perhaps investigated as a second investigation. In this case, springs, stands, masses, rulers, and timing devices would be necessary.

Investigation 13.5.1: Inverse Trigonometric Functions

Students will investigate the relationship between the sine and cosine functions and their inverses. This investigation is difficult to do when using the TI-81. Students who have a TI-81 calculator may wish to pair up with other students.

A	0°	5°	10°	15°	20°	25°	30°	. . .	90°	95°	100°	. . .	450°
sin A	0	0.0872	0.1736	0.2588	0.3420	0.4226	0.5	. . .	1	0.9962	0.9848	. . .	1
$\sin^{-1}(\sin A)$	0	5°	10°	15°	20°	25°	30°	. . .	90°	85°	80°	. . .	90°

The complete table will have values every 5°.

a. This should be the familiar sine curve.

b. Yes, this graph should be a function. There are fewer points because each point is repeated in the list.

c. This graph is not a function because each x-value has more than one y-value associated with it. When the other set of points is added, they match up for angles between 0° and 90°. However, for sines that are negative, the new angles show up between −90° and 0° instead of between their positive counterparts. In this way these points form a continuous function.

d. This is true only for angles between 0° and 90°. Otherwise, the angle is matched with the angle between −90° and 90° that has the same sine value.

e. The inverse cosine uses angles between 0° and 180°.

f. For the inverse sine function, the domain is $-1 \leq x \leq 1$ and the range is $-90° \leq y \leq 90°$. The inverse cosine has domain $-1 \leq x \leq 1$ and the range is $0° \leq y \leq 180°$.

PROBLEM SET NOTES

Problem 2 requires that students put their calculators into parametric mode. Problems 5 and 6 are spring problems, which are related to the examples in this section. The graph for the left side of Problem 7b is actually a tangent curve. However, because of the form of the equation, there are holes at the x-values that are multiples of 180°. An interesting exercise might be to work through the steps that rewrite this expression as the tangent function.

Suggested Assignments

Individual	Group	Essential	Performance assessment	Portfolio	Journal
1, 3–5, 9	2, 6–8, 10	1, 2	1	10	8

EXTENSIONS

Project: A Dampened Sine Curve

Take Another Look 13.5 (in the *Teacher's Resource Book*)

Section 13.6
Polar Curves

OBJECTIVES

- To locate points in the polar coordinate system and graph equations in this system

- To convert the coordinates of a point between rectangular and polar form

MATERIALS

Polar graph paper

RESOURCES

Transparency Master: Polar Graph Paper

Calculator Notes 13B and 13C

Quiz covering Sections 13.2 to 13.5

TEACHING NOTES

Students may have already discovered the polar mode for reporting graph coordinates during earlier parametric work. They need to practice plotting points manually and not just rely on the calculator to always make the graph. Having students physically act out the plotting of a point will help them to make important connections.

Investigation 13.6.1: Rose Curves

This investigation gives students the opportunity to discover the meaning of each element of polar equations in the form $r = a \cos n\theta$. Some students will gain much insight from this particular investigation.

a. When n is even, there are $2n$ petals. When n is odd, there are n petals.

b. When n is even, there are $2n$ petals. When n is odd, there are n petals. However, these curves are rotated from those made with the cosine. Those in part a are at the end of the petal for $x = 0$. Those in part b are at the origin when $x = 0$.

c. One equation that works is $r = 3\sqrt{\cos 2\theta}$. This is because the square root of a negative number is not real, and thus for angles where the cosine is negative, the graph does not exist, which deletes two leaves from the graph.

d. The height of a point on the auxiliary graph will be the value of r when $x = \theta$.

PROBLEM SET NOTES

Problem 6 uses the results from Problem 5c. The cardioid microphone described in Problem 6 is used quite frequently in electronics. Students who work with electronics or recording equipment may be able to share additional information with the class.

Suggested Assignments

Individual	Group	Essential	Performance assessment	Portfolio	Journal
1–4, 8	5–7	1, 2, 4, 5	1, 8	Inv. 13.6.1	

EXTENSIONS

Take Another Look 13.6

Section 13.7
Polar Coordinates and Complex Numbers

OBJECTIVES

- To locate complex numbers in either polar or rectangular form

- To discover a technique for multiplication and exponentiation of complex numbers

- To experiment with different methods of graphing recursive complex functions

MATERIALS

None

RESOURCES

Transparency Master: Polar Graph Paper

Calculator Notes 13D and 13E

TEACHING NOTES

Students were exposed to the rectangular form of complex numbers in Chapter 10. A quick review with applications and connections to polar coordinates should help make this section readily accessible. Investigation 13.7.1 is important and can be completed entirely in small groups, or parts c–f might be covered during a full class exploration. Investigation 13.7.2 will take more time to complete and may be assigned on the second day. Students will need to work cooperatively and combine results for the most efficient investigation. Interested students could be directed to the project on Julia sets for further study.

Investigation 13.7.1: Multiplication of Complex Numbers
Students will discover the pattern found when multiplying complex numbers written in polar form. This discovery investigation is important for students to understand complex numbers written in polar coordinates.

a. i. $3 + 11i$ ii. $11 + 10i$ iii. $5 + 10i$

b. i. $2 + 3i = 3.606(\cos 56.31° + i \sin 56.31°)$
   $3 + i = 3.162(\cos 18.43° + i \sin 18.43°)$
   $3 + 11i = 11.40(\cos 74.74° + i \sin 74.74°)$

  ii. $1 + 4i = 4.123(\cos 75.96° + i \sin 75.96°)$
   $3 - 2i = 3.606(\cos -33.69° + i \sin -33.69°)$
   $11 + 10i = 14.866(\cos 42.27° + i \sin 42.27°)$

  iii. $-1 + 2i = 2.236(\cos 116.56° + \sin 116.56°)$
   $3 - 4i = 5(\cos -53.13° + \sin -53.13°)$
   $5 + 10i = 63.43(\cos 63.43° + \sin 63.43°)$

The angle of the product is the sum of the angles of the factors. The modulus of the product is the product of the moduli of the factors.

d. The cosine graph is shifted 45° to the left. In the general case, the cosine graph is shifted $\Phi°$ to the left. [$\cos \theta \cos \Phi - \sin \theta \sin \Phi = \cos(\theta + \Phi)$]

e. The sine graph is shifted 45° to the left. In the general case, the sine graph is shifted $\Phi°$ to the left. [$\cos \theta \sin \Phi + \sin \theta \cos \Phi = \sin(\theta + \Phi)$]

f. $(a \cos \theta + ai \sin \theta)(b \cos \Phi + bi \sin \Phi) = ab(\cos (\theta + \Phi) + i \sin(\theta + \Phi))$
$4.25(\cos 23.4° + i \sin 23.4°) \bullet 2.5(\cos 32.5° + i \sin 32.5°) =$
$10.625(\cos 55.9° + i \sin 55.9°)$
In rectangular form: $5.968 + 8.798i$

Investigation 13.7.2: Prisoners and Escapees
In this investigation, students convert complex numbers to polar form and square the result. Students will get a modulus that either will grow very large or will shrink to zero. In part c, students are introduced to the Julia set formed by this iteration.

b. This should form a circle of radius 1, centered at the origin. The four points (0, 1), (1, 0), (−1, 0), and (0, −1) remain a constant distance of 1 from the origin under repeated iteration. Any points that lie on the boundary will have this same characteristic.

c. The points that go to zero are inside the circle. The points outside the circle are the escapee set.

PROBLEM SET NOTES

Problem 2 refers to Problem 1. Problems 6 and 10 lead up to Problem 11. The results of Problem 6 are predictable and form easily explained patterns. Problem 8 uses the steps in Problem 7. Problem 9 uses the method described in Example 4 of this section. Problem 10 is interesting in that all seed values iterate to the same point. Problem 11 refers to Investigation 13.7.2. The results from Problem 11 are surprising, as the points between the basins for each root form complicated regions. Problem 11 will be time-consuming.

Suggested Assignments

Individual	Group	Essential	Performance assessment	Portfolio	Journal
1–6	7–11	1–5	1, 2, 5	11	

EXTENSIONS

Project: More on Julia Sets

Section 13.8
Chapter Review

OBJECTIVE

• To review the mathematical terms, concepts, and problem-solving skills in Chapter 13

RESOURCES

Test on Chapter 13 to be given following this section

TEACHING NOTES

Review the important concepts of the chapter. Assign the chapter review and allow the students to work together to solve the problems while you circulate to answer questions. Students may wish to present their solutions to the class as part of the review.

PROBLEM SET NOTES

Problem 6 is a journal-writing prompt.

Suggested Assignments

Individual	Group	Essential	Performance assessment	Portfolio	Journal
1–11			1, 2, 5, 9		6

Assessing What You've Learned

Students are reminded to review their journal entries, organize their notebooks, and update their portfolios. There are also several suggestions for alternative assessment for students to complete.

Answers to Problems

Chapter 0

Problem Set 0.1

1. a. 10.63014581   **b.** 1.95   **c.** 30   **d.** 249.3796248

2. a. $(-4)^2 = 16, -4^2 = -16$ **b.** 17^2 or $(17)^2 = 289$

    c. -24^2 or $-(24)^2 = -576$ **d.**

```
17→X
            17
X²
           289
-X²
          -289
```

3. a. i.   8

      ii.   0.8

   b. $12 + \dfrac{3 - \sqrt{169 - 2^3(6)}}{2}$ $\dfrac{2 + \dfrac{11 - \sqrt{25}}{3}}{\sqrt{6^3 - 20} - \dfrac{18}{2}}$

      $12 + \dfrac{3 - \sqrt{169 - 8(6)}}{2}$ $\dfrac{2 + \dfrac{11 - 5}{3}}{\sqrt{216 - 20} - 9}$

      $12 + \dfrac{3 - \sqrt{169 - 48}}{2}$ $\dfrac{2 + \dfrac{6}{3}}{\sqrt{196} - 9}$

      $12 + \dfrac{3 - \sqrt{121}}{2}$ $\dfrac{2 + 2}{14 - 9}$

      $12 + \dfrac{3 - 11}{2}$ $\dfrac{4}{5}$

      $12 + \dfrac{-8}{2}$

      $12 + {-4}$

      8

   c. i. $12 + \left(3 - \sqrt{(169 - 2^3(6))}\right)/2$

      ii. $\left(2 + \dfrac{(11 - \sqrt{25})}{3}\right)/\sqrt{(6^3 - 20)} - 18/2$

   d. Answers will vary.

4. a. Area of a triangle

      i. 268.755   ii. 1.70154   iii. 6.8385

   b. Height of an object in free fall

      i. 87.39   ii. 1358.8416   iii. 12.68

   c. Slope of a line given two points

      i. -1.221428571 ii. Undefined   iii. -0.5423728814

5. a. $(5 + 3)8/4$ **b.** $7(5 + 3^4)$ **c.** $(1 + 2(3))4$ **d.** $(7 - 3 - 2)9$ **e.** $15 - 3(7 - 12)$

6. Answers will vary.
  a. 0.4444444444; the display shows a decimal point followed by ten 4s. This is an exact decimal value.
  b. .4444444445; the display shows a decimal point followed by nine 4s and one 5. This is an approximate decimal value.
  c. A sample answer might be that the calculator displays 10 digits, but works internally with 13.

Problem Set 0.2

1. **a.** i. $1.23439632 \cdot 10^7$
    ii. $8.164967851 \cdot 10^{-5}$
  b. i. $6.63466667 \cdot 10^{-34}$
    ii. $1.116 \cdot 10^{-33}$

2. **a.** 347,895,000 **b.** 0.000 000 000 008 247 **c.** 140,000

3. Answers will vary. The exponent will be positive when the original number is greater than or equal to 10 and will be negative when the original number is less than 1.

4. $2 \cdot 10^{18}$ neurons

5. **a.** Each person will take one-ninth of the pizza, so it is divided fairly.
  b. The last person to select will also get one-ninth of the pizza.

6. **a.** It is about 125 mi from Lake Michigan to Lake Erie. However, the distance isn't the problem here. A speed of 60 ft/sec or its equivalent, 40.9 mi/hr, isn't likely.
  b. This is faster than the average ball player can run. The distance between the bases is 90 ft.
  c. i. 260 km   ii. 253.5 km   iii. Approximately 3%

7. **a.** 14,496,768 lb or 7,248.384 T   **b.** Yes: answers will vary.

8. The hydrogen atom has about 1868 times the mass of the electron.

9. Answers will vary.

Problem Set 0.3

1. Answers will vary.
  a. Xmin = −2 or less, Xmax = 3 or more, Xscl = 1 or less,
    Ymin = 5 or less, Ymax = 21 or more, Yscl = 1 or more
  b. Xmin = 0 or less, Xmax = 4 or more, Xscl = 1 or less,
    Ymin = −4 or less, Ymax = 12 or more, Yscl = 1 or more

2. $20 \cdot 1.5^h$

a.
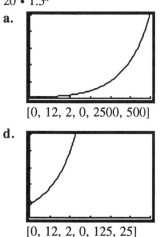
[0, 12, 2, 0, 2500, 500]

b.
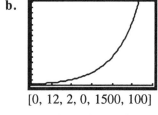
[0, 12, 2, 0, 1500, 100]

c.
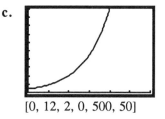
[0, 12, 2, 0, 500, 50]

d.

[0, 12, 2, 0, 125, 25]

e. The view window in part a gives the best picture because the graph fills most of the screen.

3. a.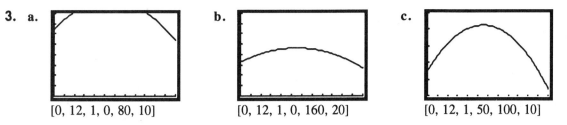

[0, 12, 1, 0, 80, 10]   [0, 12, 1, 0, 160, 20]   [0, 12, 1, 50, 100, 10]

d. The view window in part c gives the best picture because the graph fills most of the screen and the critical area of the maximum is shown.

4. Answers will vary.
   a. Range of -25 to 35 for y-values is good.
   b. Range of -50 to 300 for y-values is good.
   c. Range of -10 to 50 for y-values is good.

5. a. i. 14.4   ii. 33.76
   b. i. 0.0030448   ii. $3.43232 \cdot 10^{-6}$

6. Answers will vary. One possible answer is Xmin = 2, Xmax = 12, Ymin = 1, and Ymax = 7.

7. Answers will vary.

8. Answers will vary.

Chapter 1

Problem Set 1.1

1. 6, 9, 13.5, . . . ; geometric; $u_{10} = 230.6601563$

2. 6 ENTER seeds the sequence. Ans + 3.2 ENTER can be repeated to generate the terms; $u_{10} = 34.8$.

3. a. 2 ENTER seeds the sequence. Ans • 3 ENTER . . . ; $u_{15} = 9{,}565{,}938$
   b. 10 ENTER Ans • 0.5 ENTER . . . ; $u_{12} = 0.004\ 882\ 812\ 5$
   c. 0.4 ENTER Ans • 0.1 ENTER . . . ; $u_{10} = 4 \cdot 10^{-10}$
   d. 2 ENTER Ans + 6 ENTER . . . ; $u_{30} = 176$
   e. 1.56 ENTER Ans + 3.29 ENTER . . . ; $u_{14} = 44.33$
   f. 6.24 ENTER Ans • -2.5 ENTER . . . ; $u_{20} = -227{,}009{,}877.6$

4. a. Between 12 and 13 min   **b.** Between 28 and 29 min   **c.** Ans + 2.4 – 3.1

5. a. 399 km   **b.** During the eighth hour after the second car leaves

6. a. 10 gal   **b.** 0.625 gal   **c.** Never

7. a. $60.00   **b.** $33.75   **c.** 9 weeks

8. a. 20 ENTER Ans(1 – 0.5) + 2.4 ENTER . . .
   b. 12.4 gal   **c.** 5.275 gal   **d.** 4.8 gal

Problem Set 1.2

1. a.

Generations back	0	1	2	3	4	17	n
Ancestors in a generation	$u_0 = 1$	$u_1 = 2$	$u_2 = 4$	$u_3 = 8$	$u_4 = 16$	$u_{17} = 131{,}072$	$u_n = 2u_{(n-1)}$

b. Multiply the number in the preceding generation by 2.
c. 4,194,304. About 22 generations back, Jill would have almost 5 million ancestors.
d. 550 yr ago
e. Answers will vary.

2. Answers will vary. (For example; no, you are doubling at each step. The hypothetical income after six rounds should be 64 times as large or nearly $1 billion.)

3. About 25 time periods or between 24,000 and 25,000 yr; 100 $\boxed{\text{ENTER}}$
Ans • 0.8855 $\boxed{\text{ENTER}}$ and so on.

4. a. $\frac{0.065}{12} \approx 0.0054 = 0.54\%$ **b.** $502.71   **c.** $533.49
d. $584.80   **e.** 7.568%

5. a. 25,098   **b.** $\approx 64.07\%$ **c.** 3.2%
d. Using 0.032 as the rate you get a population of 73,553, which is too large. You need to find a smaller rate than 3.2% to compensate for the compounding effect.
e. 0.025
f. 50,147; the average is less than half the 1980 population because the relationship is nonlinear.

6. Answers will vary.

Problem Set 1.3

1. a. 747.45, 818.04   **b.** Answers will vary.   **c.** The sequence levels out at 840.

2. a. 1, 2, 6, 24, 120, 720   **b.** $u_7 = 5040$; $u_{14} \approx 8.17 \cdot 10^{10}$

3. a. $u_n = \begin{cases} 49.06 & \text{if } n = 1 \\ 1.18 + u_{(n-1)} & \text{if } n > 1 \end{cases}$ **b.** $u_n = \begin{cases} -4.24 & \text{if } n = 1 \\ 5 \cdot u_{(n-1)} & \text{if } n > 1 \end{cases}$

4. a. $u_1 = 24{,}000$ and $u_n = \left(1 + \frac{0.064}{12}\right) \cdot u_{(n-1)} - 100$
b. $24,000; $24,028; $24,056.15; $24,084.45; $24,112.90
c. The balance after 4 mo
d. $24,346.03; $25,108.03

5. a. 5557 trees   **b.** 5000 trees   **c.** No change in long run totals
d. Answers will vary.   **e.** The end result doesn't change.

6. $u_1 = 20$ and $u_n = (1 - 0.25) \cdot u_{(n-1)}$; between 10 and 11 days

7. $u_1 = 20$ and $u_n = (1 - 0.25) \cdot u_{(n-1)} + 20$; about 80 mg

8. Yes. Answers will vary.

9. a. $u_1 = 11{,}000$ and $u_n = \left(1 + \frac{0.096}{12}\right) \cdot u_{(n-1)} - 274$
b. $11,000; $10,814; $10,626.51; $10,437.52; $10,247.02
c. 49 mo with a final payment of $167.73
d. $13,319.73

10. a. The balance continues to increase.   **b.** $128

Problem Set 1.4

1. a. (1, 2.5); (2, 4); (3, 5.5); (4, 7); (5, 8.5); (6, 10)
  b. Answers will vary. One possible window is [0, 7, 1, 0, 11, 1].
  c.   **d.** The sketch will look like the graph for part c.

2. a. (0, 3929000); (1, 4871960); (2, 6041230); (3, 7491126); (4, 9288996); (5, 11518355)
  b. The initial population   **c.** 24%   **d.** Geometric
  e.

```
WINDOW FORMAT
Xmin=0
Xmax=6
Xscl=1
Ymin=0
Ymax=15000000
Yscl=5000000
```

3. a.   **b.** The graph is not linear.
  c. $(u_{20} - u_0)/u_0 = 7286\%$

[0, 200, 50, 0, 2, 900,000,000, 100,000,000]

4. No, this graph is not linear. The balance decreases very fast at the start, so it takes only about four years longer to withdraw all of the money.

5.

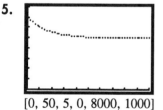

[0, 50, 5, 0, 8000, 1000]
This is a set of discrete points.

6. a. The slime takes over during the seventh day.
  b. The concentration increases to 3.333333333 ppm. The pool will never be pure chlorine.
  c. The concentration establishes equilibrium at 0.666667 ppm.
  d. You will need to add 0.225 ppm each day.

Problem Set 1.5

1. $u_{10} = 56; u_{20} = 116; u_{30} = 176$

2. a. $1,905.56   **b.** $3,631.15   **c.** $6,919.38

3. a.

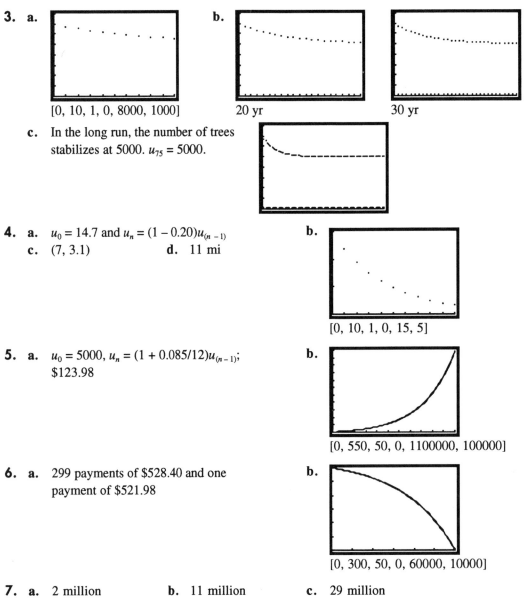

[0, 10, 1, 0, 8000, 1000]　　　　20 yr　　　　30 yr

c. In the long run, the number of trees stabilizes at 5000. $u_{75} = 5000$.

4. a. $u_0 = 14.7$ and $u_n = (1 - 0.20)u_{(n-1)}$
  c. $(7, 3.1)$　　　　**d.** 11 mi

b. [0, 10, 1, 0, 15, 5]

5. a. $u_0 = 5000$, $u_n = (1 + 0.085/12)u_{(n-1)}$; $123.98

b. [0, 550, 50, 0, 1100000, 100000]

6. a. 299 payments of $528.40 and one payment of $521.98

b. [0, 300, 50, 0, 60000, 10000]

7. a. 2 million　　　**b.** 11 million　　　**c.** 29 million
  d. 211 million　　**e.** Population outside CA – population in CA
  f. Approximately 48.68 million in 1990; 66.10 million in 1995; the long run equilibrium is 80 million in California.

8. a. 1, 1, 2, 3, 5, 8, 13, 21, 34, 55
  b. The ratios are 1, 2, 1.5, 1.6, 1.625, ... The ratios are approaching 1.618033989.

9. Answers will vary.

Problem Set 1.6

1. 2, 8, 18, 32, 50

2. a. 14,348,906
  b. It is probably impossible to find a graphing window that pictures the initial small sums and the eventual gigantic sums.

3. a. 0.3333333333

b. 0.333333333333333; the sum is the same as for ten terms because the calculator cannot display more digits.

c. $0.\overline{3}$ or 1/3.

4. a. 144   **b.** 400   **c.** n^2

5. 1200 min (20 hr); 4550 min (75.8 hr)

6. a. 500,500   **b.** 1,500,500   **c.** Answers will vary.   **d.** 2,500,500
e. Answers will vary. One possible answer is $2(1000)^2 + S(1000)$.

7. First plan: \$38,373,180,000; Second plan: \$45,035,996,273,704; The second plan is more profitable by \$44,997,623,093,704.

8. 0.3939393939

9. a. 576,443; 641,676   **b.** Answers will vary.

10. Answers will vary.

Chapter Review
Problem Set 1.7

1. a. 3, 6, 9, 12, 15, 18, 21, 24, 27, 30   **b.** $u_n = \begin{cases} 3 & \text{if } n = 1 \\ u_{(n-1)} + 3 & \text{if } n > 1 \end{cases}$
     c. 3384 cans   **d.** 13 rows

2. a. 511   **b.** 40th   **c.** 79   **d.** 820

3. a. 34.171875   **b.** Tenth   **c.** 45.5625   **d.** 887.3125

4. a. \$657.03   **b.** \$4,083.21

5. 5299 students; 5208 students

6. 359 payments of \$637.96 and one payment of \$620.46

7. a. −3, −1.5, 0, 1.5, 3   **b.** 2, 4, 10, 28, 82

Chapter 2

Problem Set 2.1

1. a. $\frac{5}{3}$, 7, 18, $36\frac{2}{3}$, 65   **b.** Neither

2. $u_6 = 2.45$; $u_{15} = 3.87$; $u_n = \sqrt{n}$ (rounded to two decimal places)

3. a.
     b. −3   **c.** −3
     d. 21   **e.** $u_n = -3n + 21$
     f. $u_{10} = -9$ **g.** $y = -3x + 21$

4. a. 4, 9, 14, 19, . . .   **b.** 14   **c.** 5
     d. $u_5 = 24$ and $u_0 = -1$ **e.** 5   **f.** −1
     g. $u_n = 5n - 1$ **h.** $y = 5x - 1$

5. a. $(1, 7)$ and $(6, 27)$ **b.** $m = 4$ **c.** 3, 7, 11, 15, 19, 23, 27
    d. $y = 4x + 3$ **e.** $u_n = 4n + 3$
    f. The slope and the common difference are the same.

6. a. $u_n = 2.5(n - 1) + 6.3 = 2.5n + 3.8$ **b.** 30th term

7. a. 231 mi   **b.** $d = 54x + 15$ **c.**
    d. If only distances on the hour are considered, it is
      arithmetic. Otherwise the distance depends on time—a
      continuous rather than discrete notion.

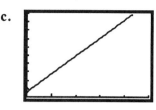

8. a. −4750, −3850, −2950, −2050, −1150, −250, 650, . . .
    b.
    c. $900 profit per car sold
    d. $900 profit per car sold
    e. −$4,750 ($y$-intercept) represents expenses even if no cars are sold;
      5.27 (x-intercept) means at least 6 cars must be sold to make any profit.
    f. $d = 900c - 4750$

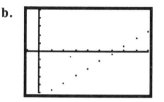

9. a. −2   **b.** 5   **c.** 7
    d. The height can be found from the equation because you need to add 7 heights of d to the original height of u_0.
    e. $u_5 = u_0 + 13d$ **f.** $u_n = u_0 + nd$

10. a. They are the same and will always be the same.
    b. The trick is to look at the total income at the end of each six-month period. Assume that the raise goes
      into effect at the beginning of the next time period. Although the total earnings are different at the end
      of the odd-numbered six-month periods, at the end of each year the total income is always the same.

	Case 1	Total earnings	Case 2	Total earnings
First 6 mo	9,200	9,200	8,950	8,950
First yr	9,200	18,400	9,450	18,400
Third 6 mo	10,200	28,600	9,950	28,350
Second yr	10,200	38,800	10,450	38,800
Fifth 6 mo	11,200	50,000	10,950	49,750
Third yr	11,200	61,200	11,450	61,200

Problem Set 2.2

1. 7650

2. 5700

3. a. 149   **b.** 5625   **c.** 5264

4. a. −6639.7   **b.** $\displaystyle\sum_{n-1}^{64} 132.1 - 6.8n$

5. a. 229   **b.** $5n - 1$ **c.** 5359

6. 88 gal

7. A sequence with positive slope (line a)
    A sequence with negative slope (line b)
    A sequence with zero slope (line c)

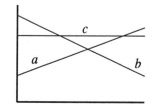

8. a. 143 seats   **b.** 4160 seats   **c.** In row 13, seventh seat from the right aisle

9. a. 12.5   **b.** 116   **c.** Add up the areas of the ten trapezoids formed at consecutive integers. $3.5 + 5.3 + \cdots + 19.7 = 116$

Problem Set 2.3

1. 9,565,938

2. $2,302.03; after 23 yr the balance is $5,139.23.

3. a. The value of $4,000 after 10 yr of compounded interest at 7.2%
   b. The value of $4,000 after 4 yr of interest compounded monthly
   c. $1500(1+0.055)^8$

4. a. iv   **b.** iii   **c.** ii   **d.** i

5. $r \approx 1.15$ (graph a)
$r = 1$ (graph b)
$r \approx 0.85$ (graph c)
Answers will vary.

6. a. ii   **b.** i   **c.** iii

7. a. ≈ 10.74 inches   **b.** 21st rebound; 31st rebound

8. a. $u_n = 80 \cdot 0.75^{(n-1)}$ **b.** $60   **c.** $33.75   **d.** Ninth week

9. 0.393939393939

10. Answers will vary.

Problem Set 2.4

1. a. 3069   **b.** 22   **c.** 2.8   **d.** 0.95

2. 21.4%

3. a.

n	1	2	3	4	5	6	7
S_n	5	15	35	75	155	315	635

   b. No
   c. When $r = 0$

4. a. 92.224   **b.** 99.9529815   **c.** 99.9997157

5. a. Neither   **b.** $\frac{761}{280}$ or about 2.718

6. a. $1^2 + 2^2 + 3^2 + 4^2 + 5^2 + 6^2 + 7^2 = 140$ **b.** $3^2 + 4^2 + 5^2 + 6^2 + 7^2 = 135$

7. a. $2^{63} \approx 9.22 \cdot 10^{18}$ **b.** $2^{64} - 1 \approx 1.84 \cdot 10^{19}$

   c. $\displaystyle\sum_{n-1}^{64} 2^{(n-1)}$

8. a. $S_{10} = 15.984375$ **b.** $S_{20} = 15.99998474$ **c.** $S_{30} = 15.99999999$ **d.** The partial sums approach 16.

Problem Set 2.5

1. $S_{10} = 60$; $S_n = 6n$; infinite

2. **a.** $S_{10} \approx 12.96$; $S_{40} \approx 13.33$
   b. $S_{10} \approx 170.48$; $S_{40} \approx 481{,}572$
   c. $S_{10} = 40$; $S_{40} = 160$
   d. The inequality $r > 1$ gives the top graph; $r = 1$ gives the middle graph; $0 < r < 1$ gives the bottom graph.
   e. When $|r| < 1$

3. $600/0.12 = 5000$ trees

4. **a.** 0.149382716   **b.** ≈ 0.1499974597 **c.** 0.15   **d.** Answers will vary.

5. The sum of this geometric series with $r = 0.9$ approaches \$10,000,000 as n gets large.

6. **a.** $\frac{1}{128}$ ft (right)   **b.** $\frac{-1}{262144}$ ft (left)   **c.** $\frac{1}{3}$

7. 50 mi

8. At age 30, Prudence has \$35,120.59 and Charity has \$2,000; at age 65, Prudence has \$716,950.60 and Charity has \$472,249.45.

9. **a.** 1.414   **b.** 0.125   **c.** P approaches 109.25 and A approaches 128.

10. **a.** $96 + 24 + 6 + 1.5 + \cdots + 3.66 \cdot 10^{-4}$ **b.** 127.9999924   **c.** 128
    d.

11. Answers will vary.

Problem Set 2.6

1. Geome tree

		1	2	3	4	n	∞
a.	Length of the last segment	1	0.5	0.25	0.125	$1\left(\frac{1}{2}\right)^{(n-1)}$	0
b.	Length of the path	1	1.5	1.75	1.875	$\dfrac{1\left(1 - \left(\frac{1}{2}\right)^{n}\right)}{1 - \frac{1}{2}}$	2
c.	Total number of segments	1	3	7	15	$2^n - 1$	∞
d.	Sum of the lengths of all segments	1	2	3	4	n	∞
e.	Height of the tree	1	1.354	1.604	1.692		1.8047
f.	Width of the tree	0	0.707	1.207	1.384		1.609

2. Koch snowflake

		1	2	3	4	n	∞
a.	Length of each segment	1	$\frac{1}{3}$	$\frac{1}{9}$	$\frac{1}{27}$	$\left(\frac{1}{3}\right)^{(n-1)}$	0
b.	Total number of segments	3	12	48	192	$3 \cdot 4^{(n-1)}$	∞
c.	Perimeter	3	4	$5\frac{1}{3}$	$\frac{64}{9}$	$\dfrac{3 \cdot 4^{(n-1)}}{3^{(n-1)}}$	∞
d.	Area	0.43301	0.577	0.641	0.67001		

3. Sierpiński triangle

		1	2	3	4	n	∞
a.	Length of last side	1	$\frac{1}{2}$	$\frac{1}{4}$	$\frac{1}{8}$	$\left(\frac{1}{2}\right)^{(n-1)}$	0
b.	Number of triangles	1	3	9	27	$3^{(n-1)}$	∞
c.	Perimeter of each	3	$\frac{3}{2}$	$\frac{3}{4}$	$\frac{3}{8}$	$\dfrac{3}{2^{n-1}}$	0
d.	Area of each	$\frac{\sqrt{3}}{4}$	$\frac{\sqrt{3}}{16}$	$\frac{\sqrt{3}}{64}$	$\frac{\sqrt{3}}{256}$	$\dfrac{\sqrt{3}}{4^n}$	0
e.	Sum of perimeters	3	4.5	6.75	10.125	$\dfrac{3^n}{2^{(n-1)}}$	∞
f.	Sum of areas	$\frac{\sqrt{3}}{4}$	$\frac{3\sqrt{3}}{16}$	$\frac{9\sqrt{3}}{64}$	$\frac{27\sqrt{3}}{256}$	$\dfrac{3^{(n-1)}\sqrt{3}}{4^n}$	0

4. Answers will vary.

Chapter Review

Problem Set 2.7

1. a. 3, 6, 9, . . . , 30

b. $u_n = \begin{cases} 3 & \text{if } n = 1 \\ u_{(n-1)} + 3 & \text{if } n > 1 \end{cases}$

c. $u_n = 3n$ **d.** 3384 cans **e.** 13 rows

2. a. 511 **b.** 40th **c.** 79 **d.** 820

3. a. 144, 1,728, 20,736, $4.3 \cdot 10^8$

b. $u_n = \begin{cases} 12 & \text{if } n = 1 \\ 12 \cdot u_{(n-1)} & \text{if } n > 1 \end{cases}$

c. $u_n = 12^n$ **d.** $9.7 \cdot 10^{12}$ bugs

4. a. 34.171875 **b.** tenth term **c.** 45.5625 **d.** 887.3125

e. The sum approaches 1024.

5. a. $657.03 **b.** $4,083.21

6. a. 5327 students **b.** 5208 students

7. a. ≈ 139.67 cm **b.** ≈ 1206.65 cm **c.** 4000 cm

8. ≈ 56.488 ft; 60 ft

9. 359 payments of $637.96 and 1 payment of $620.46

10. a. $\left(\frac{2}{3}\right)^0$, $\left(\frac{2}{3}\right)^1$, $\left(\frac{2}{3}\right)^2$, $\left(\frac{2}{3}\right)^3$, and so on. **b.** $C_n \to 0$

11. a. 2.929, 3.598, 3.995, 4.279, 4.499, 4.680, 4.833, 4.965, 5.083

b. The sum continues to get larger at a slower rate.

Chapter 3

Problem Set 3.1

1. The median is 84 and the mean is 84 for both Connie and Ozzie. Neither measure separately or combined indicates the larger test score variation for Ozzie's scores.

2. The second box plot is longer because it reflects the longer range of Ozzie's scores.

3. **a.**

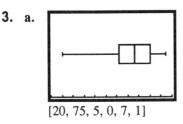

   [20, 75, 5, 0, 7, 1]

   b. {25, 51, 58, 65, 72}
   c. 56.55
   d. 98

4. **a.** Outliers for Connie: below 77.5 or above 89.5; Outliers for Ozzie: below 49 or above 121
   b. Outliers for Homer: below 30 or above 86; one outlier: 25 < 30

5. **a.** The mean is $0.70.
   c. The mean is larger than the median because of the influence of several large values in the data.

   b.

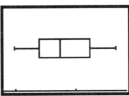

   Cost per month for toothpaste

6. **a.** {74,300, 87,050, 105,000, 153,900, 246,900}

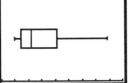

   [50000, 275000, 25000, 0, 10, 1]
   There are no outliers.

   b. {74,300, 84,650, 93,600, 105,750, 116,800}

   [70000, 120000, 25000, 0, 10, 1]

   c. Answers will vary.

7. **a.** The mean is 4601, and the median is 2477. There is one outlier, New York City.
   b. The mean is 3062, and the median is 2463. The mean was affected more.
   c. Answers will vary.
   d. The new mean would be 5601. The new median would be 3477. Each value increased by 1000.
   e. Answers will vary.

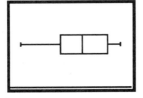

8. **a.–c.** Answers will vary.

9. a.

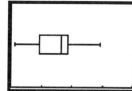

b. Scores less than −2,317 or more than 16,375 would be outliers. If I am an outlier I am more than $7,010 above the upper quartile or more than $7,009 below the lower quartile.

c. There is no mode; the median is 8279; the mean is 7683.

d. The United States is in the second quartile.

0. a. The tube price median is $2.01 and the mean is $2.13; the median cleaning rank is 66.5 and the mean rank is 67.25.

b. Price   Rank

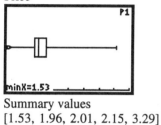

Summary values
[1.53, 1.96, 2.01, 2.15, 3.29]

Summary values
[55, 61, 66.5, 73, 86]

c. Answers will vary.

Problem Set 3.2

1. This implies than no CDs can be shipped that measure more than 12.12 cm or less than 11.88 cm.

2. Answers will vary.

3. From top to bottom the graphs are for the Northeast, Midwest, South, and West. Summary values for Northeast are {13.2, 13.75, 15.4, 16.35, 17}, for the Midwest are {14.6, 15.5, 16.45, 17.4, 19.9}, for the South are {15.4, 16.25, 17.05, 18.45, 19.9}, and for the West are {14.5, 16.85, 18.95, 19.85, 25}.

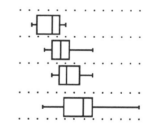

4. a. 47.1, 45.9, 47.9, 47.4, 45.1, 46.0, 45.7, 45.3

b. The mean absolute deviation is 0.875 cm.

c. 47.9, 47.4, 45.1, 45.3

. a. First period has pulse rates most alike because it has the smallest mean absolute deviation.

b. You can't really tell which class has the students with the fastest pulse. First period rates are more consistent around the mean of 79.4 because it has the lowest MAD value. Sixth period must have some very high rates and some very low rates to have the highest MAD value.

c. Answers will vary. Data sets with lower MAD values will have shorter box plots.

. a. Column 1: 19.8
Column 2: 23.6
Column 3: 17.3

b. Column 1: 5.3
Column 2: 6.2
Column 3: 4.9

c. Column 1

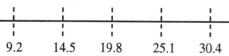

9.2   14.5   19.8   25.1   30.4

Column 2

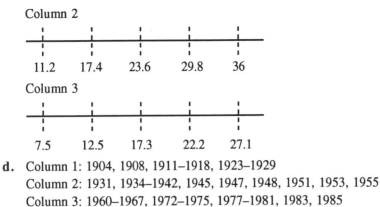

| | 11.2 | 17.4 | 23.6 | 29.8 | 36 |

Column 3

| | 7.5 | 12.5 | 17.3 | 22.2 | 27.1 |

   d. Column 1: 1904, 1908, 1911–1918, 1923–1929
       Column 2: 1931, 1934–1942, 1945, 1947, 1948, 1951, 1953, 1955
       Column 3: 1960–1967, 1972–1975, 1977–1981, 1983, 1985
   e. Column 1: 1902, 1906, 1909, 1910, 1920
       Column 2: 1943, 1950, 1958
       Column 3: 1968, 1970, 1986, 1989

7. a.–d. See answers for Problems 6a.–e.
   e. Answers will vary.

8. a. Interquartile range for Juneau, Alaska: 21
      Interquartile range for New York, New York: 30.5
   b. Juneau has more consistent temperatures ranging from 24°F to
      56°F compared to New York temperatures ranging from 32°F
      to 77°F. The mean absolute deviation for Juneau is 9.83°F
      and for New York 14.0°F.

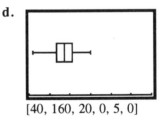

9. a. The median is 75 and the inter-
      quartile range is 19.
   c. The outliers are below 39 or above 115.
      Therefore, 147 and 158 are outliers.

   b. The mean is 80.88 and the mean absolute
      deviation is 15.9.
   d.

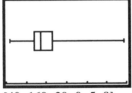

[40, 160, 20, 0, 5, 0]

[40, 160, 20, 0, 5, 0]

   e. i. The mean is 74.65 and the mean absolute deviation is 9.3.
     ii. The median is 74 and the interquartile range is 15.
   f. The mean is affected more than the median; the mean absolute deviation is affected more than the
      interquartile range. This is because the mean absolute deviation involves the mean and the interquartile
      range involves the median.

10. Answers will vary.

Problem Set 3.3

1. a. The graph should look exactly like the graph in the problem. [2, 13, 1, 0, 200, 50]
   b. It is mound shaped because 7 is the most likely dice total, then 6 and 8, then 5 and 9, and so on.
   c. The mean sum can be computed by evaluating $\frac{2(26) + 3(56) + \cdots + 12(21)}{1000}$. The median sum can
      be found by counting in from the left or right. The median will be the average of the 500th and 501st
      roll total.

2. a. This population of 95 farmers tends to plant two to five acres of sweet corn. The frequencies are on the left.

b.

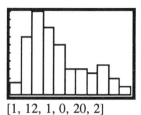

[1, 12, 1, 0, 20, 2]

c.

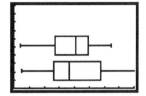

3. a.–d. Answers will vary.

4. a. 1320 students scored lower; 180 students scored higher.
b. Mary scored better than 95% of the students.
c. About the 99th percentile
d. 150 students.

5. a. HW {4, 27.5, 40.5, 49, 65}; TV {5, 26, 36.5, 58, 95}; TV has the larger spread. The spread for HW is 61, and the spread for TV is 90.

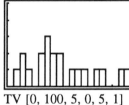

b.

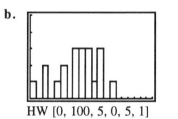

HW [0, 100, 5, 0, 5, 1]   TV [0, 100, 5, 0, 5, 1]

c. HW: MAD = 12.78, range = 61, IQR = 21.5; TV: MAD =20.56, range = 90, IQR = 32
Answers will vary on which measure best represents the data.

6. a. The sum should be 0.   **b.** 20
c. Mean of 747
  i. 47.25   ii. 747, 707, 669, 676, 767, 783, 789, 838
  iii. 757   iv. 94.5

  Mean of 850
  i. 47.25   ii. 850, 810, 772, 779, 870, 886, 892, 941
  iii. 860   iv. 94.5

d. Answers will vary. For example, The MAD and IQR are unaffected by a change in the mean, the median moves the same amount as the mean.

7. a. The MAD of the stadium capacities is 7282. The MAD of the attendance figures is 6254. Attendance MAD is less than stadium capacity MAD. This means the stadium capacity values are more spread out.
b. A larger MAD should mean the box plot is longer and the histogram distribution is not so mound shaped. A smaller MAD should mean the box plot is shorter and the histogram distribution is more mound shaped.
c. Capacity

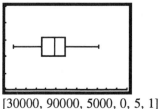   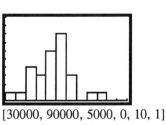

[30000, 90000, 5000, 0, 5, 1]   [30000, 90000, 5000, 0, 10, 1]

Attendance

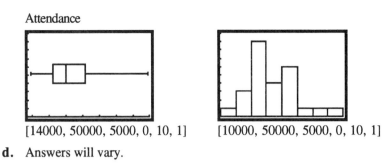

[14000, 50000, 5000, 0, 10, 1]   [10000, 50000, 5000, 0, 10, 1]

   d. Answers will vary.

8. Answers will vary.

Chapter Review

Problem Set 3.4

1. Plot B because the data is much more spread out.

2. a. Answers will vary, but the graph for plot C should be much higher. The shapes should take into account the scale on the horizontal axis and the way values are compacted between the quartiles.

   b. Seven data values are in the lower whisker in plot C. Six data values are in each whisker in plot D.

   c. Plot B has the larger MAD because the box plot is longer and the range of data values is much greater.

3. Answers will vary.

4. The mean of the extreme highs is 118°F with a MAD of 17°F. The mean of the extreme lows is ⁻60°F with a MAD of 38°F. Antarctica is two MADs from the mean high and *almost* two MADs from the mean low.

5. a. Answers will vary, but the mean absolute deviation near 0 means a tall, skinny graph.

   b. Answers will vary, but the mean absolute deviation of about 5 means a shorter but longer graph.

6. a. The mean value is 129 hr and the median value is 95 hr.

   b. The window for both graphs is [0, 600, 24, 0, 7, 1].

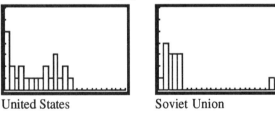

United States   Soviet Union

   c. Answers for the predictions will vary. The MAD for the Soviet flights is 70 hr and for the United States flights is 96 hr.

7. a.

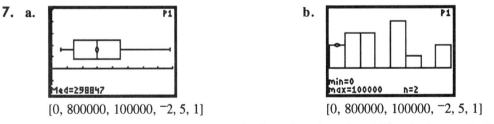

    Med=298847   min=0

                                              max=100000   n=2

    [0, 800000, 100000, ⁻2, 5, 1]   [0, 800000, 100000, ⁻2, 5, 1]

   c.–d. Answers will vary. The shape really depends on how the additional sales are distributed.

8. a. Descriptions will vary.

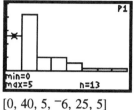

[0, 40, 5, ‾6, 25, 5]   [0, 40, 5, ‾6, 25, 5]

b. Explanations will vary.

East of the Mississippi

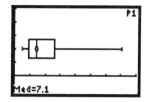

[0, 40, 5, ‾6, 15, 5]   [0, 40, 5, ‾6, 15, 5]

West of the Mississippi

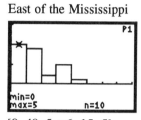
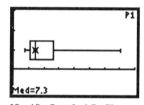

[0, 40, 5, ‾6, 15, 5]   [0, 40, 5, ‾6, 15, 5]

c. Northeast   Midwest

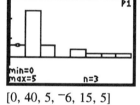
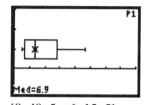

[0, 40, 5, ‾5, 10, 2]   [0, 40, 5, ‾5, 10, 2]

South   West

[0, 40, 5, ‾5, 10, 2]   [0, 40, 5, ‾5, 10, 2]

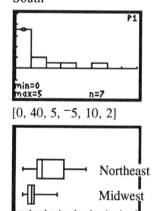
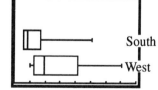

d. Answers will vary.

Chapter 4

Problem Set 4.1

1. Answers will vary. Here are some examples.
   a. Too many points are above the line.
   b. Most of the points at the left are below the line.
   c. The line doesn't follow the tendency of the data from first to last point.
   d. Points at each end are concentrated on one side of the line.
   e. This is the best of the lot.
   f. There are no points below the line.

2. For Problems 1–6, answers will vary. Possible answers are given.
   a. y-intercept is about 1.7; point (4, 4).
   b. y-intercept is about 1.8; point (3, 4).
   c. y-intercept is about 7.5; point (2, 6).
   d. y-intercept is about 2.2; point (4, 5).
   e. y-intercept is about 2.5; point (8, 7).
   f. y-intercept is about 8.6; point (7, 2).

3. Answers will vary for the best-fit line.

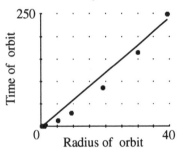

4. Answers will vary for the best-fit line.

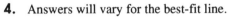
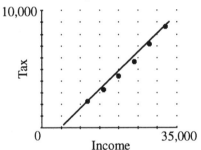

5. Answers will vary.

6. a. 6
   b. [0, 22, 2, 20, 45, 5]

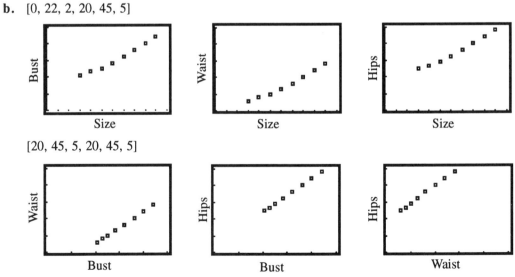

   [20, 45, 5, 20, 45, 5]

7. Answers will vary.

Problem Set 4.2

1. a. $\frac{3}{2}$ **b.** $\frac{-2}{3}$

2. a. 3 **b.** -2.8 **c.** 5 **d.** $+2.4$ **e.** -1.46875

3. a. $y = \frac{3}{2}x - 6$ **b.** $y = -1.124x + 2.643$

4. a. $y = \frac{3}{4}x - 2$ **b.** $y = \frac{-3}{2}x + \frac{7}{2}$

For Problems 5 and 6, the equation of the line should be close to that of the median-median line, whose equation is given.

5. $y = 5.59x - 8.03$

6. $y = 0.32x - 1820$

7. (size, bust) $y = 0.84x + 24.6$ (size, waist) $y = 0.79x + 17.5$
(size, hips) $y = 0.84x + 26.6$ (bust, waist) $y = 0.94x - 5.7$
(bust, hips) $y = x + 2$ (waist, hips) $y = 1.06x + 8.1$

8. 299 payments of \$528.40, 1 payment of \$521.98; $y = -1239.8x + 655{,}104.95$; root is 528.40.

Problem Set 4.3

1. a. 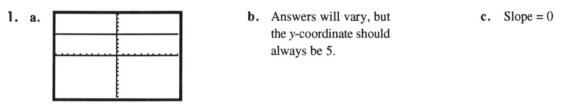 **b.** Answers will vary, but the y-coordinate should always be 5. **c.** Slope = 0

2. $y = -4$; no x-intercept, 0 slope, all points have the same y-value.

3. $x = 3$; Line(3, Ymin, 3, Ymax) or $\boxed{2\text{nd}}$ [DRAW] $\boxed{4}$ (Vertical)

4. a. The graph should show a vertical line at $x = -3$.
b. Answers will vary, but the x-coordinate should always be -3.
c. There is no slope.
d. There is no y-intercept.

5. a. For each additional story, the building height increases by about 13 ft.
b. The stories of a building are often not all the same height, the first floor or two are usually taller. The intercept of about 20 represents this difference in the height of the initial stories.
c. Domain $0 \le x \le 80$; range $0 \le y \le 1100$

6. a. \$20,497 **b.** \$847 per year of experience
c. Anita gets a \$847 raise each year. **d.** 17,109
e. Her starting salary was \$17,109. **f.** Domain $0 \le x \le 10$; answers will vary.

Note: The equations in the answers for Problems 7–10 may vary depending on the chosen point. Any line that fits the data "by eye" should be considered acceptable as long as the student can justify his or her choice of an equation.

7. a. An equation of a best-fit line using the points (44, 19) and (15, 10) is $y = 0.31x + 5.36$.
b. There is a cost increase of about 31¢ per picture.
c. (0, 5.36) **d.** There is a cost of \$5.36 for the sitting fee.
e. \$19.93 **f.** 29 prints

8. a. $y = -1.75x + 582.25$ (using the points (87, 430) and (91, 423))

  b. Years after 1900

  c. There has been a 1.75 point decrease per year in the average verbal score.

  d. 414 points for 1996, 412 for 1997, 411 for 1998, 409 for 1999, 407 for 2000

  e. 442 points

  f. There is a limit to the extrapolation in this model. Using it to predict very far beyond the given data is very unreliable.

9. The answers given are based on midrange x-values.

  a.

  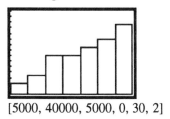

  [5000, 40000, 5000, 0, 30, 2]

  b. $y = 0.00065x - 1.125$ (using the points for incomes of $32,500 and $12,500)

  c. As family incomes increase by $1,000, the percent of students in grades 9–12 using computers at home increases by 0.65%.

  d. 39.2%

10. a. (If you choose to draw a histogram, you will have to draw it on paper because the calculator requires you to enter whole numbers for the frequencies.) $y = -5.07x + 181.3$ (using the points (17, 96.2) and (32, 19.6))

  b. Percent of men not married

  c. About 5.07% of the total male population gets married each year.

  d. −31.3%

  e. The model does not extrapolate very well, or it becomes nonlinear after age 30.

Problem Set 4.4

1. a. 10, 11, 10   **b.** 17, 16, 17

2. a. $y = -0.674x + 21.2$ **b.** $y = 2.47x + 39.6$

3. $y = 0.75x - 9.9$

4. $y = -1.8x + 72.9$

5. $y = 0.65x + 21.8$

6. The second line is $y = 4.7(x - 12.8) + 64$ or $y = 4.7x + 3.84$. The median-median line is $y = 4.7x + 3.15$.

7. a. 5, 5, 5   **b.** (30, 58.1), (55, 66.2), (80, 70)

  c. 0.238; each year the life expectancy of a male child increases by 0.238 yr.

  d. $y = 0.238x + 50.96$ **e.** $y = 0.238x + 53.11$

  f. $y = 0.238x + 51.68$ **g.** 70.24

  h. 73.34, 64.53   **i.** The year 2019

8. Answers will vary.

9. Answers will vary.

10. a. $y = -0.344x + 257.6$ **b.** A drop of 0.344 sec each year

  c. 3:45.95   **d.** Eventually the record would be 1 mi in 0 sec.

  e. Answers may vary. For example, a new world record was set in Italy on September 5, 1993, by Noureddine Morceli of 3:44.39 for the mile. The model would predict the record in 1993 to be $y = -0.344(92) + 257.6 = 225.6$ or 3:46.4.

11. Answers will vary. For example, divide the data into three groups the same way as for the median-median line. Then use the mean x and the mean y from each group. Follow the same procedure that you used for the median-median line to find an equation: $y = -0.353x + 259.8$.

12. Answers will vary.

Problem Set 4.5

1. a. −0.2   **b.** −0.4   **c.** 0.6

2. a. The residuals are below the *x*-axis on either end and above the *x*-axis in the middle.

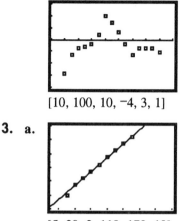

[10, 100, 10, −4, 3, 1]

b. By drawing a line that is parallel to the median-median line but with a smaller *y*-intercept, more points will lie closer to the line.

c. $y = 0.238x + 50.95$

d. 0.7 yr

3. a.

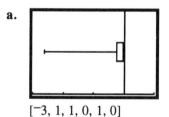

[5, 20, 2, 110, 170, 10]

$y = 5.08x + 86.3$

c. Ages 7 and 15

b.

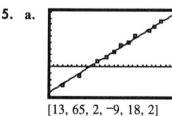

[6, 16, 2, −3, 1, 1]

The range of the residuals is from −2.6 to 0.017.

d. Answers may vary. At age 7, you are at the end of the initial growth of a child, and at age 15, you are at the end of the secondary growth of a child.

4. a.

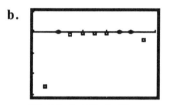

[−3, 1, 1, 0, 1, 0]

b. The residuals are not evenly divided. There are more negative values than positive ones, and the most negative value is an outlier indicating that this point does not fit the model well at all.

5. a.

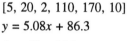

[13, 65, 2, −9, 18, 2]

$y = 0.48x − 14.2$

b.

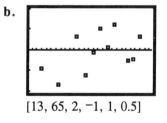

[13, 65, 2, −1, 1, 0.5]

c. Answers will vary. An improvement would be $y = 0.50x − 15$.

d. Answers will vary, but should be close to 27°C.

e. 30°F

6. a.

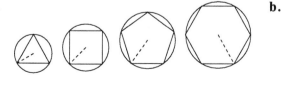

b.

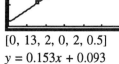

[0, 13, 2, 0, 2, 0.5]

$y = 0.153x + 0.093$

c.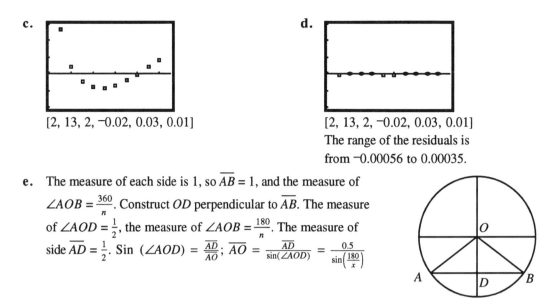

[2, 13, 2, −0.02, 0.03, 0.01]

d.

[2, 13, 2, −0.02, 0.03, 0.01]
The range of the residuals is
from −0.00056 to 0.00035.

e. The measure of each side is 1, so $\overline{AB} = 1$, and the measure of $\angle AOB = \frac{360}{n}$. Construct OD perpendicular to $\overline{AB}$. The measure of $\angle AOD = \frac{1}{2}$, the measure of $\angle AOB = \frac{180}{n}$. The measure of side $\overline{AD} = \frac{1}{2}$. Sin $(\angle AOD) = \frac{\overline{AD}}{\overline{AO}}$; $\overline{AO} = \frac{\overline{AD}}{\sin(\angle AOD)} = \frac{0.5}{\sin\left(\frac{180}{x}\right)}$

7. a. This is not a good model because the residuals form a pattern, which suggests that there is a better model to fit the data.
 b. This is a good model because the residuals are close to 0, centered around the x-axis, and do not form a pattern.
 c. This is a good model, but because there is a definite slope to the residuals, you should adjust the slope of the line.

Problem Set 4.6

1. The three summary points remain the same, so the median-median line will be the same. The outliers could change the summary points if they affect the medians of the groups.

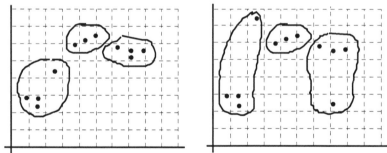

2. The least-squares equation for the line uses all of the data; the median-median equation for the line uses only three points. The least-squares line minimizes the residuals, while the median-median line ignores outliers. The least-squares equation gives you other values useful for fitting a line; the median-median equation can be found easily even without a calculator.

3. The new least-squares equation is $y = 0.4699x - 0.0013$. The new median-median line is $y = 0.4699x - 0.00195$. The outlier has less effect on the median-median line. The median-median line is said to be resistant because an outlier will not have as great an effect on this equation as it does on the least-squares equation.

4. Answers will vary.

5. a. $y = 5.235x + 84.3$ **b.** Mean age = 11; mean height = 141.89
 c. The median-median line is a better fit.

6. a. $y = 0.498x - 14.96$ **b.** Mean °F = 42.09; mean °C = 6
 c. The least-squares line is a better fit.

7. a. (400, 113,394.27), (500, 42,201.91), (600, −28,990.44), (700, −100,182.80); 2
 b. $y = 398,163.69 - 711.92x$ **c.** ≈ $559.28

8. Answers will vary.

9. Answers will vary. The closer the mean of the absolute values of the residuals is to zero, the better the fit.

10. a. $y = -1.212x + 110.2$
   b. An appropriate domain could be 10°N–60°N.
   c. Bakersfield (desert), Denver (mountain), Mexico City (mountain), Phoenix (desert), and Vancouver (Pacific currents)
   d. Answers will vary.

11. a. $y = 0.405x + 9.43$
   b. Each year 0.405% more of the labor force was women. In 1900, 9.43% of the labor force was women.
   c. Answers will vary.

12. Answers will vary.

Problem Set 4.7

1. 12

2. $y = -1.5x + 6$

3. $(-19.5, 77.4)$

4. a. $y = 59.2 - 0.536x$ **b.** $r = -0.9966$
   c. The data has a negative correlation (as the years increase, the percent of dropouts decreases), and about $(-0.9966)^2$ or 99.3% of the points lie between narrow bands on either side of the least-squares line.
   d. 20.6%   **e.** About 9 or 10 out of 10.

5. a. Volumes versus cost: $r = 0.60458$, $r^2 = 37\%$; circulation versus cost: $r = 0.5826$, $r^2 = 34\%$
   b. Answers will vary.

6. a. Seats versus cost: $r = 0.9735$; speed versus cost: $r = 0.8940$
   b. The number of seats is more closely related to cost than speed.

7. Answers will vary.

8. a. Student to faculty: $f = 0.066s + 55.08$; faculty to student: $s = 5.12f + 631.5$
   b. The correlation coefficient, r, is 0.85 for both equations.

9. a. Student to faculty: $f = 55.32 + 0.07s$; faculty to student: $s = 629.58 + 5.13f$
   b. The correlation coefficient, r, is 0.58 for both equations.

10. Answers will vary.

Problem Set 4.8

1. a. First; the points lie more on a curve than on a line.
   b. Second; these points are closest to a line.
   c. Second; the slope is negative, or as x increases, y decreases.

2. a. $y = -5.693 + 7.250x$

x	4	7	11	12.9	16	18.5
y	22	47	74	87	111	128
$y_1(x)$	23.3	45.1	74.1	87.8	110.3	128.4
Residual	−1.31	1.94	−0.06	−0.83	0.69	−0.43
Residual^2	1.710	3.772	0.003	0.695	0.478	0.188

b. −1.3 to 1.9   **c.** 5.27   **d.** 0.88   **e.** 6.85

f. The residuals are all close to the line, with the mean absolute residual only 0.88 from the line. If you find the mean of the squares of the residuals, you get 1.14, which again is rather close to the line. The line is a good fit.

3. Answers will vary.

4. The residuals have a definite pattern, which would indicate that the least-squares model may not be appropriate.

5. **a.** $y = 0.497 + 0.312x$ **b.** 4.55

c. The average (mean) distance of a point from the line is 0.33. This is a fairly accurate model.

6. **a.** 91.73   **b.** Answers will vary.

7. **a.** 303

b. Schools more than one mean absolute deviation from the mean

Boston University	University of Central Florida
Bowling Green State University	University of Cincinnati
DePauw University	University of Iowa
Florida State University	University of Massachusetts
Howard University	University of Miami
Miami University of Ohio	University of Michigan
Michigan State University	University of Nevada
New Mexico State University	University of South Florida
New York University	University of Utah
Penn State	University of Virginia
Princeton University	Webster University
Stanford University	Western Michigan University

All but two of the schools have enrollments greater than 10,000.

c. Schools more than two mean absolute deviations from the mean

Michigan State University	University of Michigan
New York University	University of South Florida
Penn State	University of Utah
University of Miami	Western Michigan University

All but three schools have enrollments greater than 30,000.

d. As the enrollment gets larger, there is more variation in the student-faculty ratios.

8. **a.** $y = 46.3 + 0.00323x$ **b.** 103 g

c. $r = 0.985$, $r^2 = 0.969$, the mean residual is 33 g, and the greatest residual is 68 g.

d. Answers will vary. One possible answer might be to discard the data for the small animals and the very large animal.

Chapter Review

Problem Set 4.9

1. −51.316

2. 23.45

3. $x = 19.94$

4. Answers will vary.

a. [1500, 3500, 250, 40, 80, 10]   **b.** [0, 110, 10, 0, 200, 20]   **c.** [0, 110, 10, 0, 110, 10]

5. $m \approx 0.024$

6. $y = 0.024x - 0.699$

7.

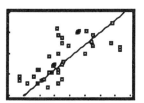

Answers will vary.

8. The domain is nonnegative numbers; that make sense in this situation. ($1667 \leq$ daily calorie supply ≤ 3336). The units of the domain are calories.

9. The units of slope are years of life expectancy per number of calories.

0. For each calorie you would expect your life expectancy to increase by 0.024 yr.

1. Answers will vary between 2300 and 2400.

2. Answers will vary between 46 and 52.

3. 55.5 yr

4. (34, 51), (57, 53), (88, 69)

5. $m \approx 0.33$

6. $y = 0.33x + 37.7$

7.

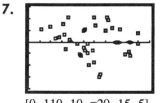

[0, 110, 10, −20, 15, 5]

The residuals seem to be evenly distributed above and below the line. There is no pattern in the residuals, which indicates a line is a good model.

8. The residual for Ethiopia is 1.89.

9. Guinea

0. $y = 166.8 - 1.26x$

1. For every 1 percent increase in the availability of health services, the number of infant deaths decreases by 1.26.

2. $y = -1.31x + 176.23$

Least-squares   Median-median

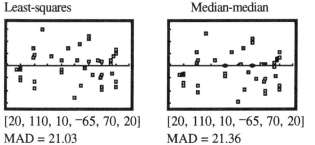

[20, 110, 10, −65, 70, 20]   [20, 110, 10, −65, 70, 20]
MAD = 21.03   MAD = 21.36

The least-squares line is slightly better than the median-median line if you compare the MADs.

3. Least-squares model: 97.33; median-median model: 104.45

4. $r \approx -0.77$, $r^2 \approx 0.6$; 60% of the points lie in a narrow band on either side of the least-squares line.

5. $y = 165.41 - 1.25x$; $r \approx -0.86$, $r^2 \approx 0.74$

6. 74% of the points will lie in a narrow band on either side of the least-squares line.

7. Answers will vary.

Chapter 5

Problem Set 5.1

1. a. Answers will vary. The curve, which appears to be a parabola, might describe the relationship between the amount of time the ball is in the air and how far away from the ground it is.
   b. Answers will vary. Some possible units are seconds and feet.
   c. Answers will vary. One possible answer is a domain of 60 sec and a range of 200 ft.
   d. No, the distance is not measured directly.

2. Answers will vary. For example, Zeke the fish was swimming around his bowl one day when the owner came into the room and bumped the table Zeke was on. The upset disoriented him and caused him to float downward. Then he swam to the bottom to eat the food that had fallen that morning. When he finished, he floated to the surface for a nap.

3. a.

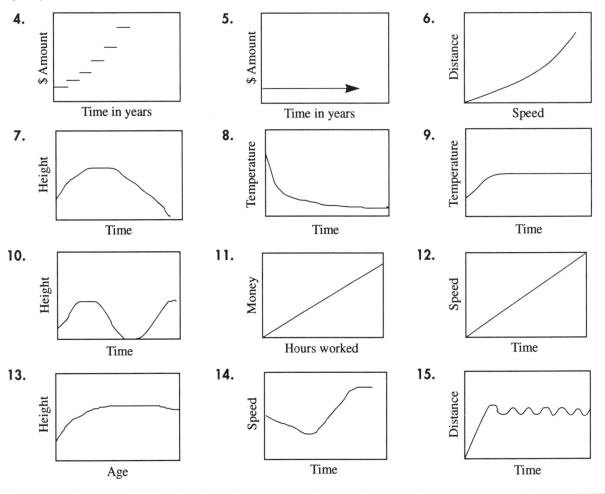

b. It is moving fastest at point *H*.
c. It is moving slowest at point *A*.
d. The speed of the roller coaster would be about the same at points *C* and *G*.

There will be many different correct answers for Problems 4–21. The graph and description should match up to justify the choice made. Be sure to consider discrete situations.

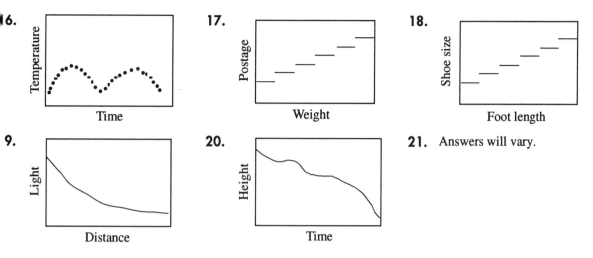

16. Temperature / Time

17. Postage / Weight

18. Shoe size / Foot length

9. Light / Distance

20. Height / Time

21. Answers will vary.

Problem Set 5.2

1. Graph A: (4, 17), (5, 21)
Graph B: (3, 14.0625), (4, 10.547), (5, 7.910), (6, 5.933), (7, 4.449)
Graph C: (2, 10), (3, 20), (4, 40), (5, 80), (6, 160)

2. a.

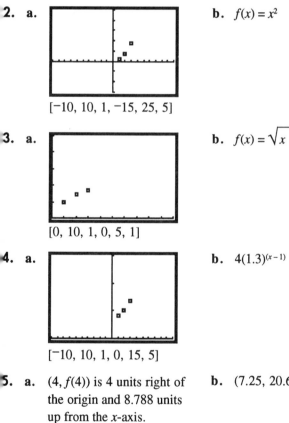

$[-10, 10, 1, -15, 25, 5]$

b. $f(x) = x^2$

c.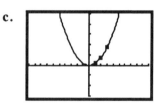

3. a.

$[0, 10, 1, 0, 5, 1]$

b. $f(x) = \sqrt{x}$

c.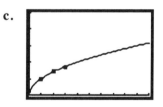

4. a.

$[-10, 10, 1, 0, 15, 5]$

b. $4(1.3)^{(x-1)}$

c.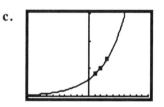

5. a. $(4, f(4))$ is 4 units right of the origin and 8.788 units up from the x-axis.

b. (7.25, 20.616)

c. 16.93 is the height of the segment.

d.

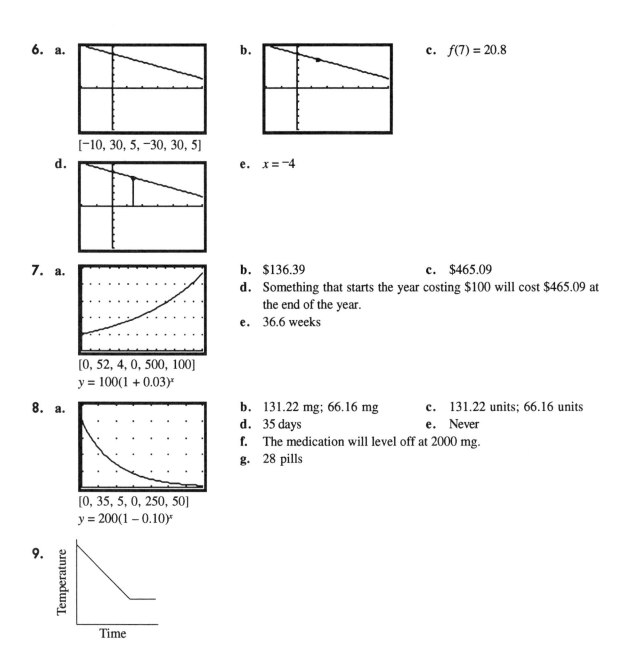

6. a.

[−10, 30, 5, −30, 30, 5]

b.

c. $f(7) = 20.8$

d.

e. $x = {}^-4$

7. a.

[0, 52, 4, 0, 500, 100]
$y = 100(1 + 0.03)^x$

b. $136.39 **c.** $465.09

d. Something that starts the year costing $100 will cost $465.09 at the end of the year.

e. 36.6 weeks

8. a.

[0, 35, 5, 0, 250, 50]
$y = 200(1 - 0.10)^x$

b. 131.22 mg; 66.16 mg **c.** 131.22 units; 66.16 units

d. 35 days **e.** Never

f. The medication will level off at 2000 mg.

g. 28 pills

9.

Problem Set 5.3

1. a. There are many correct answers including $(4, 0)$, $(2, {}^-4)$, $(1, {}^-6)$, and $(0, {}^-8)$.

b. Each of the points listed works in both forms of the equation.

c. Select another point and demonstrate that it works for both equations.

d. Answers will vary.

2. The slope is ${}^-0.549$; the y-intercept is 4.314; the x-intercept is 7.857.

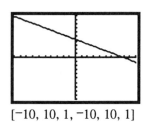

[−10, 10, 1, −10, 10, 1]

3. a. The slope is $\frac{-758}{660} \approx -1.1485$;
$y = -1.1485x - 2.7921$

b. $y = -1.1485x - 0.7921$

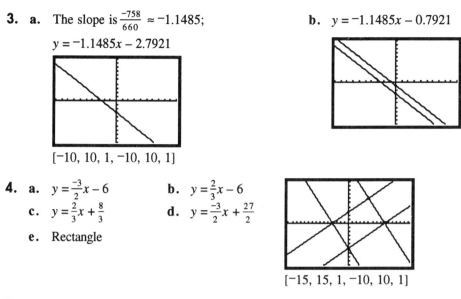

$[-10, 10, 1, -10, 10, 1]$

4. a. $y = \frac{-3}{2}x - 6$　　**b.** $y = \frac{2}{3}x - 6$

c. $y = \frac{2}{3}x + \frac{8}{3}$　　**d.** $y = \frac{-3}{2}x + \frac{27}{2}$

e. Rectangle

$[-15, 15, 1, -10, 10, 1]$

5. a. Answers will vary with the calculators. For a TI-82, a window would be $[-4.7, 4.7, 1, -3.1, 3.1, 1]$.

b. Answers will vary with the calculators. For a TI-82, a window would be $[0, 9.4, 1, 0, 6.2, 1]$.

6. $y = \frac{-3}{4}x + 2; y = \frac{2}{3}x - 1$

7. a. Answers will vary. Some possible points are $(1, 1.414)$, $(2, 2.828)$ $(3, 4.243)$, $(4, 5.657)$, and so on. The equation of a best-fit line is $y = 1.414x$.

b. $k \approx 1.414$　　　**c.** 9.05　　　**d.** 24.25

8. a. \$12,500; this is the original value of the equipment.

b. $(10, 0)$; after 10 yr, the equipment has no value.

c. -1250; each year the value of the equipment decreases by \$1,250.

d. $y = -1,250x + 12,500$

e. After 4.8 yr

9. a. 80.8　　　**b.** $y = \frac{1}{5}x + 65$　　　**c.** 95

0. a. Answers will vary. Examples are $(500, 35,203.96)$, $(600, -88,776.24)$, **b.**
$(550, -26,786.14)$, $(520, 10,407.92)$, $(540, -14,388.12)$.

c. $y = -1,239.80x + 65,5104.96$

d. 655,104.96; if no payments were made,
\$655,104.96 would be owed to the bank.

e. 528.40; this is the monthly payment that would pay off the loan in 25 yr.

f. -1239.80; each dollar increase in the monthly payment will reduce the final balance by \$1,239.80.

1. The average value is \$6,875.

Year	0	1	2	3	4	5	6	7	8	9	10
Value	12,500	11,250	10,000	8,750	7,500	6,250	5,000	3,750	2,500	1250	0

Problem Set 5.4

1. a. $y = x^2 - 6$　　**b.** $y = x^2 - 3$　　**c.** $y = x^2 + 2$　　**d.** $y = x^2 + 4$

2. a. i. $f(x) = x^2 - 6$　　　　　　ii. $f(x) = x^2 + 2$

b. i. $y = x^2 - 5$, down 5 units　　　ii. $y = x^2 + 4$, up 4 units

c. $f(x) + c$ is c units up or down from $f(x)$. It goes up if c is positive and down if c is negative.

3. a. $y = (x - 4)^2$ **b.** $y = (x - 7)^2$ **c.** $y = (x + 5)^2$

4. a. The graph moves 3 units to the right.   **b.** The graph moves 3 units to the left.
   c. The graph moves 2 units up.   **d.** The graph moves 2 units down.

5. a. $y = (x - 2)^2$ **b.** $y = (x - 2)^2 - 5$ **c.** $y = (x + 6)^2$ **d.** $y = (x + 6)^2 + 2$

6. a. Move the graph 5 units right and then 3 units down.   **b.** $y = (x - 5)^2 - 3$
   c. $(5, -3)$ **d.** $(6, -2), (4, -2), (7, 1), (3, 1)$ **e.** $b = 1; c = 4$

7. a. $y = -x^2$ **b.** $y = -x^2 + 2$ **c.** $y = -(x - 6)^2$ **d.** $y = -(x - 6)^2 - 3$

8. $y = -(x - 2)^2 + 2$

9. For $+1$, the graph opens upward. For -1, it opens downward. The graph is shifted horizontally by h units, to the right if h is positive, and left if h is negative. The graph is shifted vertically by k units, up if k is positive, and down if k is negative.

10. A parabola with an equation of $y = -(x - 25)^2 + 625$

11. A parabola with an equation of $y = (x - 0.5)^2 - 0.25$

Number of teams	1	2	3	4	5	6	7	8	9	10
Number of games	0	2	6	12	20	30	42	56	72	90

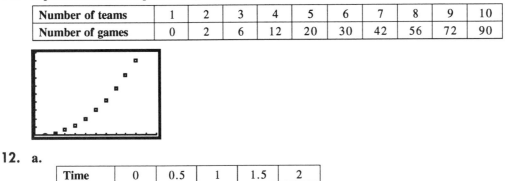

12. a.

Time	0	0.5	1	1.5	2
Height	64	60	48	28	0

Average height = 40 ft

b.

Time	0	0.25	0.5	0.75	1	1.25	1.5	1.75	2
Height	64	63	60	55	48	39	28	15	0

Average height = 41.3 ft

c.

Time	0	0.1	0.2	0.3	0.4	0.5	0.6	0.7	0.8	0.9	1
Height	64	63.8	63.4	62.6	61.4	60	58.2	56.2	53.8	51.0	48

Time	1.1	1.2	1.3	1.4	1.5	1.6	1.7	1.8	1.9	2
Height	44.6	41.0	37.0	32.6	28	23.0	17.8	12.2	6.24	0

Average height = 42.13

d. The ball starts out moving slowly and speeds up as it falls. As you increase the frequency of the measurements, you are adding more large numbers to the list. This makes the average increase.

Problem Set 5.5

1. a. $y = \sqrt{x} + 3$ **b.** $y = \sqrt{x} - 4$ **c.** $y = \sqrt{x} + 1$
   d. $y = \sqrt{x} - 3$ **e.** $y = \sqrt{x + 5}$ **f.** $y = \sqrt{x - 2}$
   g. $y = \sqrt{x + 5} + 2$ **h.** $y = \sqrt{x - 3} + 1$ **i.** $y = \sqrt{x - 1} - 4$

2. a. If x is replaced with $(x-3)$, the graph moves 3 units to the right; if it is replaced with $(x+3)$, the graph moves 3 units to the left.

b. If y is replaced with $(y-2)$, the graph moves 2 units up; if it is replaced with $(y+2)$, the graph moves 2 units down.

3. a. $y = -\sqrt{x}$ **b.** $y = -\sqrt{x} - 3$ **c.** $y = -\sqrt{x+6} + 5$

4. a. Answers will vary. Some possible answers are $(-4, -2)$, $(-3, -1)$, and $(0, 0)$.

b. $y = \sqrt{x+4} - 2$ **c.** $y = -\sqrt{x-2} + 3$

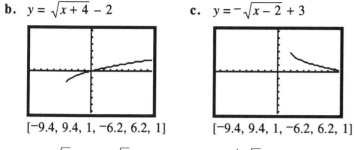

$[-9.4, 9.4, 1, -6.2, 6.2, 1]$ $[-9.4, 9.4, 1, -6.2, 6.2, 1]$

5. a. $y_1 = \sqrt{x}$, $y_2 = -\sqrt{x}$ **b.** $y = \pm\sqrt{x}$; $y^2 = x$

6. a. There are x-values on each parabola that have more than one y-value.

b. $y = \pm\sqrt{x+4}$; $y = \pm\sqrt{x} + 2$ **c.** $y^2 = x + 4$; $(y-2)^2 = x$

7. First, rewrite the parabola in the form $y = \pm\sqrt{x+3} + 2$.

$[-10, 10, 1, -6, 6, 1]$

8. a. $y = \sqrt{-x}$ **b.** $y = -\sqrt{-x}$

9. a.–d. Answers will vary.

0. Answers will vary; $v = 8\sqrt{d}$ works.

1. Change the second line of the program to $A\sqrt{(X-H)+K(→)Y_4}$.

Problem Set 5.6

1. a. $y = |x| + 2$ **b.** $y = |x| - 5$

2. a. $y = |x + 4|$ **b.** $y = |x - 3|$

3. a. $y = |x| - 1$ **b.** $y = |x - 4| + 1$

4. a. $y = |x + 5| - 3$ **b.** $y = |x - 6|$ **c.** $y = -|x|$

5. a. $y = (x - 5)^2$ **b.** $y = -|x + 4|$ **c.** $y = -|x + 4| + 3$

6. a. $y = -(x + 3)^2 + 4$ **b.** $y = \pm\sqrt{x-4} + 3$ **c.** $y = -|x - 3| - 1$

7. a. $y = -|x - 2| + 3$

b. The negative sign in front flips the graph over the x-axis. The $(x-2)$ in the radical moves the graph 2 units to the right and the $^+3$ moves the graph up 3 units.

8. a. The graph will move 5 units to the right.
   b. The graph will flip over the *y*-axis.
   c. The graph will move 3 units up.
   d. The graph will flip over the *x*-axis.

9. (1, 3); (7, 3); 1 and 7

10. $y_1 = |x + 3|$, $y_2 = 5$; the solutions are 2 and $^-8$, the *x*-coordinates of the intersection points.

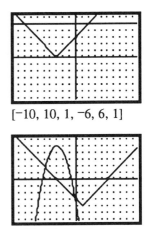

$[-10, 10, 1, -6, 6, 1]$

11. $y_1 = ^-(x + 3)^2 + 5$, $y_2 = |x - 1| - 4$; the solutions are the *x*-coordinates of the intersection points ($^-4.8$, 1.8) and ($^-0.2$, $^-2.8$).

$[-10, 10, 1, -6, 6, 1]$

12. $|x| = \begin{cases} ^-x & \text{if } x < 0 \\ x & \text{if } x \geq 0 \end{cases}$

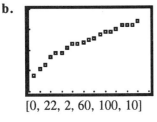

13. a. Original mean = 83.75; original MAD = 5.975; New mean = 89.75; new MAD = 5.975. The mean increases. The MAD remains the same.

   b.

$[0, 22, 2, 60, 100, 10]$

   c.

$[0, 22, 2, 60, 100, 10]$
The graph is shifted up 6 units.

14. $y = |x - 18.4|$; at 18.4 mi

Problem Set 5.7

1. $y = 2\sqrt{1 - x^2}$

2. a. $y = 3\sqrt{1 - x^2}$ **b.** $y = 0.5\sqrt{1 - x^2}$

3. a.   **b.**   **c.**

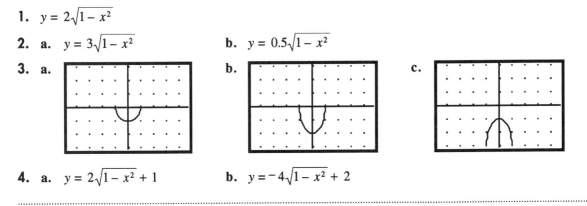

4. a. $y = 2\sqrt{1 - x^2} + 1$ **b.** $y = ^-4\sqrt{1 - x^2} + 2$

5. Graph 1

    a. $f(x + 3) + 1$

    b. $y = \sqrt{1 - (x + 3)^2} + 1$

Graph 2

    a. $2f(x - 3) + 1$

    b. $y = 2\sqrt{1 - (x - 3)^2} + 1$

6. Graph 1: $y = -5\sqrt{1 - (x + 2)^2} + 3$

    Graph 2: $y = 4\sqrt{1 - (x - 3)^2} - 2$

7. **a.** $y = \sqrt{1 - x^2} + 2$ **b.** $y = \sqrt{1 - (x + 3)^2}$ **c.** $y = 2\sqrt{1 - x^2}$

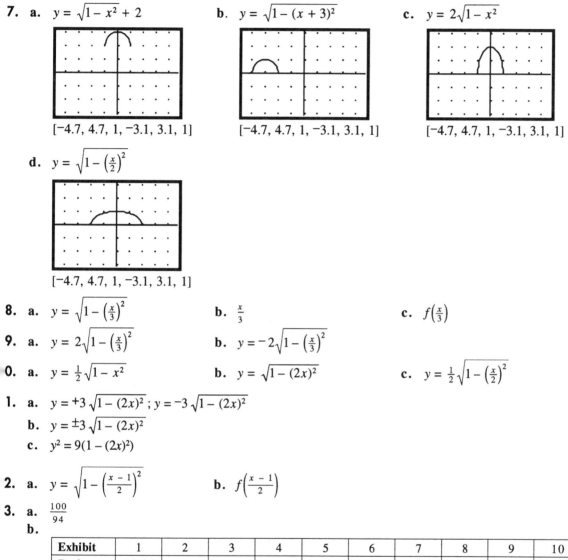

    [−4.7, 4.7, 1, −3.1, 3.1, 1]   [−4.7, 4.7, 1, −3.1, 3.1, 1]   [−4.7, 4.7, 1, −3.1, 3.1, 1]

    d. $y = \sqrt{1 - \left(\frac{x}{2}\right)^2}$

    [−4.7, 4.7, 1, −3.1, 3.1, 1]

8. **a.** $y = \sqrt{1 - \left(\frac{x}{3}\right)^2}$ **b.** $\frac{x}{3}$ **c.** $f\left(\frac{x}{3}\right)$

9. **a.** $y = 2\sqrt{1 - \left(\frac{x}{3}\right)^2}$ **b.** $y = -2\sqrt{1 - \left(\frac{x}{3}\right)^2}$

10. **a.** $y = \frac{1}{2}\sqrt{1 - x^2}$ **b.** $y = \sqrt{1 - (2x)^2}$ **c.** $y = \frac{1}{2}\sqrt{1 - \left(\frac{x}{2}\right)^2}$

11. **a.** $y = +3\sqrt{1 - (2x)^2}$; $y = -3\sqrt{1 - (2x)^2}$

    b. $y = \pm 3\sqrt{1 - (2x)^2}$

    c. $y^2 = 9(1 - (2x)^2)$

12. **a.** $y = \sqrt{1 - \left(\frac{x - 1}{2}\right)^2}$ **b.** $f\left(\frac{x - 1}{2}\right)$

13. **a.** $\frac{100}{94}$

    b.

Exhibit	1	2	3	4	5	6	7	8	9	10
Rating	72.34	75.53	77.66	81.92	84.04	84.04	86.17	88.30	88.30	89.36

Exhibit	11	12	13	14	15	16	17	18	19	20
Rating	90.43	91.49	93.62	94.68	94.68	95.74	97.87	97.87	97.87	100

    c. Original scores: mean = 83.75, MAD = 5.975; New scores: mean = 89.10, MAD = 6.36

    d. The scores have been stretched by a factor of $\frac{100}{94}$. All scores increased so the mean increased. The high scores differ from the original by more than the lower ones, so they are more spread and the mean absolute deviation is increased.

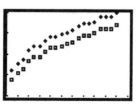

    e. Answers will vary.

14. a. Average value $= 0.546$

x	-1	-0.5	0	0.5	1
$f(x)$	0	0.87	1	0.87	0

b. Average value $= 0.690$

x	-1	-0.8	-0.6	-0.4	-0.2	0	0.2	0.4	0.6	0.8	1
$f(x)$	0	0.6	0.8	0.92	0.98	1	0.98	0.92	0.8	0.6	0

    c. For x-values spaced 0.1 units apart, the average value $= 0.739$.
        For x-values spaced 0.01 units apart, the average value $= 0.781$.
    d. The average value will approach 0.785.
    e. Answers will vary depending on the calculator.

15. Answers will vary.

Problem Set 5.8

1. a. 4   **b.** 2   **c.** -4 and 4
    d. -2, 0, and 3.5   **e.** $0 \le y \le 4$ **f.** $-4 \le x \le 4$

2. a.

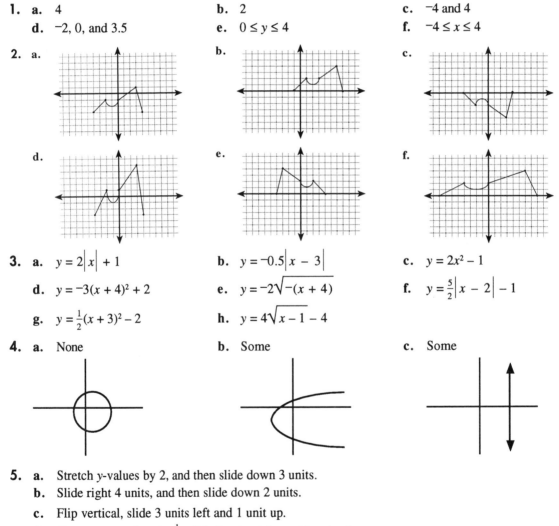

3. a. $y = 2\left|x\right| + 1$ **b.** $y = -0.5\left|x - 3\right|$ **c.** $y = 2x^2 - 1$

    d. $y = -3(x + 4)^2 + 2$ **e.** $y = -2\sqrt{-(x + 4)}$ **f.** $y = \frac{5}{2}\left|x - 2\right| - 1$

    g. $y = \frac{1}{2}(x + 3)^2 - 2$ **h.** $y = 4\sqrt{x - 1} - 4$

4. a. None   **b.** Some   **c.** Some

5. a. Stretch y-values by 2, and then slide down 3 units.
    b. Slide right 4 units, and then slide down 2 units.
    c. Flip vertical, slide 3 units left and 1 unit up.
    d. Compress y-values by $\frac{1}{2}$, slide 2 units right and 3 units down.

6. a. $y = 2x^2 - 16x + 33$ **b.** $y = -x^2 - 6x - 7$ **c.** $0.5x^2 - 2x - 1$

7. a. 2.53   **b.** 2.6   **c.** $\frac{8}{3}$
    d. 10.667   **e.** The same

8. Evaluate the function at many points. Then average these to find the average value (2). Multiply this average value by the width of the interval (3) to get the area, which is 6.

9. Average daily inventory: 300; average daily holding cost: $6

10. a. $y = \frac{2}{3}x + 4$ **b.** $y = \frac{2}{3}x + 4$

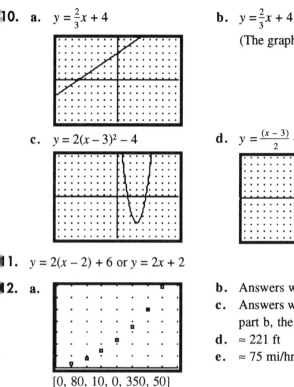

(The graph is the same as that in part a.)

c. $y = 2(x - 3)^2 - 4$ **d.** $y = \frac{(x-3)}{2} - 1$

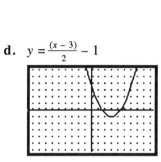

11. $y = 2(x - 2) + 6$ or $y = 2x + 2$

12. a.

[0, 80, 10, 0, 350, 50]

b. Answers will vary. One possible equation is $y = 0.07(x - 3)^2 + 21$.
c. Answers will depend on the equation. For the equation given in part b, the sum is 0.19.
d. ≈ 221 ft
e. ≈ 75 mi/hr

13. Answers will vary.

Problem Set 5.9

1. a. 12 L/min
   c. Between 40 and 45 sec
   b.

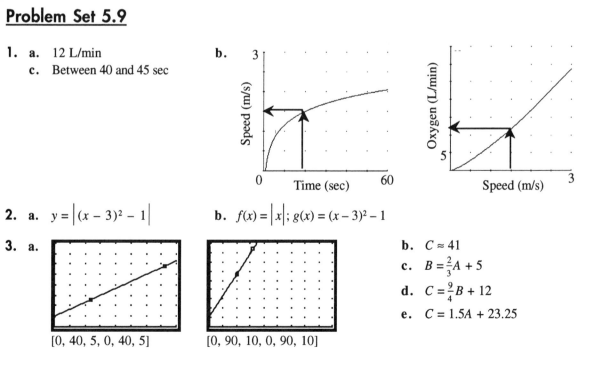

2. a. $y = \left| (x - 3)^2 - 1 \right|$ **b.** $f(x) = |x|$; $g(x) = (x - 3)^2 - 1$

3. a.

[0, 40, 5, 0, 40, 5]   [0, 90, 10, 0, 90, 10]

b. $C \approx 41$
c. $B = \frac{2}{3}A + 5$
d. $C = \frac{9}{4}B + 12$
e. $C = 1.5A + 23.25$

4. a.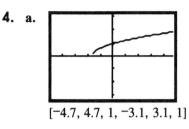

[−4.7, 4.7, 1, −3.1, 3.1, 1]

b.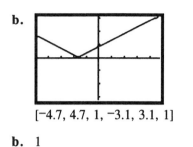

[−4.7, 4.7, 1, −3.1, 3.1, 1]

c.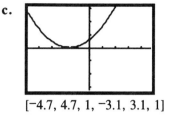

[−4.7, 4.7, 1, −3.1, 3.1, 1]

5. a. 2   **b.** 1

6. a. 2   **b.** 6

c. Answers will vary. Select 1 from g: $f(g(1)) = f(2) = 1$. The composition of f and g will always give back the original number because they "undo" the effects of each other.

7. a. $g(f(2)) = 2$

b. $f(g(-1)) = -1$

c. $g(f(x)) = g(2x - 1) = x$ for all x

d. $f(g(x)) = f\left(\frac{1}{2}x + \frac{1}{2}\right) = x$

e. The two functions "undo" the effects of each other, thus giving back the original starting value.

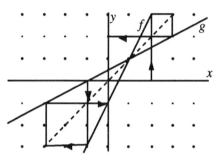

8. a. $f(g(3)) = 4$

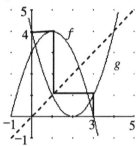

b. $f(g(2)) = 3$

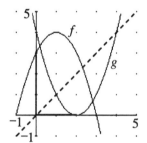

c. $g(f(0.5)) = 3.0625$

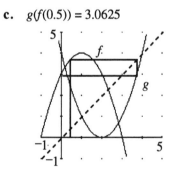

d. $g(f(1)) = 4$

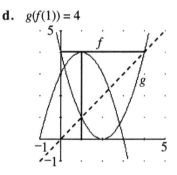

9. Answers will vary.

10. $y = 3\sqrt{1 - x^2}$

Chapter Review
Problem Set 5.10

1. For a time there are no pops. Then the popping rate begins slowly to increase. When the popping reaches a furious intensity, it seems to nearly level out. Shortly thereafter, it peaks. Then the number of pops per second drops radically to a minimal value and tapers off quickly until the last pop is heard.

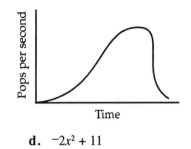

2. **a.** -7 **b.** -1 **c.** 100 **d.** $-2x^2 + 11$
    e. $(-2x + 8)^2$ **f.** $(-2x + 7)^2 - 2$

3. **a.** The graph is translated 3 units down.   **b.** The graph is translated 3 units right.

4. **a.** Slide the graph 2 units left and then 3 units down.
    b. Double all of the x-values. Then reflect the graph over the x-axis and slide the graph up 1 unit.
    c. Shrink the x-values by dividing them by 2, double the y-values, slide the graph 1 unit to the right, and then slide the graph 3 units up.

5. **a.** $y = \frac{2}{3}x - 2$ **b.** $y = \pm\sqrt{x + 3} - 1$ **c.** $y = \pm\sqrt{1 - (x - 2)^2}$

6. **a.** Slide the graph down 2 units.   **b.** Slide the graph 2 units to the right and then 1 unit up.

    c. Reflect the graph over the x-axis.   **d.** Double all the y-values. Then slide the graph 1 unit to the left and 3 units down.

    e. Reflect the graph over the y-axis, and then slide the graph up 1 unit.   **f.** Double all the x-values, and then slide the graph 2 units down.

g. Reflect the graph over the *x*-axis, slide the graph 3 units to the right, and then slide the graph 1 unit up.

h. Multiply all the *x*-values by 1.5. Then multiple all the *y*-values by ⁻2, and slide the graph 1 unit right and 2 units down.

7. a. Parent function: $y = \sqrt{1 - x^2}$; equation is $y = 3\sqrt{(1 - x^2)} - 1$.

   b. Parent function: $y = \sqrt{1 - x^2}$; equation is $y = 2\sqrt{1 - \left(\frac{x}{5}\right)^2} + 3$.

   c. Parent function: $y = \sqrt{1 - x^2}$; equation is $y = 4\sqrt{1 - \left(\frac{x - 3}{4}\right)^2} - 1$.

   d. Parent function: $y = x^2$; equation is $y = (x - 2)^2 - 4$

   e. Parent function: $y = x^2$; equation is $y = {}^-2(x + 1)^2$

   f. Parent function: $y = \sqrt{x}$; equation is $y = {}^-\sqrt{{}^-(x - 2)} - 3$

   g. Parent function: $y = |x|$; equation is $0.5|x + 2| - 2$

   h. Parent function: $y = |x|$; equation is $y = {}^-2|x - 3| + 2$

Chapter 6

Problem Set 6.1

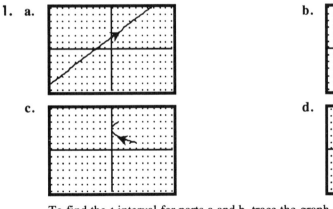

1. a.

   b.

   c.

   d.

   To find the *t*-interval for parts a and b, trace the graph. For part a, $^-3 \le t \le 2.5$ works. For part b, $^-2.5 \le t \le 2.5$ works.

2. a.

   b.

   The graph is shifted to the right 2 units.

c.

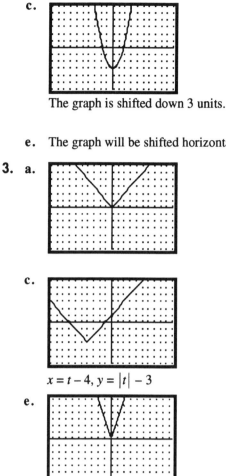

The graph is shifted down 3 units.

d.

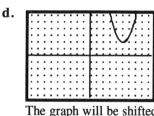

The graph will be shifted to the right 5 units and up 2 units.

e. The graph will be shifted horizontally *a* units and vertically *b* units. Answers will vary for the graphs.

3. a.

b.

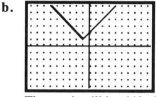

The graph will be shifted to the left 1 unit and up 2 units.

c.

$x = t - 4, y = |t| - 3$

d.

The graph is stretched twice as wide.

e.

The graph is vertically stretched by a factor of 3.

f. The 3 stretches the graph vertically, the 2 slides it 2 units to the right, and the $^{-}4$ slides it down 4 units.

4. a. This looks like the family of half-circles from Chapter 5. The parametric equations would be $x = t$ and $y = 2\sqrt{1 - \left(\frac{t}{2}\right)^2}$.

b. Slide the graph 2 units to the right. The parametric equations would be $x = t + 2$ and $y = 2\sqrt{1 - \left(\frac{t}{2}\right)^2}$.

c. Flip the graph over the *x*-axis and slide up 1 unit. The parametric equations would be $x = t$ and $y = -2\sqrt{1 - \left(\frac{t}{2}\right)^2} + 1$.

d. Stretch the graph horizontally by a factor of 2 and slide up 1 unit. The parametric equations would be $x = 2t$ and $y = 2\sqrt{1 - \left(\frac{t}{2}\right)^2} + 1$.

5. a.

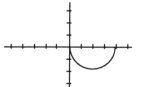

The graph is reflected over the *x*-axis.

b.

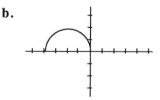

The graph is reflected over the *y*-axis.

6. a. The graph is translated 2 units left and 2 units up, so $x = f(t) - 2$ and $y = g(t) + 2$.

b. The graph is stretched vertically by a factor of 2 so $x = f(t)$ and $y = 2g(t)$.

c. The graph is stretched horizontally by a factor of 2 so $x = 2f(t)$ and $y = g(t)$.

d. The graph is reflected over the x-axis and is translated 1 unit left so $x = f(t) - 1$ and $y = -g(t)$.

Problem Set 6.2

1. a. $y = (x - 1)^2$

    b. $y = \frac{2}{3}x + \frac{5}{3}$

    c. $y = \pm\sqrt{x} + 3$

    d. $y = \sqrt{4 - (x + 1)^2}$

2. a. $y = \frac{x + 7}{2}$

    b. $y = \pm\sqrt{x} + 1$

    c. $y = \frac{2x - 4}{3}$

    d. $y = 2(x + 2)^2$

3. a.

b.

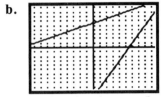

$x = 2t - 1$ and $y = t + 5$

    c. All pairs of coordinates of the original graph are switched in the new graph.

4. $-\sqrt{6.2} \leq t \leq \sqrt{6.2}$

5. a. The graph is reflected over the x-axis.

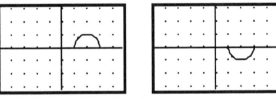

    b. The graph is reflected over the y-axis.

    c. The graph is reflected over the x-axis and then the y-axis (or over the y-axis and then the x-axis).

6. There are many possibilities for these equations, for example $x_1 = 3 + t$ and $y_1 = 2 + 2t$; $x_2 = 3 + 2t$ and $y_2 = 2 - t$.

7. a. Tanker A: $x = 18t$ and $y = 1$; Tanker B: $x = 22(t - 5)$ and $y = 2$

    b. [0, 50, .5, 0, 900, 100, −1, 3, 1]

    c. $t = 27.5$ hr, $d = 495$ mi

    d. Tanker A: $x = 18t$ and $y = 1$; Tanker B: $x = 900 - 22t$ and $y = 2$. The time interval is $21.25 \leq t \leq 23.75$. The distances are between 382.5 and 427.5 mi out from Corpus Christi.

Problem Set 6.3

1. **a.** 17.334   **b.** 57.577   **c.** 22.780
   d. 8.220   **e.** 15.832   **f.** 16.761

2. **a.** 31.19°   **b.** 29.91°   **c.** 49.69°
   d. 36.25°   **e.** 43.90°   **f.** 45.88°

3. **a.** 25.3°   **b.** 66.7 cm

4. **a.** The graph is a line segment at a 39° angle with the horizontal axis. The initial and end points depend on the interval used for t.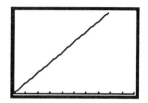
   b. Trace and select a point. Find the inverse tangent of the ratio of the x- and y-values of the point. The angle is 39°.

5. The graph is a line segment at an angle of 45° with the horizontal axis. The initial and end points depend on the interval used for t. The angle with a tangent ratio $\frac{y}{x}$ or $\frac{t \sin 45°}{t \cos 45°}$ is 45°.

6. $x = t \cos 57°$ and $y = t \sin 57°$; an interval that includes $\frac{-3.1}{\sin 57°} \le t \le \frac{3.1}{\sin 57°}$

7. $x = t \cos 29°$, $y = t \sin 29°$

8. $x = t$, $y = t \tan 29°$

9. **a.** $x = t \cos 47°$, $y = t \sin 47°$; $\frac{-3.1}{\sin 47°} \le t \le \frac{3.1}{\sin 47°}$ (The t-interval assumes you are using a "friendly" window on a TI-82 or TI-83 in which the distance between the pixels is 0.1.)
   b. $x = t \cos 115°$, $y = t \sin 115°$; $\frac{-3.1}{\sin 115°} \le t \le \frac{3.1}{\sin 115°}$

10. **a.** $x = 10t \cos 30°$, $y = 10t \sin 30°$
    b. $0 \le t \le 10$
    c. The 10 represents 10 mi/hr, t represents time in hours, 30° is the angle with the x axis, x is the horizontal position at any time, and y is the vertical position at any time.
    d. Points on the graph are drawn as a simulation of the actual position of the tanker at any time t.

11. **a.** $x = 18t \cos 17°$, $y = 18t \sin 17°$; 41.7 hr
    b. ≈ 717 mi east and ≈ 219 mi north

12. **a.** From due north, a heading of 285° is an angle in the second quadrant, 15° above the horizontal axis.
    b. 23.2 hr
    c. ≈ 492.6 mi west and 132 mi north
    d. Use $x = 900 - 22t \cos 15°$, $y = 22t \sin 15°$; the tankers meet at a point approximately 411 mi east of Corpus Christi, and 131 mi north of St. Petersburg, or just about at New Orleans.

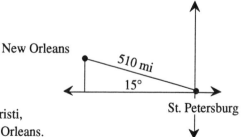

Problem Set 6.4

1. There are many other possibilities for these equations. Use a "friendly" window in which the distance between pixels is 0.1.
   a. $x = 3 \cos t$, $y = 3 \sin t$; $0° \le t \le 360°$ with Tstep of 72
   b. $x = 3 \cos t$, $y = 3 \sin t$; $18° \le t \le 738°$ with Tstep of 144
   c. $x = 3 \cos t$, $y = 3 \sin t$; $30° \le t \le 390°$ with Tstep of 120
   d. $x = 3 \cos t$, $y = 3 \sin t$; $0° \le t \le 1080°$ with Tstep of 135

2. a. $x = 1 \cos t, y = 1 \sin t$

b.

Angle A	0°	30°	45°	60°	90°	120°	135°
$\cos A$	1	0.866	0.707	0.5	0	−0.5	−0.707
$\sin A$	0	0.5	0.707	0.866	1	0.866	0.707

c. Cosine A is the x-coordinate of the point where the line extending the central angle A crosses the perimeter of the unit circle.

d. Sine A is the y-coordinate of the point where the line extending the central angle A crosses the perimeter of the unit circle.

3. a. $x = 2 \cos t + 2, y = 2 \sin t$ **b.** $x = 2 \cos t - 3, y = 2 \sin t$

c. $x = 2 \cos t, y = 2 \sin t + 4$ **d.** $x = 2 \cos t, y = 2 \sin t - 2$

e. $x = 2 \cos t + 3, y = 2 \sin t + 2$

4. a. $\cos t = \frac{x}{3}, \sin t = \frac{y}{3}$ **b.** $(\cos t)^2 = \frac{x^2}{9}, (\sin t)^2 = \frac{y^2}{9}$

c. $(\cos t)^2 + (\sin t)^2 = \frac{x^2}{9} + \frac{y^2}{9}$ **d.** $1 = \frac{x^2}{9} + \frac{y^2}{9}$

e. $9 = x^2 + y^2$ or $x^2 + y^2 = 9$ **f.** 3

5. a. $x = 2 \cos t + 3, y = 2 \sin t + 2; \cos t = \frac{x - 3}{2}, \sin t = \frac{y - 2}{2}$

b. $(\cos t)^2 = \frac{(x - 3)^2}{4}, (\sin t)^2 = \frac{(y - 2)^2}{4}; (\cos t)^2 + (\sin t)^2 = \frac{(x - 3)^2}{4} + \frac{(y - 2)^2}{4}$

c. $1 = \frac{(x - 3)^2}{4} + \frac{(y - 2)^2}{4}$ **d.** $4 = (x - 3)^2 + (y - 2)^2$

e. $(x - 3)^2 + (y - 2)^2 = 4, h = 3, k = 2, r = 2$ **f.**

6. a. $x = 2 \cos t$ **b.** $x = 4 \cos t$ **c.** $x = 2 \cos t$
     $y = 3 \sin t$ $y = \sin t$ $y = 4 \sin t$

7. a. $x = 4 \cos t$ **b.** $x = 3 \cos t + 4$ **c.** $x = 2.5 \cos t$ **d.** $x = 2 \cos t + 1$
     $y = 3 \sin t$ $y = 2 \sin t$ $y = 1.5 \sin t + 2$ $y = 3.5 \sin t + 3$

8. a. For Problem 7a   **b.** For Problem 7c

     a. $\cos t = \frac{x}{2}, \sin t = \frac{y}{3}$ **a.** $\cos t = \frac{x}{2.5}, \sin t = \frac{y - 2}{1.5}$

     b. $(\cos t)^2 + (\sin t)^2 = \frac{x^2}{4} + \frac{y^2}{9}$ **b.** $(\cos t) + (\sin t) = \frac{x^2}{6.25} + \frac{(y - 2)^2}{2.25}$

     c. $1 = \frac{x^2}{4} + \frac{y^2}{9}$ **c.** $1 = \frac{x^2}{6.25} + \frac{(y - 2)^2}{2.25}$

c. For the ellipse in 8a, the center is at $(0, 0)$ and the lengths of the axes are 4 units and 3 units. For the ellipse in 8b, the center is at $(0, 2)$ and the lengths of the axes are 2.5 units and 1.5 units.

9. Many answers are possible. Those listed below are only one way of generating each figure.

     a. $x = 5t, y = 2t$; Tmin = −9.4, Tmax = 9.4, Tstep = 0.5

     b. $x = 5 \cos t, y = 3 \sin t$; Tmin = 0, Tmax = 360, Tstep = 10

     c. $x = 6 \cos t, y = 6 \sin t$; Tmin = 0, Tmax = 720, Tstep = 144

     d. $x = 2 \cos t + 4, y = 2 \sin t + 3$; Tmin = 0, Tmax = 360, Tstep = 10

10. a. $x = 2 \cos t + 4, y = 2 \sin t + 3$, Tmin = 0, Tmax = 720, Tstep = 144

     b. $x = 2 \cos t + 4, y = {}^-(2 \sin t + 3)$.

     c. $x = {}^-(2 \cos t + 4), y = 2 \sin t + 3$.

     d. $x = {}^-(2 \cos t + 4), y = {}^-(2 \sin t + 3)$

     e. Tmin = 0, Tmax = 720, Tstep = 144

     f. Answers will vary.

Problem Set 6.5

1. Pat moves at a compass heading of 53.1°; the pilot is on a heading of 265.4°.

2. (Assuming the river flows toward the top of the page and the boat is heading from left to right.)
   a. $y = 2t$
   b. $x = 6t$
   c.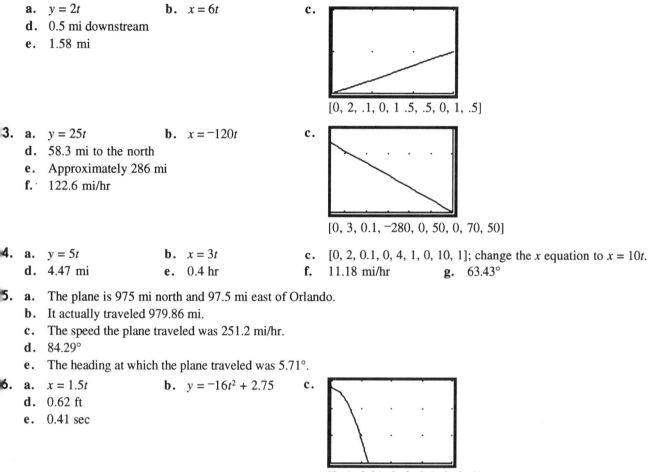

   d. 0.5 mi downstream
   e. 1.58 mi

   $[0, 2, .1, 0, 1 .5, .5, 0, 1, .5]$

3. a. $y = 25t$
   b. $x = -120t$
   c.
   d. 58.3 mi to the north
   e. Approximately 286 mi
   f. 122.6 mi/hr

   $[0, 3, 0.1, -280, 0, 50, 0, 70, 50]$

4. a. $y = 5t$
   b. $x = 3t$
   c. $[0, 2, 0.1, 0, 4, 1, 0, 10, 1]$; change the x equation to $x = 10t$.
   d. 4.47 mi
   e. 0.4 hr
   f. 11.18 mi/hr
   g. 63.43°

5. a. The plane is 975 mi north and 97.5 mi east of Orlando.
   b. It actually traveled 979.86 mi.
   c. The speed the plane traveled was 251.2 mi/hr.
   d. 84.29°
   e. The heading at which the plane traveled was 5.71°.

6. a. $x = 1.5t$
   b. $y = -16t^2 + 2.75$
   c.
   d. 0.62 ft
   e. 0.41 sec

   $[0, 1, 0.01, 0, 2, 0.5, 0, 3, 1]$

7. a. 0.43 sec
   b. 4.16 ft/sec

8. a. $x = 650t, y = -16t^2 + 5.5$
   b. The dart falls short; it hits the ground at about 381 ft from the biologist.
   c. She should hold the gun between 9.1 ft and 10.6 ft high.
   d. 162.5 ft; the original height makes no difference because it takes 0.25 sec to drop 1 ft; using $x = vt$ or $x = 0.25v$, the horizontal distance it travels as it drops 1 ft is dependent on the velocity.

9. The third step. Check the y coordinate when x is 8, 16, 24, to see if the ball is above the level of the stair. (It might be interesting to use a grid and draw or graph the stairs.)

10. Answers will vary.

11. Answers will vary.

Problem Set 6.6

1. a. $y = -4t \sin A$
   b. $y = 3t$
   c. 48.59°
   d. $x = 4t \cos 48.59°$ (for the boat) and $x = 0$ (for the river)
   e. $x = 4t \cos 48.59°$ and $y = -4t \sin 48.59° + 3t$

2. a.

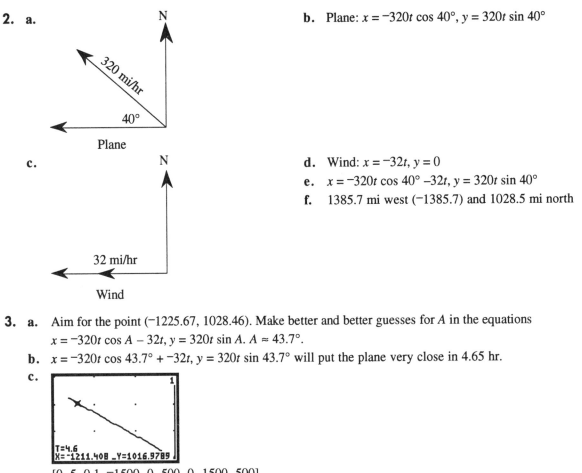

b. Plane: $x = {}^-320t \cos 40°$, $y = 320t \sin 40°$

c.

d. Wind: $x = {}^-32t$, $y = 0$

e. $x = {}^-320t \cos 40° - 32t$, $y = 320t \sin 40°$

f. 1385.7 mi west ($^-1385.7$) and 1028.5 mi north

3. a. Aim for the point ($^-1225.67$, 1028.46). Make better and better guesses for A in the equations $x = {}^-320t \cos A - 32t$, $y = 320t \sin A$. $A \approx 43.7°$.

b. $x = {}^-320t \cos 43.7° + {}^-32t$, $y = 320t \sin 43.7°$ will put the plane very close in 4.65 hr.

c.

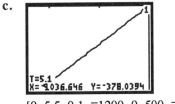

T=4.6
X=-1211.408 _Y=1016.9789

[0, 5, 0.1, −1500, 0, 500, 0, 1500, 500]

4. a. The plane makes a 20° angle with the axis.
The wind makes a 70° angle with the axis.

b. Plane: $x = {}^-220t \cos 20°$, $y = {}^-220t \sin 20°$
Wind: $x = 40t \cos 70°$, $y = {}^-40t \sin 70°$

c. $x = {}^-220t \cos 20° + 40t \cos 70°$,
$y = {}^-220t \sin 20° - 40t \sin 70°$

d. The plane will be 965.26 mi west and 564.16 mi south of its starting point.

e. The actual distance is 1118.04 mi from the start.

f. The actual heading is 239.70°.

5. a. If there was no wind, the plane would land at the coordinates ($^-1033.66$, $^-376.22$) in 5 hr. Because of the wind, the pilot needs to adjust and fly slightly north of the airport.

b. Let A be the angle with the horizontal in the equations $x = {}^-220t \cos A + 40t \cos 70°$, $y = {}^-220t \sin A - 40t \sin 70°$. $A = 9.56°$ gets the plane very close in about 5.08 hr.

c.

T=5.1
X=-1036.646 Y=-378.0394

Zoom in and trace to find ($^-1033$, $^-377$).

[0, 5.5, 0.1, −1200, 0, 500, −400, 0, 500]

6. a. You need the vertical component of Superman to balance the vertical component of the wind
($y = 75t \sin A = 32t \sin 30°$); $A = 12.32°$; this is a heading of $257.68°$

b. $-75t \cos 12.32° + -32t \cos 30° = -800$ **c.** 7.92 hr

7. a.

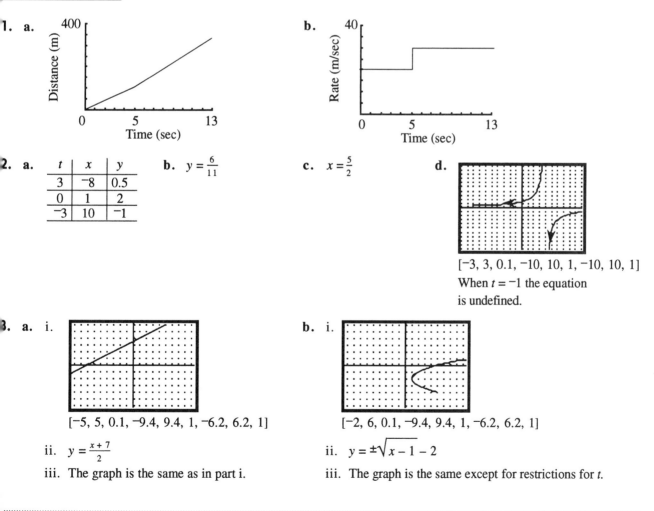

N

8 mi/hr   10°

Wind

$x = 8t \cos 10°$
$y = -8t \sin 10°$

b.

N

10 mi/hr   75°

Bird

$x = 10t \cos 75°$
$y = 10t \sin 75°$

c. $x = 8t \cos 10° + 10t \cos 75°$; $y = -8t \sin 10° - 10t \sin 75°$; 83.73 mi east and 88.39 mi south

d. $136.6°$ heading

e. Answers will vary.

8. a. 4,000 mi/hr   **b.** 90 mi   **c.** $0.43°$

9. Answers will vary.

Chapter Review

Problem Set 6.7

1. a.

Distance (m) vs Time (sec), axes 400 and 13, 5

b.

Rate (m/sec) vs Time (sec), axes 40 and 13, 5

2. a.

t	x	y
3	$^-8$	0.5
0	1	2
$^-3$	10	$^-1$

b. $y = \frac{6}{11}$ **c.** $x = \frac{5}{2}$ **d.**

$[-3, 3, 0.1, -10, 10, 1, -10, 10, 1]$
When $t = -1$ the equation
is undefined.

3. a. i.

$[-5, 5, 0.1, -9.4, 9.4, 1, -6.2, 6.2, 1]$

ii. $y = \frac{x + 7}{2}$

iii. The graph is the same as in part i.

b. i.

$[-2, 6, 0.1, -9.4, 9.4, 1, -6.2, 6.2, 1]$

ii. $y = \pm\sqrt{x - 1} - 2$

iii. The graph is the same except for restrictions for t.

c. i.

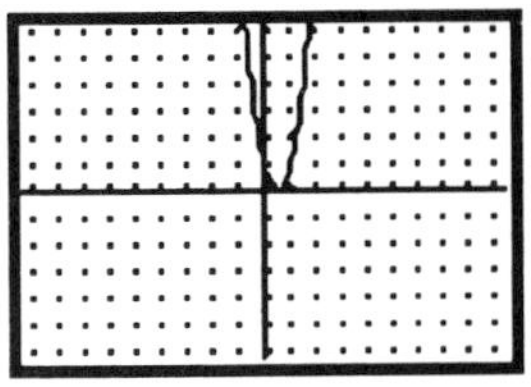

[⁻4, 3, 0.1, ⁻9.4, 9.4, 1, ⁻6.2, 6.2, 1]

  ii. $y = (2x - 1)^2$

  iii. The graph in this window is the same as in part i.

d. i.

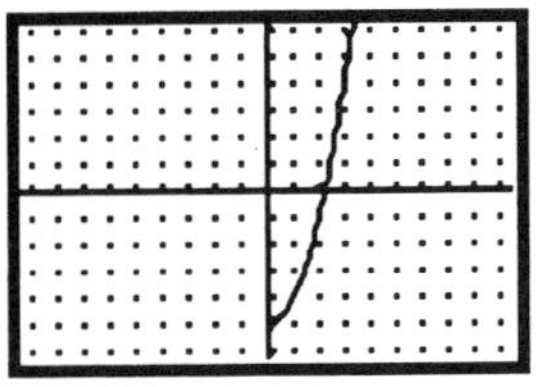

[⁻5, 10, 0.1, ⁻9.4, 9.4, 1, ⁻6.2, 6.2, 1]

  ii. $y = x^2 - 5$

  iii. The parametric graph shows only one side of the parabola. The equation in ii gives the complete parabola.

4. Problem 3a

  i. $x = ⁻(2t - 5), y = t + 1$

  ii. $x = 2t - 5, y = ⁻(t + 1)$

  iii. $x = 2t - 5, y = t + 4$

  iv. $x = 2t - 9, y = t - 1$

Problem 3c

  i. $x = -\frac{t+1}{2}, y = t^2$

  ii. $x = \frac{t+1}{2}, y = ⁻(t^2)$

  iii. $x = \frac{t+1}{2}, y = t^2 + 3$

  iv. $x = \frac{t+1}{2} - 4, y = t^2 - 2$

5. a. 42.83°   **b.** 28.30°   **c.** 22.98   **d.** 12.86

   e. 21.36   **f.** 17.11

6.

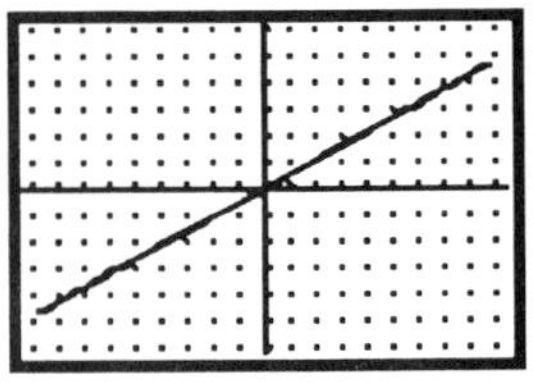

[⁻10, 10, 0.1, ⁻9.4, 9.4, 1, ⁻6.2, 6.2, 1]; angle is 28°.

7. Using the edge of the pool as the point (0, 0), the x-equation would be $x = 4t + 1.5$ and the y-equation would be $y = ⁻4.9t^2 + 10$. She hits at a point 7.2 m from the edge.

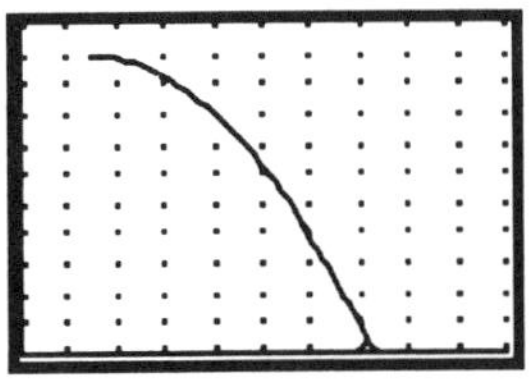

8. 1.43 ft/sec

9. No, he will miss the monkey.

10. He will hit the monkey. Both the monkey and the dart are falling at the same rate.

11. Flying at a heading of 107.77° will take him to his destination if the wind averages 25 mi/hr. If the wind were 30 mi/hr continuously, he could miss his destination by as much as 8 mi.

12. Answers will vary.

Chapter 7

Problem Set 7.1

1. a. $y = 1.151(1 + 0.015)^x$

b.

Year	Population (in billions)
1991	1.151
1992	1.168
1993	1.186
1994	1.204
1995	1.222
1996	1.240
1997	1.259
1998	1.277
1999	1.297
2000	1.316

   c. 2063, 3.364 billion

   d. Answers will vary. (The dangers involved in this long-range prediction are great.)

2. **a.** $y = 2.56(2.5)^x$; fifth day: 250; sixth day: 625   **b.** $7.56(2.5)^{3.5} \approx 63.25$

    c. 728 cm   **d.** 11 days 13 hr; 9 p.m. on day 11

3. **a.** 49   **b.** 79.7023   **c.** 129.6418   **d.** 210.8723   **e.** 343

    f. 30.7023; 49.9395; 81.2305; 132.1277. Answers will vary. These numbers do not form an arithmetic sequence.

    g. 1.627; 1.627; 1.627; 1.627. Answers will vary. The ratios are the same numbers. They form a geometric sequence.

    h. Answers will vary. Decimal powers form a geometric sequence.

4. Answers will vary between 2000 and 2300. The actual value is approximately 2056.

5. **a.** The radiation after 75 days is 60 rads.

    b. The radiation after 80 days is 52.23 rads.

    c. The initial radiation was 480 rads.

    d. The radiation was 960 rads for one time period, 25 days, before we started keeping track.

    e. After one time period the radiation was 240 rads.

    f. 22.74 rads

6. **a.** $f(x) = 5000(1 + 0.065)^x$ **b.** $6,850.43

    c. Amount invested after 5 yr   **d.** $6,568.78

    e. Amount invested after 4 yr 4 mo   **f.** $5,000, the initial investment

    g. $8,145.72; answers will vary for the meaning.

7. **a.** The water temperature drops 6% each minute.

    b. 23°C

    c. The temperature after 7.4 min is 14.55°C.

    d. 16.11°C

    e. After 13 min, 28 sec ($\approx$ 13.47 min), the water at the bottom of the glass has cooled to 10°C.

    f. 24.66 min

Problem Set 7.2

1. **a.** $49^{5/2}$ is the square root of 49 raised to the fifth power = 16,807.

    b. $16^{3/4}$ is the fourth root of 16 raised to the third power = 8.

    c. $64^{5/3}$ is the cube root of 64 raised to the fifth power = 1024.

    d. $32^{2/5}$ is the fifth root of 32 squared = 4.

2. **a.** 16 kg   **b.** 25 kg   **c.** 91 cm

3. a. $x^{1/4}$　　　　**b.** $x^{3/5}$　　　　**c.** $x^{7/3}$　　　　**d.** $x^{4/5}$

4. a. 128　　　　**b.** 81　　　　**c.** 625　　　　**d.** 27

5. a. Cincinnati　　　　**b.** Answers will vary.

6. a. $\sqrt[3]{x^2}$　　　　**b.** $\sqrt[4]{x^{11}}$ or $x^2\sqrt[4]{x^3}$

7. a. $x = \frac{3}{2}$ or 1.5　　　　**b.** $x = \frac{7}{5}$ or 1.4

8. a. $u_n = \begin{cases} 1 & \text{if } n = 0 \\ u_{n-1}(1.04) & \text{if } n > 0 \end{cases}$　　　　**b.** $b(x) = 1.04^x$　　　　**c.** About 100 yr

9. Answers will vary. One possibility is to enter $y = x \wedge (1/5)$.

10. a. 4000 is the initial investment.
　　b. You are earning 7.2% interest on your investment.
　　c. The interest is compounded monthly.
　　d. This is one month after the investment was made.
　　e. This is at the time the investment was made.
　　f. This is one month before the investment was made.
　　g. $x \approx 115.9$

11.

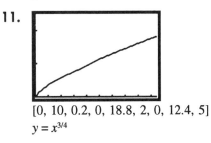

[0, 10, 0.2, 0, 18.8, 2, 0, 12.4, 5]
$y = x^{3/4}$

Problem Set 7.3

1. a. $\frac{1}{27} = 0.037037\ldots$　　　　　**b.** $\frac{1}{5} = 0.2$

　　c. -216　　　　　**d.** $\frac{1}{144} = 0.0069444\ldots$

　　e. $\frac{16}{9} = 1.777\ldots$　　　　　**f.** $\frac{7}{2} = 3.5$

　　g. $-\frac{3}{2} = -1.5$　　　　　**h.** 1

2. a. $\frac{1}{8x^3}$　　　**b.** $\frac{2}{x^3}$　　　**c.** $x^{7/6}$　　　**d.** $2x^{3/2}$

3. One egg over easy

4. a. False　　　**b.** False　　　**c.** False　　　**d.** False
　　e. True　　　**f.** True

5. a. -2　　　**b.** -3　　　**c.** -5　　　**d.** 0

6. As the base increases, the graphs become steeper. They all intersect the y-axis at (0, 1). The graph of $y = 6^x$ should be the steepest one. It will contain the points (0, 1) and (1, 6).

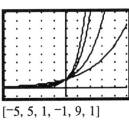

[−5, 5, 1, −1, 9, 1]

7. As the base increases, the graphs flatten out. They all intersect the y-axis at (0, 1). All of these equations involve raising a number between 0 and 1 to a power. The graph of the equation $y = 0.1^x$ should be steeper than any of these given. It will contain the points (0, 1) and (−1, 10).

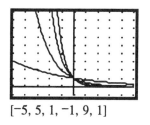

[−5, 5, 1, −1, 9, 1]

8. Each equation in Problem 6 involves a base larger than 1. In Problem 7 each base is less than 1.
   a. $y = 2.5^x$ **b.** $y = 0.35^x$

9. a. Each function in Problem 6 is increasing. None of the functions in Problem 7 are increasing.
   b. A function is a decreasing function if and only if for each $x_1 > x_2, f(x_1) \le f(x_2)$.

10. a. The graph will be reflected across the y-axis. It is the same as $y = a\left(\frac{1}{b}\right)^x$
   b. The graph will be reflected across the x-axis.
   c. The graph will be translated 2 units to the right.

11. a. False   **b.** False   **c.** False   **d.** False

Problem Set 7.4

1. a. $x = t + 2, y = 2t - 3$ **b.** $x = t + 1, y = t^2$

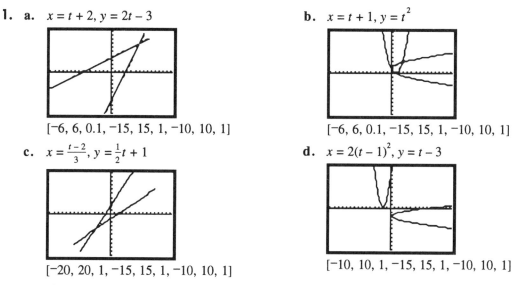

[−6, 6, 0.1, −15, 15, 1, −10, 10, 1]   [−6, 6, 0.1, −15, 15, 1, −10, 10, 1]

c. $x = \frac{t-2}{3}, y = \frac{1}{2}t + 1$ **d.** $x = 2(t-1)^2, y = t - 3$

[−20, 20, 1, −15, 15, 1, −10, 10, 1]   [−10, 10, 1, −15, 15, 1, −10, 10, 1]

e. The original graph and its inverse are symmetric with respect to the line $y = x$.
f. $x = t, y = t$

2. Graph c is the inverse because the x- and y-coordinates have been switched from the original graph and both graphs are symmetric to the line $y = x$.

3. a. $y = 2x - 11$ **b.** $x = 2t - 1, y = t + 5$ **c.** $x = 2y - 11$
   d. The nonparametric equations are exactly the same except that the variables have been switched.

4. a. $x = (y - 3)^2 + 2$ or $y = 3 \pm \sqrt{x - 2}$ **b.** $x = t + 3, y = t^2 + 2$
   c. $y = (x - 3)^2 + 2$ **d.** Answers will vary.

5. Answers will vary; $t \ge 3$ works and so does $t \le 3$.

6. Answers will vary; $t \le 0$ works and so does $t \ge 0$.

7. a. Answers will vary. One possibility: $x = t$ and $y = (t + 1)^2 - 2$.
   b. $x = (t + 1)^2 - 2, y = t$

c. $x = (y + 1)^2 - 2$ or $y = \pm\sqrt{x + 2} - 1$

d. $f(x) = (x + 1)^2 - 2$. The inverse is not a function, so it will take two equations to write it:
$y = \sqrt{x + 2} - 1$ and $y = -\sqrt{x + 2} - 1$.

8. a. $f(x) = 2x - 3$ and $f^{-1}(x) = \frac{x + 3}{2}$ **b.** $f(x) = \frac{4 - 3x}{2}$ and $f^{-1}(x) = \frac{4 - 2x}{3}$

    c. $f(x) = \frac{-1}{2}x^2 + \frac{3}{2}$; the inverse is not a function, so $f^{-1}(x)$ notation doesn't apply: $y = \pm\sqrt{-2x + 3}$.

9. a. i. $\frac{x + 140}{6.34}$ **ii.** 15.75   **iii.** 15.75   **iv.** $f(f^{-1}(x)) = f^{-1}(f(x)) = x$

    b. i. $\frac{x - 32}{1.8}$ **ii.** 15.75   **iii.** 15.75   **iv.** $f(f^{-1}(x)) = f^{-1}(f(x)) = x$

10. a. $f(x) = -0.0066x + 14.6175$ **b.** $f^{-1}(x) = -152.51x + 2229.30$

    c. $f(x) = -0.0036x + 58.5586$ **d.** $g^{-1}(x) = -281.52x + 16,485.41$

    e. $-15.27°F$

    f. Let $f(x) = -0.0066x + 14.6175$ equal the function that relates (altitude in meters, temperature in °C) and let $h(x) = 1.8x + 32$ equal the function that relates (°C, °F). Then $h(f(x))$, with an input of altitude in meters, will give an output in °F.

11. a. $y = 100 - C$ **b.** $y = \frac{F - 212}{-1.8}$

12. Answers will vary.

13. Answers will vary. Problem 1 is correct. Problem 2 is incorrect. Problem 3 is incorrect. Problem 4 is incorrect.

Problem Set 7.5

1. a. 2.187   **b.** 29.791   **c.** No solution   **d.** 625

    e. 1   **f.** 512   **g.** 0.951   **h.** 0.426

2. a. $9x^4$ **b.** $8x^6$ **c.** $216x^{-18}$

3. 0.109 or 10.9%

4. a. $P = 4 \cdot 1.02^t$ where t is number of years since 1975.

    b. Answers will vary.

    c. Answers will vary.

5. 3.2%

6.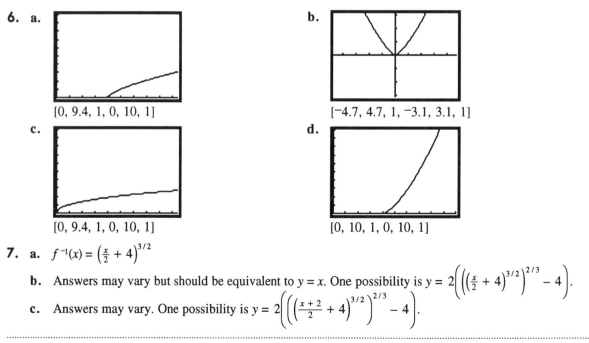

    a. $[0, 9.4, 1, 0, 10, 1]$ **b.** $[-4.7, 4.7, 1, -3.1, 3.1, 1]$

    c. $[0, 9.4, 1, 0, 10, 1]$ **d.** $[0, 10, 1, 0, 10, 1]$

7. a. $f^{-1}(x) = \left(\frac{x}{2} + 4\right)^{3/2}$

    b. Answers may vary but should be equivalent to $y = x$. One possibility is $y = 2\left(\left(\left(\frac{x}{2} + 4\right)^{3/2}\right)^{2/3} - 4\right)$.

    c. Answers may vary. One possibility is $y = 2\left(\left(\left(\frac{x + 2}{2} + 4\right)^{3/2}\right)^{2/3} - 4\right)$.

8. a.

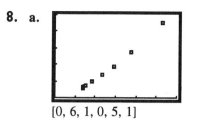

[0, 6, 1, 0, 5, 1]

b. The least-squares line of best fit is $y = -0.8118 + 9.681x$. The residuals form a definite pattern, which means the line is not a good fit.

c. Answers will vary but should be close to $y = 0.37x^{1.5}$. For this equation there is no pattern in the residuals.

9. a. Answers will vary depending on the equation found in Problem 8; $x \approx 1,229,200$ km.

b. $y \approx 17.25$ days

10. Answers will vary.

Problem Set 7.6

1. a. $10^x = 1000$ **b.** $5^x = 625$ **c.** $7^x = \sqrt{7}$ **d.** $8^x = 2$

    e. $5^x = \frac{1}{25}$ **f.** $6^x = 1$

2. a. 3   **b.** 4   **c.** $\frac{1}{2}$ **d.** $\frac{1}{3}$

    e. -2 **f.** 0

3. a. $3 < \log 1250 < 4$ **b.** $2 < \log 125 < 3$ **c.** $1 < \log 12.5 < 2$ **d.** $0 < \log 1.25 < 1$

    e. $-1 < \log 0.125 < 0$ **f.** $-2 < \log 0.0125 < -1$

4. The window used for all of the graphs is $[-4.7, 4.7, 1, -3.1, 3.1, 1]$.

a.

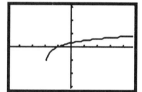

The graph is shifted 2 units to the left of $y = \log x$.

b.

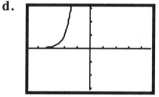

The graph of $y = \log x$ is stretched vertically by a factor of 3.

c.

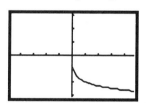

The graph is flipped over the x-axis and then shifted 2 units down from $y = \log x$.

d.

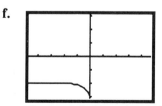

The graph is shifted 2 units to the left of $y = 10^x$.

e.

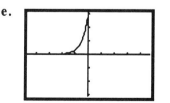

The graph of $y = 10^x$ is stretched vertically by a factor of 3.

f.

The graph is flipped over the x-axis and then shifted 2 units down from $y = 10^x$.

5. In about 25 min

6. a. About 1980   **b.** 13%   **c.** About 5.6 yr

7. a. $C_1 = 32.7$, $C_2 = 65.4$, $C_3 = 130.8$, $C_6 = 1046.4$, $C_7 = 2092.8$, $C_8 = 4185.6$
   b. $y = 16.35(2)^x$
   c. Answers will vary, but string lengths are related to the frequencies. Longer lengths have shorter frequencies.

8. a. $y = 100(0.999879)^x$ **b.** Approximately 6002 yr ago; answers will vary.

9. a. $y = ab^x$ **b.** $(0, 88.7)$, $(6, 92.9)$ **c.** $a = 88.7$ **d.** $b = 1.0077$
   e. 23 or 24 clicks

10. Answers will vary.

Problem Set 7.7

1. a. $\log 10$ **b.** $\log 100$ **c.** $\log 900$ **d.** $\log 200$
   e. To get the answer, multiply the arguments.
   f. Answers are the same as for parts 1a.–1d.
   g. $\log a + \log b = \log ab$
   h. Logs are exponents, and when you multiply exponential expressions with the same base, you add the exponents.

2. a. $\log 5$ **b.** $\log 20$ **c.** $\log 30$ **d.** $\log 40$
   e. To get the answer, divide the arguments.   **f.** Answers are the same as for parts 2a.–d.
   g. $\log a - \log b = \log \frac{a}{b}$
   h. Logs are exponents, and when you divide exponential expressions with the same base, you subtract the exponents.

3. a. i. 0.3   ii. 0.9   **b.** $\log 2^3 = 3 \log 2$
   c. i. 1.7   ii. 3.4   **d.** $\log 50^2 = 2 \log 50$
   e. Answers are the same.   **f.** $\log a^b = b \log a$
   g. Yes   **h.** $\frac{1}{2} \log a$

4. a. True   **b.** False; $\log 5 + \log 3 = \log 15$ **c.** True
   d. True   **e.** False; $\log 9 - \log 3 = \log 3$ **f.** False; $\log \sqrt{7} = \frac{1}{2} \log 7$
   g. False; $\log 35 = \log 5 + \log 7$ **h.** True   **i.** False; $\log 3 - \log 4 = \log \frac{3}{4}$
   j. True

5. Answers will vary. For example, the log of a product is the sum of the logs. The log of a quotient is the difference of the logs. The log of a number raised to a power is the power times the log of the number.

6. Answers will vary. For example, if a horizontal line will intersect f in more than one point, its inverse is not a function.

7. a. $y = 261.6 \cdot 2^{x/12}$
   b.

	Note	Frequency		Note	Frequency
Do	C	261.6	**Sol**	G	392.0
	C#	277.2		G#	415.3
Re	D	293.6	**La**	A	440.0
	D#	311.1		A#	466.1
Mi	E	329.6	**Ti**	B	493.8
Fa	F	349.2	**Do**	C	523.2
	F#	370.0			

8. 2

9. a. $x + y$ **b.** $z - x$ **c.** $3z$ **d.** $2(x + z)$

10. **a.** 4   **b.** 1.292   **c.** 0.774   **d.** 2.465

11.

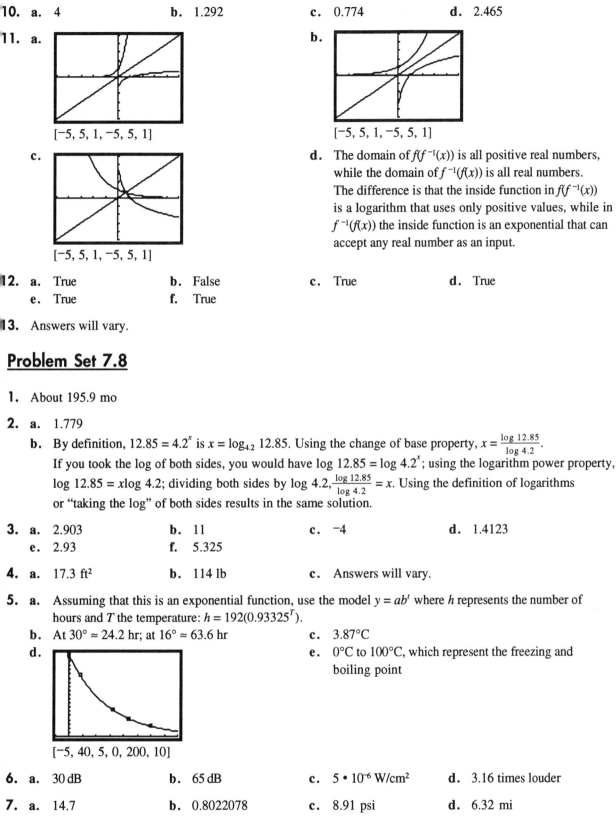

a. [−5, 5, 1, −5, 5, 1]

b. [−5, 5, 1, −5, 5, 1]

c. [−5, 5, 1, −5, 5, 1]

d. The domain of $f(f^{-1}(x))$ is all positive real numbers, while the domain of $f^{-1}(f(x))$ is all real numbers. The difference is that the inside function in $f(f^{-1}(x))$ is a logarithm that uses only positive values, while in $f^{-1}(f(x))$ the inside function is an exponential that can accept any real number as an input.

12. **a.** True   **b.** False   **c.** True   **d.** True

     e. True   **f.** True

13. Answers will vary.

Problem Set 7.8

1. About 195.9 mo

2. **a.** 1.779

     b. By definition, $12.85 = 4.2^x$ is $x = \log_{4.2} 12.85$. Using the change of base property, $x = \frac{\log 12.85}{\log 4.2}$. If you took the log of both sides, you would have $\log 12.85 = \log 4.2^x$; using the logarithm power property, $\log 12.85 = x\log 4.2$; dividing both sides by $\log 4.2, \frac{\log 12.85}{\log 4.2} = x$. Using the definition of logarithms or "taking the log" of both sides results in the same solution.

3. **a.** 2.903   **b.** 11   **c.** −4   **d.** 1.4123

     e. 2.93   **f.** 5.325

4. **a.** 17.3 ft²   **b.** 114 lb   **c.** Answers will vary.

5. **a.** Assuming that this is an exponential function, use the model $y = ab^t$ where h represents the number of hours and T the temperature: $h = 192(0.93325^T)$.

     b. At 30° ≈ 24.2 hr; at 16° ≈ 63.6 hr   **c.** 3.87°C

     d.

[−5, 40, 5, 0, 200, 10]

     e. 0°C to 100°C, which represent the freezing and boiling point

6. **a.** 30 dB   **b.** 65 dB   **c.** $5 \cdot 10^{-6}$ W/cm²   **d.** 3.16 times louder

7. **a.** 14.7   **b.** 0.8022078   **c.** 8.91 psi   **d.** 6.32 mi

8. **a.** $y = 100(0.999879)^x$ **b.** About 11,500 yr   **c.** Around 1,900 B.C.

     d. Less than 0.001% remains. There is virtually nothing left to measure so you could not use carbon-14 for dating coal.

9. a. 96.5%   **b.** $y = 100(0.965)^x$ **c.** 19.456 min
d. In one day, the carbon-11 is virtually gone, so you could never use it to date an archaeological find.

10. a.–d. Answers will vary.

Problem Set 7.9

1. $y = 0.21\sqrt{x}$ ... (x, y) ... $(x, \log y)$

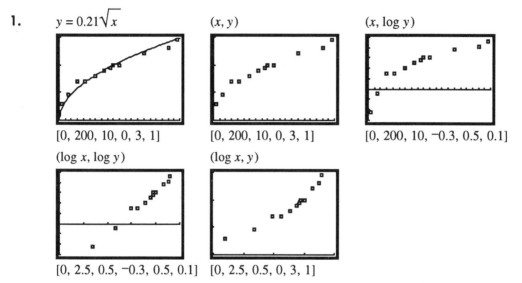

[0, 200, 10, 0, 3, 1] ... [0, 200, 10, 0, 3, 1] ... [0, 200, 10, −0.3, 0.5, 0.1]

$(\log x, \log y)$ ... $(\log x, y)$

[0, 2.5, 0.5, −0.3, 0.5, 0.1] ... [0, 2.5, 0.5, 0, 3, 1]

The graph of $(\log x, \log y)$ appears to be the most linear; $y \approx 0.303x^{0.417}$. (Answers will vary depending on the method used to find the equation of the line. Be sure to check your answer graphically to make sure it appears to fit).

2. a.

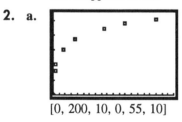

[0, 200, 10, 0, 55, 10]

b. $(\log x, y)$

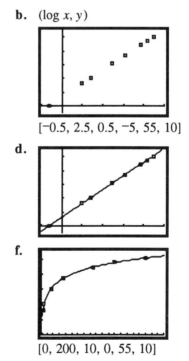

[−0.5, 2.5, 0.5, −5, 55, 10]

c. The equation should be close to $y = 20x + 6$.

d.

e. $y = 20 \log x + 6$ (Answers will vary depending on the method used to find the equation of the line. Be sure to check your answer graphically to make sure the equation fits.)

f.

[0, 200, 10, 0, 55, 10]

3. a.–e. Answers will vary, but the equation should be close to $y = a(0.5)^x$ where a represents the starting amount of M&Ms.

4. a.

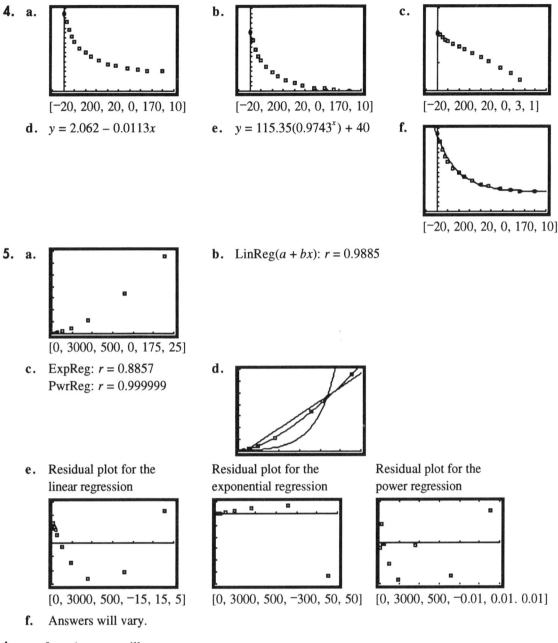

[−20, 200, 20, 0, 170, 10]

b.

[−20, 200, 20, 0, 170, 10]

c.

[−20, 200, 20, 0, 3, 1]

d. $y = 2.062 - 0.0113x$

e. $y = 115.35(0.9743^x) + 40$

f.

[−20, 200, 20, 0, 170, 10]

5. a.

[0, 3000, 500, 0, 175, 25]

b. LinReg($a + bx$): $r = 0.9885$

c. ExpReg: $r = 0.8857$
PwrReg: $r = 0.999999$

d.

e. Residual plot for the linear regression

Residual plot for the exponential regression

Residual plot for the power regression

[0, 3000, 500, −15, 15, 5]   [0, 3000, 500, −300, 50, 50]   [0, 3000, 500, −0.01, 0.01. 0.01]

f. Answers will vary.

6. a.–d. Answers will vary.

7. a. The equation should be close to $y = 3.56x^{0.5}$.
b. Answers will vary. A power regression probably provides the best fit.

8. a. 3.65 gal; 3.35 gal; 3.1 gal

b. $u(n) = \begin{cases} 4 & \text{if } n = 0 \\ u_{(n-1)}(1 - 0.15) + 0.25 & \text{if } n > 0 \end{cases}$

c.

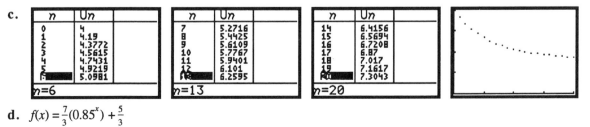

n	Un
0	4
1	4.19
2	4.3772
3	4.5615
4	4.7431
5	4.9219
6	5.0981

$n=6$

n	Un
7	5.2716
8	5.4425
9	5.6109
10	5.7767
11	5.9401
12	6.101
13	6.2595

$n=13$

n	Un
14	6.4156
15	6.5694
16	6.7208
17	6.87
18	7.017
19	7.1617
20	7.3043

$n=20$

d. $f(x) = \frac{7}{3}(0.85^x) + \frac{5}{3}$

Chapter Review

Problem Set 7.10

1. **a.** $\frac{1}{16}$ **b.** $-\frac{1}{3}$ **c.** 125   **d.** 7   **e.** $\frac{1}{4}$

   f. $\frac{27}{64}$ **g.** $^{-}1$ **h.** 12   **i.** 0.6

2. **a.** $\log xy$ **b.** $\log z - \log v$ **c.** $2.1x^{6.8}$ **d.** $k \log w$ **e.** $x^{1/5}$ **f.** $\frac{\log t}{\log 5}$

3. **a.** 2.153   **b.** 2.231   **c.** 2.344   **d.** $1.242 \cdot 10^{23}$ **e.** 3.041   **f.** 45.897
   g. 5902   **h.** 612

4. **a.** 0.50   **b.** 2.4998   **c.** 0.63; the first 0.63 min is free.   **d.** $4.19   **e.** 3.98 min

5. **a.**

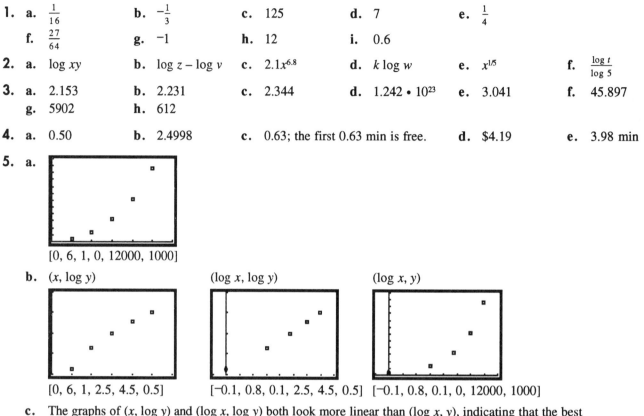

[0, 6, 1, 0, 12000, 1000]

   b. $(x, \log y)$ $(\log x, \log y)$ $(\log x, y)$

[0, 6, 1, 2.5, 4.5, 0.5]   [$^{-}$0.1, 0.8, 0.1, 2.5, 4.5, 0.5]   [$^{-}$0.1, 0.8, 0.1, 0, 12000, 1000]

   c. The graphs of $(x, \log y)$ and $(\log x, \log y)$ both look more linear than $(\log x, y)$, indicating that the best fit for the original data is either a power regression or an exponential regression. The exponential regression on the calculator gives you $y = 249.15(2.20)^x$ with $r = 0.988$. The power regression gives you $y = 398.14x^{1.98}$ with $r = 0.997$. To determine which is indeed the best fit for the original data, you need to calculate the residuals. Answers will vary as to which regression provides the better fit.

   d. Using the exponential regression: 1990 = 299,166; 1995 = 15,367,552; 2000 = 789,532,012
   Using the power regression: 1990 = 30,787; 1995 = 73,804; 2000 = 135,062

   e. Using the power regression: 1981 + 52 yr or the year 2033.
   Using the exponential regression: 1981 + 11 yr or the year 1992.

   f. Answers will vary.

6. **a.** There are many ways to select data points: using midpoints of the intervals, using one point for each year, and other methods. The equations generated will vary depending on the choice of method. However, the answers for parts b and c should be similar. Using (55, 0.75) as the first value, and each time the wage changed as a data point, the power regression equation is $y \approx (1.3592 \cdot 10^{-6})x^{3.3185}$. The exponential regression equation is $y = 0.067(1.05)^x$. Answers will vary as to which is the better model for the data.

   b. Power regression: 2000, $5.40; 2010, $7.12; 2020, $9.39; exponential regression: 2000, $8.81; 2010, $14.35; 2020, $23.38

   c. Power regression: $0.28; exponential regression: $0.43

7. Answers will vary.

Chapter 8

Problem Set 8.1

Many of the questions in this problem set ask the student to devise a method to randomly select an outcome or to generate a set of random numbers. In these answers, one example is given, but it is by no means the only method.

1. Answers will vary.

2. **a.** Answers will vary.
   b. Theoretically, $\frac{1}{5}$ of the students or 20 should be assigned to each bus.
   c. Alter the Random Number Generator Routine to seq (int 5rand + 1,x,1,99,1)→L₁. You will need to do one more roll to get 100 rolls.
   d. Answers will vary.   **e.** Answers will vary.

3. Each one of these procedures for producing random numbers has shortcomings.
   a. Middle numbers (3 through 7) occur more commonly than 1, 2, 8, or 9.
   b. Very few pencils will be 0 in. or 1 in. in length.
   c. Books tend to open to pages that are used more than others.
   d. Answers will vary. You could alter the Random Number Generator Routine to seq (int 9rand + 1,x,1,99,1)→L₁. (See Calculator Note 8B.)

4. **a.** Answers will vary.
   b. Answers will vary. You could alter the Random Number Generator Routine to seq (int 6rand + 1,x,1,99,1)→L₁. (See Calculator Note 8B.)
   c. Answers will vary.
   d. Answers will vary.
   e. Answers will vary. Long-run averages should tend toward 6 turns.

5. **a.–d.** Answers will vary.
   e. Answers will vary. Average numbers should be about 22 boxes.

6. **a.** Answers will vary.
   b. The long-range pattern should be that $\frac{1}{6}$ of all rolls are a 3, $\frac{1}{6}$ of all rolls are a 1, and so on.
   c. When the data points are collected from other classmates, the points should level out to a straight line. If you considered 5's instead of 3's, the data should level out to the same value as with the 3's.
   d. Answers will vary.   **e.** Ideally, P(3) = $\frac{1}{6}$

7. **a.** i. $-2 < y < 4$ ii. {1, 2, 3}

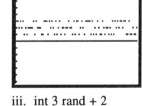

   b. i. 5 rand – 4   ii. int 4 rand – 4   iii. int 3 rand + 2

8. **a.** Answers will vary. Long-run averages should tend toward 2 children.
   b. 1 girl

Problem Set 8.2

1. **a.** 36 different outcomes
   b. 6 different outcomes, all in the column representing green 4
   c. 12 different outcomes, all in the rows representing white 2 and white 3
   d. 3 different outcomes

2. **a.** $x + y = 9$ (4 different outcomes)
   b. $x + y = 6$ (5 different outcomes)
   c. $x - y = 1$ or $y - x = 1$ (10 different outcomes)
   d. $x + y = 6$ and $x - y = 2$ (1 outcome)
   e. $x + y \leq 5$ (10 different outcomes)

3. **a.** $4; \frac{4}{36}$ **b.** $5; \frac{5}{36}$ **c.** $10; \frac{10}{36}$ **d.** $1; \frac{1}{36}$ **e.** $10; \frac{10}{36}$

4. **a.** Initially the cumulative probabilities are unsettled, making many jogs up and down, but tend to be between 0.5 and 0.7.
   b. In the long run the probabilities tend toward 0.6.
   c. If the proportion graph tended toward 1, this would mean that in the long run success was a certainty.
   d. If the proportion graph tended toward 0, this would mean that in the long run there is no chance of something happening.
   e. The range of values possible for any probabilities is from 0 to 1.

5. **a.** 144   **b.** 44   **c.** 0.306   **d.** $\frac{44}{144} = 0.306$ **e.** 0.694   **f.** 0; 0

6. **a.** 21.08   **b.** 40   **c.** 0.527
   d. Modify the program Ratio of Success in Calculator Note 8D. Change the indicated lines to :√X→Y₁, :10Rand→X, and 4Rand→B. Answers will vary.
   e. Answers will vary.

7. **a.** $x + y \leq 6$ **b.**   **c.** 0.28

```
8

0        8
```

8. **a.** $x - y \leq 10$ or $y - x \leq 10$ **b.** 0.31

9. **a.** 0.32   **b.** 0.5   **c.** 0.21875

Problem Set 8.3

1. **a.** 24   **b.** $\frac{1}{4}$ **c.** $\frac{2}{24}$ or $\frac{1}{12}$ **d.** $\frac{1}{24}$ **e.** $\frac{23}{24}$ **f.** $\frac{12}{24}$ or $\frac{1}{2}$

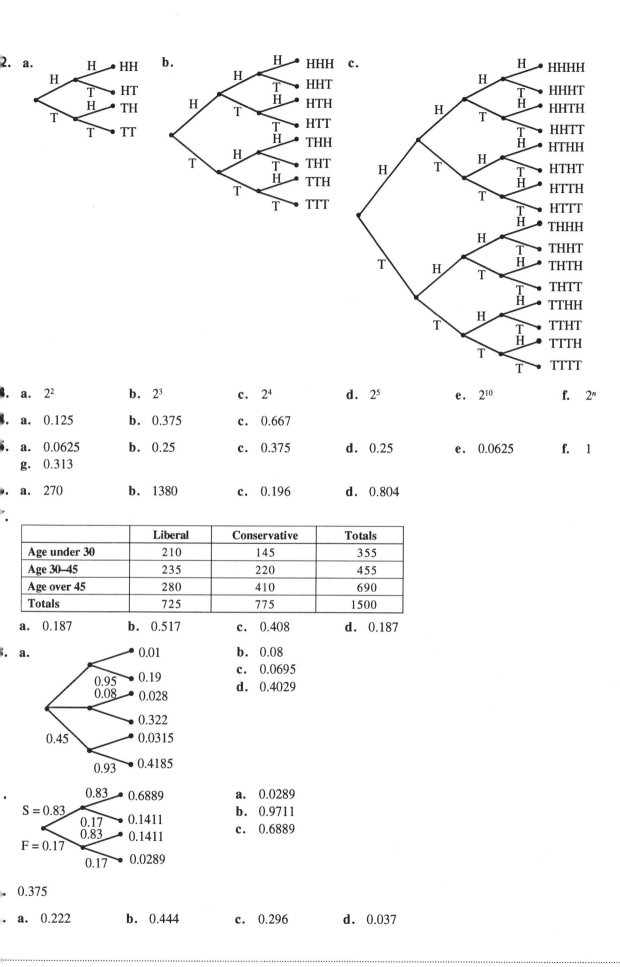

2. a.

H → H → HH
→ T → HT
T → H → TH
→ T → TT

b.

H → H → HHH
→ T → HHT
H → T → H → HTH
→ T → HTT
T → H → H → THH
→ T → THT
→ T → H → TTH
→ T → TTT

c.

HHHH
HHHT
HHTH
HHTT
HTHH
HTHT
HTTH
HTTT
THHH
THHT
THTH
THTT
TTHH
TTHT
TTTH
TTTT

3. **a.** 2^2 **b.** 2^3 **c.** 2^4 **d.** 2^5 **e.** 2^{10} **f.** 2^n

4. **a.** 0.125 **b.** 0.375 **c.** 0.667

5. **a.** 0.0625 **b.** 0.25 **c.** 0.375 **d.** 0.25 **e.** 0.0625 **f.** 1
g. 0.313

6. **a.** 270 **b.** 1380 **c.** 0.196 **d.** 0.804

7.

	Liberal	Conservative	Totals
Age under 30	210	145	355
Age 30–45	235	220	455
Age over 45	280	410	690
Totals	725	775	1500

a. 0.187 **b.** 0.517 **c.** 0.408 **d.** 0.187

8. a.

0.95 → 0.01
0.08 → 0.19
→ 0.028
→ 0.322
0.45 → 0.0315
0.93 → 0.4185

b. 0.08
c. 0.0695
d. 0.4029

9.

0.83 → 0.6889
S = 0.83
0.17 → 0.1411
0.83 → 0.1411
F = 0.17
0.17 → 0.0289

a. 0.0289
b. 0.9711
c. 0.6889

10. 0.375

11. **a.** 0.222 **b.** 0.444 **c.** 0.296 **d.** 0.037

Problem Set 8.4

1. a. Answers will vary. **b.** Answers will vary.

c.

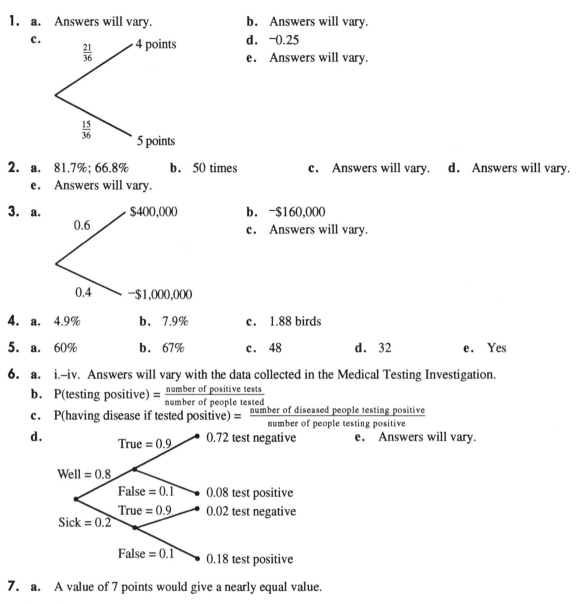

$\frac{21}{36}$ → 4 points

$\frac{15}{36}$ → 5 points

d. ‾0.25
e. Answers will vary.

2. a. 81.7%; 66.8%   **b.** 50 times   **c.** Answers will vary.   **d.** Answers will vary.
e. Answers will vary.

3. a.

0.6 → $400,000

0.4 → ‾$1,000,000

b. ‾$160,000
c. Answers will vary.

4. a. 4.9%   **b.** 7.9%   **c.** 1.88 birds

5. a. 60%   **b.** 67%   **c.** 48   **d.** 32   **e.** Yes

6. a. i.–iv. Answers will vary with the data collected in the Medical Testing Investigation.

b. P(testing positive) = $\frac{\text{number of positive tests}}{\text{number of people tested}}$

c. P(having disease if tested positive) = $\frac{\text{number of diseased people testing positive}}{\text{number of people testing positive}}$

d.

Well = 0.8
  True = 0.9 • 0.72 test negative
  False = 0.1 • 0.08 test positive

Sick = 0.2
  True = 0.9 • 0.02 test negative
  False = 0.1 • 0.18 test positive

e. Answers will vary.

7. a. A value of 7 points would give a nearly equal value.

b. Answers will vary.

8. Answers will vary.

Problem Set 8.5

1. a. 3 colors

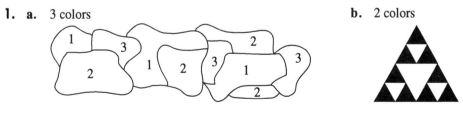

b. 2 colors

2. a.–e. Answers will vary.

3. a. 3

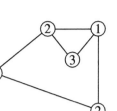

b. 4

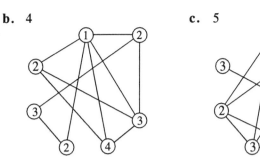

c. 5

4. Draw the diagram as suggested in the problem. Connect each vertex (class) with an edge to any other class with which they should not be grouped. Any two vertices (classes) that are connected by an edge must be different colors or numbers. The best schedule will have 5 exam periods. The following is one possible solution.

Period 1: L1, L2, L3, L5, H3, P3, S3
Period 2: M1, M2, M4, S2, S4, P1
Period 3: E1, E2, E3, E4
Period 4: H1, H2, M3, M5, P2
Period 5: S1, L4, L6, H3, P3

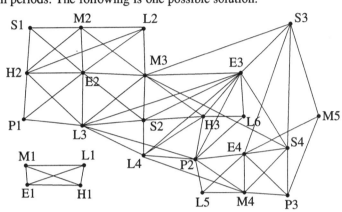

5. 5 storage areas: A (1, 2, 10); B (3, 11); C (4, 8); D (9, 12); E (5, 6, 7)

Problem Set 8.6

1.

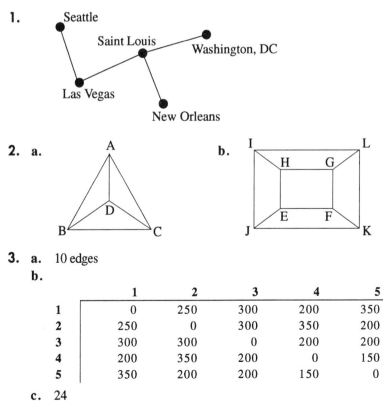

2. a.

b.

3. a. 10 edges

b.

	1	2	3	4	5
1	0	250	300	200	350
2	250	0	300	350	200
3	300	300	0	200	200
4	200	350	200	0	150
5	350	200	200	150	0

c. 24

d. 1-2-5-4-3-1 or 1-2-3-5-4-1 or their reversals are all $1,100.

4. a. $[29 \quad 211]$ **b.** $[36.65 \quad 203.35]$ **c.** $[43.1525 \quad 196.8475]$

5. a.

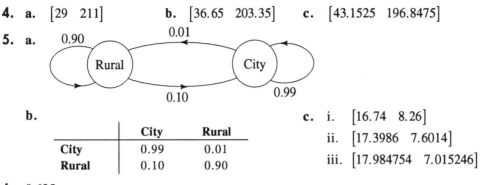

b.

	City	Rural
City	0.99	0.01
Rural	0.10	0.90

c. i. $[16.74 \quad 8.26]$
ii. $[17.3986 \quad 7.6014]$
iii. $[17.984754 \quad 7.015246]$

6. 0.625

Problem Set 8.7

1. $[43.15 \quad 196.84]$

2. a.

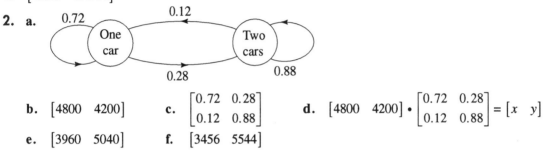

b. $[4800 \quad 4200]$ **c.** $\begin{bmatrix} 0.72 & 0.28 \\ 0.12 & 0.88 \end{bmatrix}$ **d.** $[4800 \quad 4200] \cdot \begin{bmatrix} 0.72 & 0.28 \\ 0.12 & 0.88 \end{bmatrix} = [x \quad y]$

e. $[3960 \quad 5040]$ **f.** $[3456 \quad 5544]$

3. Answers will vary. For example, there are 20 million people living in California and 220 million people living in the United States outside of California. Each year 2 million people immigrate to California and 11 million people immigrate to the United States outside of California.

4. a. $[7 \quad 54]$ **b.** $\begin{bmatrix} 0.815 & 0.185 \\ 0.0925 & 0.9075 \end{bmatrix}$ **c.** $\begin{bmatrix} 15.6 & {}^-10.8 \\ 10.7 & 42.2 \end{bmatrix}$ **d.** $\begin{bmatrix} 180 & {}^-230 \\ 54 & 322 \end{bmatrix}$

5. a. $[29 \quad 211]$ **b.** $[36.65 \quad 203.35]$ **c.** $[43.1525 \quad 196.84751]$ **d.** $[80 \quad 160]$

6. a. $\begin{bmatrix} 0.815 & 0.185 \\ 0.0925 & 0.9075 \end{bmatrix}$ **b.** $\begin{bmatrix} 0 & 0 & 0 \\ 0 & 4 & 0 \\ 0 & 0 & 0 \end{bmatrix}$

7. a.

	Low	Average	High
Low	0.5	0.45	0.05
Average	0.25	0.5	0.25
High	0.3	0.3	0.4

b. After one generation $[0.32 \quad 0.4575 \quad 0.2225]$
After two generations $[0.341125 \quad 0.4395 \quad 0.219375]$
After three generations
$[0.34625 \quad 0.43906875 \quad 0.21468125]$
In the long run
$[0.3474903475 \quad 0.4401544402 \quad 0.2123552124]$

8. 0.375

9. a. $\begin{bmatrix} 7 & 3 & 0 \\ {}^-19 & {}^-7 & 8 \\ 5 & 2 & {}^-1 \end{bmatrix}$ **b.** $\begin{bmatrix} {}^-2 & 5 \\ 8 & 7 \end{bmatrix}$ **c.** $[13 \quad 29]$ **d.** This is not possible because the number of columns in [A] does not match the number of rows in [B].

e. $\begin{bmatrix} 4 & {}^-1 \\ 4 & {}^-2 \end{bmatrix}$ **f.** This is not possible because the dimensions aren't the same. The dimensions must be the same in order to add or subtract.

10. Answers will vary.

Chapter Review
Problem Set 8.8

1. Answers will vary.

2. Answers will vary.
    a. Look for a well shuffled full deck after each draw to ensure a random pick each time.
    b. A painfully slow method if you need many numbers. Will randomness depend on who is called?
    c. This depends on randomness involved in falling off and besides, the numbers 1–12 aren't equally likely.

3. a. int 10 rand + 3   **b.** int 10 rand − 7   **c.** 5 rand − 2

4. a. $\frac{1}{2}$ **b.** 17.765

5. a. 64 possible outcomes   **b.** 10 possible outcomes
    c. $\frac{10}{64} \approx 0.156$ **d.** $\frac{49}{64} \approx 0.766$

6. a. There are 32 branches.   **b.** 10 ways   **c.** 0.375

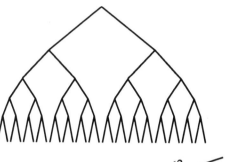

7. a.

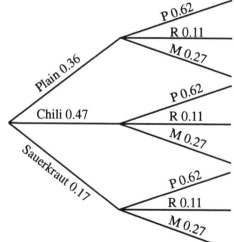

    b. 0.0517
    c. 0.8946
    d. 0.3501

8. a.

	9th grade	10th grade	11th grade	12th grade	Total
Ice cream	18	37	85	114	254
Whipped cream	5	18	37	58	118
Total	23	55	122	172	372

    b. 0.673   **c.** 0.303
    d. 0.071   **e.** 0.317

9. 11.05

10. $[479.167 \quad 520.833]$; $[400 \quad 600]$

11. Answers will vary.

12. Answers will vary.

Chapter 9

Problem Set 9.1

1. a. $(0, 1)$, $(1, 2)$, $(5, 26)$ **b.** When $x < 0$ or when $1 < x < 5$; when $0 < x < 1$ or $x > 5$

2. a. Answers will vary. **b.** 1.25, 1.176470588, 0.0735294118; y_3 is the difference between y_1 and y_2.
 c. $y_3 = 0$ **d.** The graph never crosses the x-axis. **e.** The equations do not intersect.

3. $(9.063, 2.393)$

4. a. The springs are the same length when 48.57 g of mass are added.
 b. When 120 g have been added, the second spring is 10 cm longer.
 c. Answers will vary.

5. Answers will vary.

6. a. No; when 25 pogo sticks are sold, the cost line is above the income line.
 b. Yes; about $120 **c.** About 120 pogo sticks **d.** About $80

7. a. Answers will vary depending on the regression equations used. If least-squares lines are used, they intersect
 in approximately the year 2022.
 b. Answers will vary. The least-squares lines are $y = 162.04 - 0.54x$ for men and $y = 198.76 - 0.84x$ for women
 if 1900 is listed as $x = 0$.
 c. Answers will vary.
 d. For the 1994 Olympics, $x = 94$. Using the men's model, the predicted time would be $y = 162.04 - 0.54(94) =$
 111.28 sec = 1.85 min or 1:51. The model is off 1:51.29 – 1:51 = 0.29 sec. Using the women's model, the
 predicted time would be $y = 198.76 - 0.84(94) = 119.8$ sec = 2.00 min. The model is off by 2:02.19 – 2:00 =
 2.19 sec. The actual times are close to the predicted times of the models. The residual for the 1994 mens'
 time is 0.005 min and for the 1994 women's time is 0.0365 min.

8. a. A cost equation modeling the Phrequent
 Phoner Plan is $Cost = 20 + 17(\text{int } x - 1)$,
 and a cost equation modeling the Pals and
 Buddies Plan is $Cost = 50 + 11(\text{int } x - 1)$.

 b.

[0, 10, 1, 0, 200, 20]

 c. If the time of the phone call is less than 6 min, the
 Phrequent Phoner Plan is less expensive. For times
 between 6 and 7 min, the plans charge the same rate.
 If the time of the phone call is greater than or equal to
 7 min the Phrequent Phoner Plan is more expensive than
 the Pals and Buddies Plan.

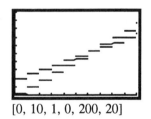

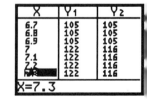

Problem Set 9.2

1. a. $(-4.7, 29.57)$ **b.** $\left(6\frac{2}{3}, 1\frac{4}{9}\right)$ **c.** $(-3.36, 9.308)$

2. a. $(13.42, 4.47)$ and $(-13.42, -4.47)$ **b.** $(1.41, -2.59)$ and $(-1.41, -5.41)$

3. a. $y = 47 + 11.5x$; $y = 59 + 4.95x$ **b.** $x \approx 1.83$ yr **c.** Answers will vary.

4. a. $(-0.53297, 2.71429)$ **b.** $\left(8, -\frac{5}{2}\right)$

5. Graphing windows will vary.

a.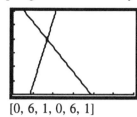

[0, 6, 1, 0, 6, 1]

b.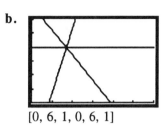

[0, 6, 1, 0, 6, 1]

c. $1.8y = 8.46x - 7.2$
    $4.7y = -8.46x + 32.9$
d. $y \approx 3.954$
e. Answers will vary.

6. a. Multiply by 3; $y \approx 2.475$; $(-0.9088, 2.4746)$
   b. Multiply by -3; $y \approx -6.786$; $(6.286, -6.786)$

7. a. Multiply by -3.6; $x \approx -0.9088$; $(-0.9088, 2.4746)$
   b. Multiply by 2; $x \approx 6.286$; $(6.286, -6.786)$

8. a. Multiply the first equation by 5 and the second equation by 3; $(0.727, 2.409)$.
   b. Multiply the first equation by 2; $(1.41, -2)$ and $(-1.41, -2)$.

9. $80°$

10. Answers will vary.

11. The 31st term; 21

Problem Set 9.3

1. a. ii, iii   **b.** The lines are parallel.   **c.** The result is a numerical impossibility.
   d. The lines have the same slope.

2. Answers will vary. Samples are given below.
   a. $y = 2x + b$ where b is any number except 4.   **b.** $y = \frac{-1}{3}x + b$ where b is any number except -3.
   c. $2x + 5y = b$ where b is any number except 10.   **d.** $x - 2y = b$ where b is any number except -6.

3. a. ii, iii   **b.** The lines are the same.   **c.** The result is a true statement.
   d. They have the same slope and the same intercept; or they are multiples of each other.

4. Answers will vary. Samples are given below.
   a. $2y = 4x + 8$, or multiply the original equation by any other number.
   b. $3y = -x - 9$, or multiply the original equation by any other number.
   c. $4x + 10y = 20$, or multiply the original equation by any other number.
   d. $2x - 4y = -12$, or multiply the original equation by any other number.

5. a. $t = 0.25$, $x = 1.75$, $y = -1.5$ **b.** No solution

6. They pass over the same spot about 18 min apart. It doesn't seem as if there is any danger. At the closest point they are about 34 mi apart.

7. $a = 100$ and $b = 0.7$

8. $y_1 = 6 - 23 \text{ int } -x$, $y_2 = 550 - 175 \text{ int}\left(\frac{-x}{16}\right)$; y_1 is more expensive when $46 < x \le 48$ or $x > 54$ oz.

9. $\tan 50° = \frac{h}{x}$; $\tan 40° = \frac{h}{10 + x}$; $x \approx 23.8$ m and $h \approx 28.36$ m

10. a. Answers will vary. If a least-squares model is used for both populations, the lines intersect approximately in the year 1996.
   b. 903,634 people
   c. The least-squares lines are $y = -830,011.6 + 18,051.82x$ and $y = 293,0012.7 - 21,099.93x$.

11. There are two possible answers: 12 peacocks, 16 pigeons, 20 swans, and 24 *sārasa* birds or 0 peacocks, 32 pigeons, 40 swans, and 0 *sārasa* birds.

Problem Set 9.4

1. a. $\begin{bmatrix} 15 & -19 \\ 22 & -27 \end{bmatrix}$ b. $\begin{bmatrix} 7 & -18 & -7 \\ 12 & -27 & 42 \\ 1 & -4 & -21 \end{bmatrix}$ c. This is not possible because you need the same number of rows in the second matrix as you have columns in the first matrix.

2. a. $a = 3, b = -7, c = -2, d = 8$ b. $a = \frac{-1}{14}, b = \frac{5}{28}, c = \frac{3}{14}, d = \frac{-1}{28}$

3. a. Yes, it's an inverse.   b. Yes, it's an inverse.
   c. Answers will vary. Two matrices are inverses if when you multiply them together you get the identity matrix as the answer.

4. a. $\begin{bmatrix} 4 & -3 \\ -5 & 4 \end{bmatrix}$ b. $\begin{bmatrix} -0.5555 & 1.4444 & 0.1111 \\ 0.5 & -1 & 0 \\ -1.6666 & 2.3333 & 0.3333 \end{bmatrix}$ c. $\begin{bmatrix} 1.4 & -0.6 \\ -2 & 1 \end{bmatrix}$
   d. $\begin{bmatrix} -0.1190 & 0.1905 & 0.1667 \\ -0.0238 & 0.2381 & -0.1667 \\ -0.3095 & 0.0952 & -0.1667 \end{bmatrix}$

5. a. $\begin{bmatrix} 5.2 & 3.6 \\ -5.2 & 2 \end{bmatrix}\begin{bmatrix} x \\ y \end{bmatrix} = \begin{bmatrix} 7 \\ 8.2 \end{bmatrix}$ b. $\begin{bmatrix} \frac{1}{4} & \frac{-2}{5} \\ \frac{3}{8} & \frac{2}{5} \end{bmatrix}\begin{bmatrix} x \\ y \end{bmatrix} = \begin{bmatrix} 3 \\ 2 \end{bmatrix}$

6. a. $\begin{bmatrix} 4 \\ 3 \end{bmatrix}$ b. $\begin{bmatrix} -3 \\ 1 \end{bmatrix}$ c. $\begin{bmatrix} 0.5 \\ 6 \\ 3 \end{bmatrix}$ d. $\begin{bmatrix} -1 \\ 1 \\ -2 \\ 3 \end{bmatrix}$

7. a. $2l + 2w = 44$ b. $2l + b = 40$ c. $f = 1.8c + 32$
      $l = 2 + 2w$ $b = l - 2$ $f = 3c - 0.4$
      $l = \frac{46}{3}$ and $w = \frac{20}{3}$ $b = 12$ and $l = 14$ $c = 27°$ and $f = 80.6°$

8. a. The three equations are: $7t + 3a + 9s = 19.55$; $9t + 10a = 13$; $8t + 7a + 10s = 24.95$
      Rides for the timid cost $0.50. Rides for the adventurous cost $0.85. Rides for the thrill seekers cost $1.50.
   b. $28.50
   c. Carey would have been better off buying a ticket book for $28.50 because it cost her $24.95 + $5.00 or $29.95.

9. a. $14,600; $13,100   b. $y = 12,500 + 0.6x$ c. $y = 6800 + 1.8x$
   d. More than 4750 tickets   e. Answers will vary.

10. There are 12 students in the second hour, 18 in the third hour, and 24 in the seventh hour.

11. The price of a citron is 8; the price of a fragrant wood apple is 5.

Problem Set 9.5

1. $y \geq 2.4x + 2$ and $y \leq -x^2 - 2x + 6.4$; All inequations are shaded so that the feasible region is not shaded.

2.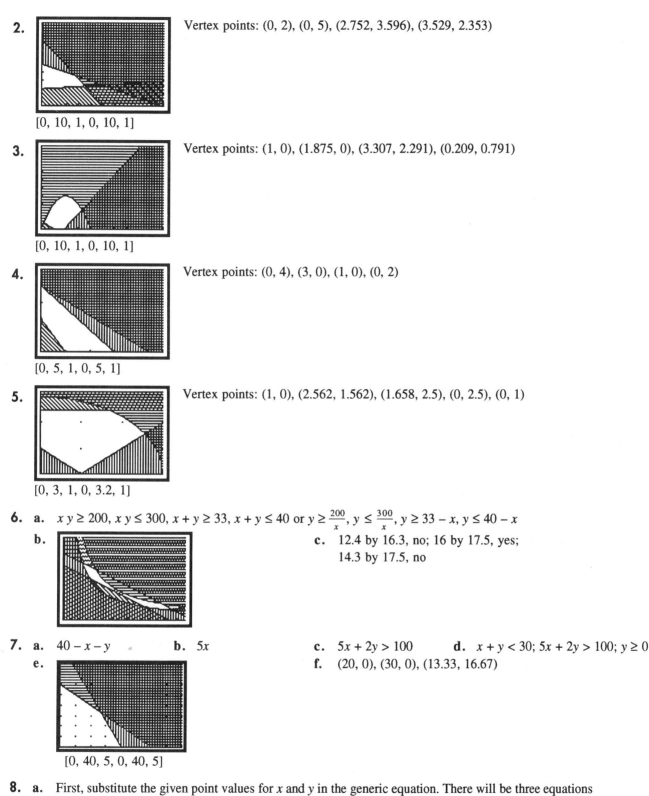

[0, 10, 1, 0, 10, 1]

Vertex points: (0, 2), (0, 5), (2.752, 3.596), (3.529, 2.353)

3.

[0, 10, 1, 0, 10, 1]

Vertex points: (1, 0), (1.875, 0), (3.307, 2.291), (0.209, 0.791)

4.

[0, 5, 1, 0, 5, 1]

Vertex points: (0, 4), (3, 0), (1, 0), (0, 2)

5.

[0, 3, 1, 0, 3.2, 1]

Vertex points: (1, 0), (2.562, 1.562), (1.658, 2.5), (0, 2.5), (0, 1)

6. a. $x\,y \geq 200$, $x\,y \leq 300$, $x + y \geq 33$, $x + y \leq 40$ or $y \geq \frac{200}{x}$, $y \leq \frac{300}{x}$, $y \geq 33 - x$, $y \leq 40 - x$

b.

c. 12.4 by 16.3, no; 16 by 17.5, yes;
14.3 by 17.5, no

7. a. $40 - x - y$ **b.** $5x$

c. $5x + 2y > 100$ **d.** $x + y < 30$; $5x + 2y > 100$; $y \geq 0$

e.

[0, 40, 5, 0, 40, 5]

f. (20, 0), (30, 0), (13.33, 16.67)

8. a. First, substitute the given point values for x and y in the generic equation. There will be three equations in three variables, a, b, and c. Set up a matrix equation in the form [A] [X] = [B] and find [X].

b. The parabola is $3x^2 + 16x - 12$.

c. Answers will vary.

9. Answers will vary.

Problem Set 9.6

Change the window format to Grid On in order to see the integer points in the feasible region. All inequations are shaded such that the feasible region is not shaded. Points on the border are part of the interior also because the inequations are not strict inequations.

1. i. a. $y \leq \frac{-2x+6}{3}$, $y \leq 6 - 4x$, $x > 0$, $y > 0$

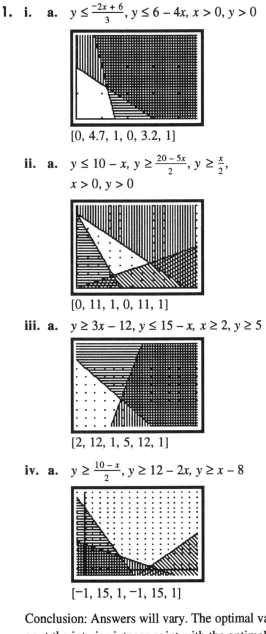

$[0, 4.7, 1, 0, 3.2, 1]$

b. $(0, 0)$, $(1.5, 0)$, $(1.2, 1.2)$, $(0, 2)$
c. $(0, 0)$, $(0, 1)$, $(0, 2)$, $(1, 0)$, $(1, 1)$;
The maximum value of 7 occurs at $(1, 1)$.
d. The maximum value of 12 occurs at $(1.2, 1.2)$.

ii. a. $y \leq 10 - x$, $y \geq \frac{20-5x}{2}$, $y \geq \frac{x}{2}$,
$x > 0$, $y > 0$

$[0, 11, 1, 0, 11, 1]$

b. $(3.3333, 1.6667)$, $(6.6667, 3.3333)$, $(0, 10)$
c. $(0, 10)$, $(1, 8)$, $(1, 9)$, $(2, 6)$, $(2, 7)$, $(2, 8)$, $(3, 3)$,
$(3, 4)$, $(3, 5)$, $(3, 6)$, $(3, 7)$, $(4, 2)$, $(4, 3)$, $(4, 4)$,
$(4, 5)$, $(4, 6)$, $(5, 3)$, $(5, 4)$, $(5, 5)$, $(6, 3)$, $(6, 4)$.
The minimum value of 10 occurs at $(4, 2)$.
d. The minimum value of 8.3333 occurs at $(3.3333, 1.6667)$.

iii. a. $y \geq 3x - 12$, $y \leq 15 - x$, $x \geq 2$, $y \geq 5$

$[2, 12, 1, 5, 12, 1]$

b. $(2, 5)$, $(5.6667, 5)$, $(6.75, 8.25)$, $(2, 13)$
c. $(2, 5)$, $(2, 6) \ldots (2, 13)$; $(3, 5)$, $(3, 6) \ldots (3, 12)$
$(4, 5)$, $(4, 6) \ldots (4, 11)$; $(5, 5)$, $(5, 6) \ldots (5, 10)$
$(6, 6)$, $(6, 7) \ldots (6, 9)$
The maximum value of 21 occurs at $(6, 9)$.
d. The maximum value of 21.75 for vertex points occurs at $(6.75, 8.25)$.

iv. a. $y \geq \frac{10-x}{2}$, $y \geq 12 - 2x$, $y \geq x - 8$

$[-1, 15, 1, -1, 15, 1]$

b. $(4.6667, 2.6667)$, $(8.6667, 0.6667)$
c. There are an infinite set of possible interior points.
The minimum value of 20 occurs at $(4, 4)$.
d. The minimum value of 19.3333 occurs at $(4.6667, 2.6667)$.

Conclusion: Answers will vary. The optimal value is always located at the vertex of a region closest to or at the interior integer point with the optimal value.

2. a.

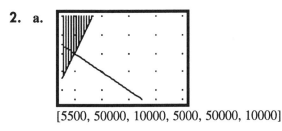

$[5500, 50000, 10000, 5000, 50000, 10000]$

b. $(10,000, 30,000)$; $3,800$

3. a. There are zero or more of each species in the region. (There cannot be a negative number of birds.)

b. The area required by species X plus the area required by species Y is no more than 180,000 m².

c. The total food requirements of species X plus the total food requirements of species Y is no more than 72,000 kg.

d. 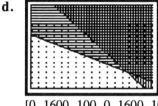 The vertices of the region are (0, 0), (1500, 0), (1263.2, 315.8), and (0, 1034.5).

[0, 1600, 100, 0, 1600, 100]

e. The maximum number of nesting pairs is 1578.

4. Answers will vary.

Problem Set 9.7

1.

	Number of shawls (x)	Number of afghans (y)	Constraining value
Spinning (hr)	1	2	≤ 8
Dyeing (hr)	1	1	≤ 6
Weaving (hr)	1	4	≤ 14
Profit	$16	$20	

$x + 2y \le 8$, $x + y \le 6$, $x + 4y \le 14$, $x \ge 0$, $y \ge 0$: Profit $= 16x + 20y$

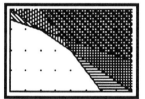 Vertices: (0, 0), (6, 0), (4, 2), (2, 3), (0, 3.5)
The maximum profit occurs at (4, 2) or 16(4) + 20(2) = $104.
They should make four shawls and two afghans.

[0, 8, 1, 0, 4, 1]

2.

	Siberians	Poodles	Constraining value
Number of poodles		y	≤ 20
Number of Siberians	x		≤ 15
Food	6	2	≤ 100
Training	250	1000	≤ 10000
Profit	80	200	

$y \le 20$, $x \le 15$, $6x + 2y \le 100$, $250x + 1,000y \le 10,000$, $x \ge 0$, $y \ge 0$: Profit $= 80x + 200y$

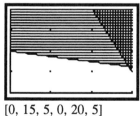 The vertices of the feasible region are (0, 0), (15, 0), (15, 5), (14.5455, 6.3636), and (0, 10).
To maximize profits, they should raise 14 Siberians and
6 poodles: 80(14) + 200(6) = $2,320.

[0, 15, 5, 0, 20, 5]

3. x = the number of newspaper ads; y = the number of radio ads; Newspaper minimum: $x \geq 4$; radio minimum: $y \geq 5$; cost: $50x + 100y \leq 1000$ or $y \leq \frac{1000 - 50x}{100}$; optimize number of people reached: $8{,}000x + 15{,}000y$

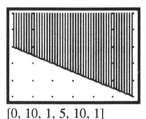

[0, 10, 1, 5, 10, 1]

The vertices of the feasible region are (4, 5), (4, 8), and (10, 5).
To maximize the number of people reached, place ten radio ads and five newspaper ads: $8{,}000(10) + 15{,}000(5) = 155{,}000$ people.
Answers will vary. One assumption may be that people who listen to the radio are independent of people who read the newspaper.

4.

	Hectares of coffee (x)	Hectares of cocoa (y)	Constraining values
Available land	x	y	$\leq 500{,}000$
Hectares of coffee (x)	x		$\geq 100{,}000$
Hectares of cocoa (y)		y	$\geq 200{,}000$
Production		y	$\leq 270{,}000$
Available workers	$2x$	$5y$	$\leq 1{,}750{,}000$
Profit	$220x$	$310y$	

$x + y \leq 500{,}000$, $x \geq 100{,}000$, $y \geq 200{,}000$, $y \leq 270{,}000$, $2x + 5y \leq 1{,}750{,}000$: Profit $= 220x + 310y$

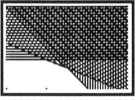

[100000, 400000, 100000, 200000, 400000, 100000]

The vertices of the feasible region are (100,000, 200,000), (300,000, 200,000), (250,000, 250,000), (100,000, 270,000), and (200,000, 270,000).
The maximum profit occurs when you plant 250,000 hectares of coffee and 250,000 hectares of cocoa: Profit $= 220x + 310y = 220(250{,}000) + 310(250{,}000) = \$132{,}500{,}000$.

5.

	Number of barrels of low-sulfur oil	Number of barrels of high-sulfur oil	Constraining values
Total barrels	x	y	≥ 1200
Percentage	$0.02x$	$0.06y$	$\leq 0.04(x + y)$
Cost	$18.50x$	$14.70x$	

$x + y \geq 1200$ or $y \geq 1200 - x$; $0.02x + 0.06y \leq 0.04(x + y)$: Cost $= 18.50x + 14.70y$

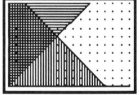

[0, 1500, 100, 0, 1000, 100]

The vertices of the feasible region are (1200, 0) and (600, 600). The minimum cost will occur when you use 600 barrels of the low-sulfur and 600 barrels of the high-sulfur oil. Cost $= 18.50(600) + 14.70(600) = \$19{,}920$.

Problem Set 9.8

1. Only parts b and d have solutions; all other coefficient matrices have a determinant of zero.

2. **a.** Dependent; the point (16, −5.333333) works in both equations.
  c. Dependent; the point (21, −17, 1) works in all equations.
  e. Inconsistent; the point (16, 15.667, −3.862) does not work in the first equation, but does work in the other two.
  f. Inconsistent; the point (1, 1.209, 1.116, 0.256) does not work in the first equation, but does work in the other three.

3.

	True/false (w)	Fill in the blank (x)	Matching (y)	Essay (z)	Constraints
Points	$2w$	$4x$	$6y$	$10z$	$= 100$
Time	$1w$	$2x$	$5y$	$6z$	$= 60$
Lines	$4w$	$3x$	$15y$	$9z$	$= 110$

The equations are: $2w + 4x + 6y + 10z = 100$, $1w + 2x + 5y + 6z = 60$, and $4w + 3x + 15y + 9z = 110$. Two integer solutions are (2, 6, 2, 6) and (5, 1, 1, 8).

4. a.–b. Answers will vary.

5. Answers will vary.

6. Answers will vary.

Chapter Review

Problem Set 9.9

1. (0.634, ⁻0.598) and (2.366, 4.598)

2. a. Answers will vary. No window is really good to see the intersection, but one possible window is [0, 20, 2, 0, 45, 5].

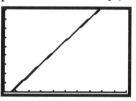

b.

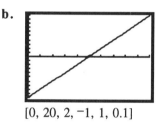

[0, 20, 2, ⁻1, 1, 0.1]

c. $3.2x - 4 = 3.1x - 3$ **d.** $x = 10$

e. Equation 1 can be rewritten as $0 = 3.2x - 4 - y$. Now substitute the second equation, which equals y, into the above equation, resulting in $0 = 3.2x - 4 - (3.1x - 3)$. Solving this resulting equation for x will give you the x-intercept for y_3.

3. a. (⁻1.325, 10.183) **b.** (8.4, 5.3)

4. a. $(\frac{2}{3}, 1)$ **b.** (1, 0)

5. 5a is consistent; 5c and 5d are inconsistent; 5b is dependent.

6. a. $\begin{bmatrix} 0.8 & {}^-0.6 \\ 0.2 & {}^-0.4 \end{bmatrix}$ **b.** $\begin{bmatrix} {}^-0.0353 & 0.1882 & {}^-0.0235 \\ 0.2118 & {}^-0.1294 & 0.1412 \\ {}^-0.3765 & 0.3412 & 0.0824 \end{bmatrix}$

c. None **d.** $\begin{bmatrix} {}^-0.0893 & 0.1429 & 0.125 \\ {}^-0.0536 & 0.2857 & {}^-0.125 \\ {}^-0.5179 & 0.4286 & 0.125 \end{bmatrix} = \begin{bmatrix} {}^-\frac{5}{56} & \frac{1}{7} & \frac{1}{8} \\ {}^-\frac{3}{56} & \frac{2}{7} & {}^-\frac{1}{8} \\ {}^-\frac{29}{56} & \frac{3}{7} & \frac{1}{8} \end{bmatrix}$

7. a. $\begin{bmatrix} 3.758 \\ 2.613 \end{bmatrix}$ **b.** $\begin{bmatrix} {}^-39.143 \\ 24.592 \\ 8.816 \\ {}^-34.449 \end{bmatrix}$

8. a. $y \leq \frac{12 - 2x}{3}$, $y \leq 18 - 6x$, $y \geq \frac{2 - x}{2}$, $x > 0$, $y \geq 0$

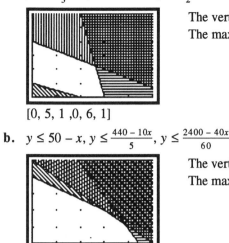

[0, 5, 1 ,0, 6, 1]

The vertices are (0, 4), (2.625, 2.25), (3, 0), (2, 0), and (0, 1).
The maximum value occurs at (0, 4): 1.65(0) + 5.2(4) = 20.8.

b. $y \leq 50 - x$, $y \leq \frac{440 - 10x}{5}$, $y \leq \frac{2400 - 40x}{60}$

The vertices are (0, 40), (30, 20), (38, 12), and (44, 0).
The maximum value occurs at (30, 20): 6(30) + 7(20) = 320.

[0, 50, 10, 0, 50, 10]

9. A new heater will pay for itself in about 4.4 yr.

10. a. $2x + 1y + 3z = 5$

   b. $4x + 0y + 1z = 6$; $0x + 2y + 1z = 2$

   c. $x = 1.375$; $y = 0.75$; $z = 0.5$

   d. Change the matrix to fractions. The multiplier is 8; 11, 6, 4.

   e. 11 parts of mixture 1, 6 parts of mixture 2, 4 parts of mixture 3

11. Answers will vary.

12. Answers will vary.

Chapter 10

Problem Set 10.1

1. a. $y = 10,000x^4 + 5,000x^2 + 2,000$ **b.** Answers will vary.
   c. 1.006   **d.** 7.2%

2. a. $\left(1 - \frac{p}{100}\right)$ **b.** $30x^3$ **c.** 55   **d.** 45%

3. a. $50x^3 + 70x^2 + 90x$ **b.** 0.3976   **c.** 60.24%

4. a. 1, 3, 6, 10, 15, 21, 28   **b.** D_1 = 2, 3, 4, 5, 6, 7; D_2 = 1, 1, 1, 1, 1
   c. Second degree: you need to find the differences twice before the differences are all equal.
   d. They are the number of pieces needed to build a triangle with n rows.

5. a. D_1 = 15.1, 5.3, −4.5, −14.3, −24.1, −33.9; D_2 = −9.8, −9.8, . . .
   b. D_1 = 59.1, 49.3, 39.5, 29.7, 19.9, 10.1; D_2 = −9.8, −9.8, . . .
   c. Second degree
   d. $h = -4.9t^2 + 20t + 80$

6. a. b = 1, 5, 14, 30, 55, 91   **b.** D_1 = 4, 9, 16, 25, 36; D_2 = 5, 7, 9, 11;
   D_3 = 2, 2, 2; degree = 3

   c. $b = \frac{1}{3}n^3 + \frac{1}{2}n^2 + \frac{1}{6}n$ **d.** 204 blocks   **e.** 12 layers

Problem Set 10.2

1. a. $y = x^2 - 4x + 7$ **b.** $y = x^2 + 8x + 14$ **c.** $y = 2x^2 - 20x + 46$ **d.** $y = -0.5x^2 - x + 3.5$
e. $y = -3x^2 + 24x - 48$ **f.** $y = 1.5x^2 - 3$

2. a. $y = -0.5x^2 - Hx - 0.5H^2 + 4$ **b.** $y = Ax^2 - 8Ax + 16A$
c. $y = Ax^2 - 2AHx + AH^2 + K$

3. a. $y = (x + 3)^2 - 2$; $y = x^2 + 6x + 7$
b. $y = -(x - 4)^2 + 3$; $y = -x^2 + 8x - 13$
c. $y = 2(x - 2)^2 - 4$; $y = 2x^2 - 8x + 4$
d. $y = -0.5(x + 1.5)^2 + 3$; $y = -0.5x^2 - 1.5x + 1.875$
e. $y = A(x - H)^2 + K$; $y = Ax^2 - 2AHx + AH^2 + K$

4. a. $3, 2, -5$ **b.** $3, 2 + d, 14s^2$ **c.** $2, 12, 22$ **d.** $-3, 30, -76$

5. a. $A, -2AH, K + AH^2$ **b.** $a = A$ **c.** $b = -2AH$; $H = \frac{-b}{2a}$ **d.** $c = K + AH^2$; $K = c - \frac{b^2}{4a}$
e. Answers will vary.

6. a. $(2.17, -2.08)$; $y = 3(x - 2.17)^2 - 2.08$ **b.** $(-3, 2)$; $y = (x + 3)^2 + 2$
c. $(-1, -9)$; $y = (x + 1)^2 - 9$ **d.** $(1.375, 35.25)$; $y = -16(x - 1.375)^2 + 35.25$
e. $(1.25, 12.125)$; $y = -2(x - 1.25)^2 + 12.125$

7. $T = 0.031w^2 - 2.31w + 37.8$; (37.3 mi/hr, $-5.23°$F)

8. a. Number sold = 200, 195, 190, 185, 180
b. Revenue = 400, 409.50, 418, 425.50, 432; D_1 = 9.5, 8.5, 7.5, 6.5; $D_2 = -1, -1, -1$
c. $y = -50x^2 + 300x$
d. \$450; \$3

9. a.

Width	5	10	15	20	25
Length	35	30	25	20	15
Area	175	300	375	400	375

b. $a = -w^2 + 40w$ **c.** Width = 20 m, area = 400 m²
d. 0 m or 40 m **e.** Greater than 40 m or less than 0 m

10. a.–c. Answers will vary.

Problem Set 10.3

1. a. x-intercepts, 7.5, -2.5, 3.2; y-intercept, 150 **b.** $y = 2.5x^3 - 20.5x^2 - 6.875x + 150$
c.

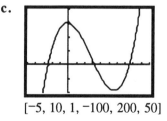

$[-5, 10, 1, -100, 200, 50]$

2. a. $y = -4.9(x - 0.7)(x - 2.8)$ **b.** $(1.75, 5.4)$; at 1.75 sec, the ball reaches a height of 5.4 m.
c. -9.604; the well is 9.6 m deep. **d.** The maximum changes, but the roots stay the same.

3. a. x-intercepts, -1.5 and -6; y-intercept, -2.25; vertex, $(-3.75, 1.265625)$
b. x-intercept, 4; y-intercept, 48; vertex, (4, 0)

    c.   *x*-intercepts, 3, ⁻2, and 5; *y*-intercept, 60; no vertex

    d.   *x*-intercepts, 3 and ⁻3; *y*-intercept, ⁻135; no vertex

4. Answers will vary, but the graphs will have the following shapes and number of intercepts. Each window is [⁻9.4, 9.4, 1, ⁻6.2, 6.2, 1].

    a. $y = (x - 3)^2$ **b.** $y = (x - 3)^2 + 1$

    c. $y = (x - 3)^3 + 1$ **d.** $y = (x - 3)(x - 5)^2$

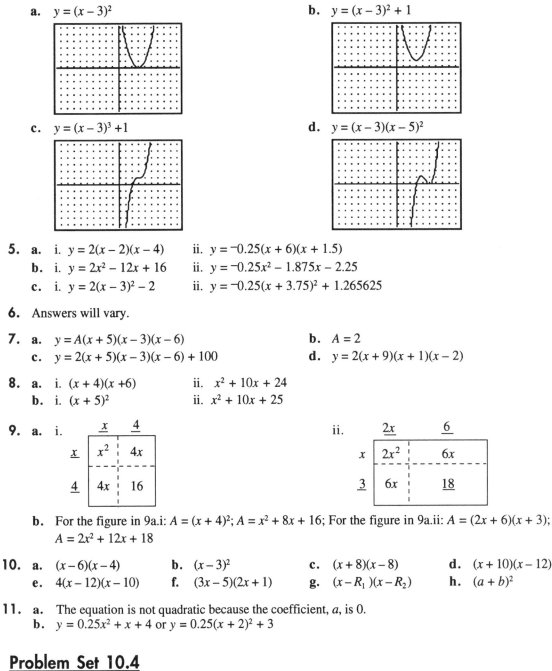

5. **a.**   i. $y = 2(x - 2)(x - 4)$ ii. $y = {}^{-}0.25(x + 6)(x + 1.5)$

    b.   i. $y = 2x^2 - 12x + 16$ ii. $y = {}^{-}0.25x^2 - 1.875x - 2.25$

    c.   i. $y = 2(x - 3)^2 - 2$ ii. $y = {}^{-}0.25(x + 3.75)^2 + 1.265625$

6. Answers will vary.

7. **a.** $y = A(x + 5)(x - 3)(x - 6)$ **b.** $A = 2$

    c. $y = 2(x + 5)(x - 3)(x - 6) + 100$ **d.** $y = 2(x + 9)(x + 1)(x - 2)$

8. **a.**   i. $(x + 4)(x + 6)$ ii. $x^2 + 10x + 24$

    b.   i. $(x + 5)^2$ ii. $x^2 + 10x + 25$

9. **a.**   i.

                                                        ii.

    b.   For the figure in 9a.i: $A = (x + 4)^2$; $A = x^2 + 8x + 16$; For the figure in 9a.ii: $A = (2x + 6)(x + 3)$; $A = 2x^2 + 12x + 18$

10. **a.** $(x - 6)(x - 4)$ **b.** $(x - 3)^2$ **c.** $(x + 8)(x - 8)$ **d.** $(x + 10)(x - 12)$

    e. $4(x - 12)(x - 10)$ **f.** $(3x - 5)(2x + 1)$ **g.** $(x - R_1)(x - R_2)$ **h.** $(a + b)^2$

11. **a.**   The equation is not quadratic because the coefficient, *a*, is 0.

    b. $y = 0.25x^2 + x + 4$ or $y = 0.25(x + 2)^2 + 3$

Problem Set 10.4

1. **a.** $(2x - 3)^2$ **b.** $\left(x + \frac{5}{2}\right)^2$ **c.** $(x - y)^2$

2. **a.** ⁻2.7, 7.3   **b.** ⁻7.95, ⁻0.95   **c.** $-\frac{1}{2}$, 2

3. **a.** $3x^2 - 13x - 10 = 0$ **b.** $x^2 - 5x - 13 = 0$

         $a = 3, b = {}^{-}13, c = {}^{-}10$ $a = 1, b = {}^{-}5, c = {}^{-}13$

         $\frac{-2}{3}$, 5 or ⁻0.667, 5 $\frac{5 \pm \sqrt{77}}{2}$ or ⁻1.887, 6.887

c. $3x^2 + 5x + 1 = 0$

$a = 3, b = 5, c = 1$

$\frac{-5 \pm \sqrt{13}}{6}$ or $-1.434, -0.232$

d. $3x^2 - 3x - 2 = 0$

$a = 3, b = -3, c = -2$

$\frac{3 \pm \sqrt{33}}{6}$ or $-0.457, 1.457$

e. $x^2 - 15x + 50 = 0$

$a = 1, b = -15, c = 50$

$x = 5, 10$

4. a. At time $t = 1.81$ sec the projectile is located approximately at $(6.05, 0)$.

b. At time $t = 2.56$ sec the projectile is located approximately at $(19.9, 0)$.

c. At time $t = 9.48$ sec the projectile is located approximately at $(9, 0)$.

5. Answers will vary. Those listed below are only examples.

a. $(x - 3)(x + 3) = 0$ **b.** $(x - 4)(5x + 2) = 0$ **c.** $(x - R_1)(x - R_2) = 0$ **d.** $-4.9(x - 1.1)(x - 4.7) = 0$

6. Answers will vary. The calculator will give an error message or produce an answer in complex form. The value under the radical is negative. The graph does not cross the x-axis. Example: $y = x^2 + 1$.

7. a. Many solutions are possible depending on which points are selected. The example below uses points $(10, 19)$, $(40, 116)$, and $(60, 248)$:

$$y = 0.07x^2 - 0.13x + 13.6.$$

b. Answers will vary depending on which three points were chosen. With real data, the point selection is very important.

c. Answers will vary. Choose points that are spread out rather than ones that are close together.

8. $\left(7 + 0.5\sqrt{300}\right)^2 - 14\left(7 + 0.5\sqrt{300}\right) - 26$

$49 + 7\sqrt{300} + 75 - 98 - 7\sqrt{300} - 26$

$49 + 75 - 98 - 26 + 7\sqrt{300} - 7\sqrt{300}$

$124 - 124 = 0$

$\left(7 - 0.5\sqrt{300}\right)^2 - 14\left(7 - 0.5\sqrt{300}\right) - 26$

$49 - 7\sqrt{300} + 75 - 98 + 7\sqrt{300} - 26$

$49 + 75 - 98 - 26 - 7\sqrt{300} + 7\sqrt{300}$

$124 - 124 = 0$

9. a. $y = \sqrt{400 - x^2}$ **b.** 17.3 ft   **c.** 8.7 ft   **d.** Pythagorean theorem: $a^2 + b^2 = c^2$

10. Pr9m3:QUADFORM

```
:Disp "A"
:Input A
:Disp "B"
:Input B
:Disp "C"
:Input C
:B2-4AC→D
:(-B+√D)/2A→X
:(-B-√D)/2A→R
:Disp X
:Disp R
```

11. Yes; $x = 40t \cos 60°$; $y = -16t^2 + 40t \sin 60°$

12. Answers will vary.

Problem Set 10.5

1. $y = -4.9x^2 = 227$ m; $y = -16x^2 = 740$ ft

2. a. $H(t) = -4.9t^2 + 100t + 25$

b. Height = 25 m; velocity = 100 m/sec

c. 10.2 sec

d. 535 m

e. 3.28 sec and 17.1 sec

f. 20.7 sec

3. a. $y = -20x^2 + 332x$ **b.** $8.30 each for a total of $1,377.80

4. a. $y = x(80 - 2x)$ **b.** 20 by 40 ft, area = 800 ft²

5. a. $y = 0.5x^2 + 0.5x + 1$ **b.** 5 cuts = 16 pieces; 10 cuts = 56 pieces; no

6. a. $y = (26 - 2x)(21 - 2x)$ **b.** $0 \le A \le 546$ in².   **c.** 3.395 in.

7. $y = 11000x^2 - Mx - M$

8. a. $y = -4x^3 + 38x^2 + 482x - 3640$ **b.** At $10.25, the maximum profit is $985.
c. At $6.50 or at $13.43 the profit would be 0.

9. a. $L = -4t^2 - 6.8t + 49.2$ **b.** 49.2 L   **c.** 2.76 min

Problem Set 10.6

1. a. $y = x - 4$ **b.** $y = (x - 4)^2$ **c.** $y = (x - 4)^3$

2. a.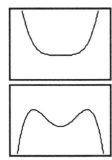
[−6, 6, 1, −150, 500, 100]

b.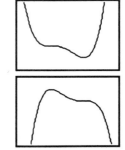
[−6, 6, 1, −700, 100, 100]

c.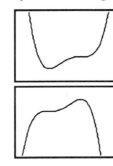
[−6, 6, 1, −1000, 100, 100]

d.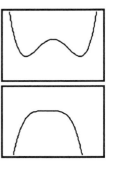
[−6, 6, 1, −1800, 100, 100]

e. When the exponent is 1, the curve passes through the axis. When the exponent is 2, the curve appears to bounce off the axis at the intercept.

3. a. 4 x-intercepts   **b.** Fifth degree   **c.** $y = -x(x + 5)^2(x + 1)(x - 4)$

4. a. Different values of A merely stretch the graph vertically, keeping all x-intercepts the same.
b. If $A = -2$, the graph will reflect over the x-axis.
c. They are both "U" shaped, but the quadratic is wider while the fourth degree graph is flatter at the bottom.
d. They both go from the lower left corner to the upper right corner. The first equation is a straight line, while the cubic has a flat spot at the x-intercept of 3.
e. The graph should start from the upper left corner, bounce off −4, go straight through −1, bounce off 3 from below, "s" through 5, and end up going to the upper right corner.

5. Answers will vary. You should come up with a basic "W" shape, either going up or turned upside down. The points of the W can vary in relative height or be basically the same.

6. False; answers will vary.

7. **a.** $y = (x + 5)^2(x + 2)(x - 1)$ **b.** $y = {}^-(x + 5)^2(x + 2)(x - 1)$
  c. $y = (x + 5)^2(x + 2)(x - 1)^2$ **d.** $y = {}^-(x + 5)(x + 2)^3(x - 1)$
  e. $\{-5, -5, -2, 1\}$ $\{-5, -5, -2, 1\}$ $\{-5, -5, -2, 1, 1\}$ $\{-5, -2, -2, -2, 1\}$

8. Answers will vary. Those provided here are based on a width of 21.6 cm.
  a. 15.9 and 30 cm²   **b.** 0 and 21.6 cm   **c.** $area = Ax(x - 21)(x - R_3)$
  d. $15.9 = {}^-55.8A(3 - R_3)$ and $30 = {}^-93.6A(6 - R_3)$; $area = {}^-.012x(x - 21)(x + 21.6)$
  e. $x = 21.5$ cm for an area of 45.2 cm²

Problem Set 10.7

1. **a.** $2 \pm i\sqrt{2}$ or $2 \pm 1.41i$; complex   **b.** $\pm i$; complex
  c. $\dfrac{-1 \pm i\sqrt{3}}{2} = {}^-0.5 \pm 0.866i$; complex

2. **a.** $x^2 - 2x - 15 = 0$ **b.** $x^2 + 7x + 12.25 = 0$
  c. $x^2 + 25 = 0$ **d.** $x^2 - 4x + 5 = 0$

3. **a.** $y = (x + 4)(x - 5)(x + 2)^2$ **b.** $y = {}^-2(x + 4)(x - 5)(x + 2)^2$
  c. $y = Ax(3x - 1)(5x + 2)$ **d.** $y = (x^2 + 25)(x + 1)^3(x - 4)$

4. **a.** $10.83i, {}^-0.83i$ **b.** $2i, i$
  c. The solutions do not come in conjugate pairs because the coefficients of the equation are imaginary.

5. **a.** $b^2 < 4ac$ **b.** $b^2 \geq 4ac$ **c.** $b^2 = 4ac$

6. When $x = {}^-2, 3,$ or 6, the y-value is 50. The y-intercept is $^-166$.

7. **a.**

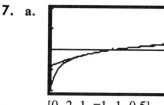

[0, 2, 1, −1, 1, 0.5]

  b. 1
  c. $0.0723\left[6(x - 1) - 3(x - 1)^2 + 2(x - 1)^3\right]$
  $= 0.0723\left[(x - 1)\left(6 - 3(x - 1) + 2(x - 1)^2\right)\right]$
  d. $1.75 \pm 1.56i$

8. **a.**

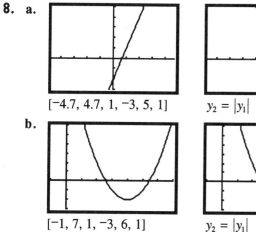

[−4.7, 4.7, 1, −3, 5, 1] $y_2 = |y_1|$

  b.

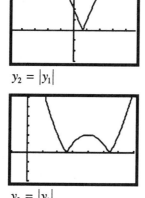

[−1, 7, 1, −3, 6, 1] $y_2 = |y_1|$

c.

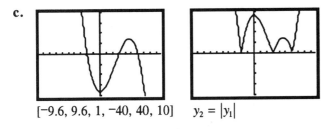

$[-9.6, 9.6, 1, -40, 40, 10]$ $y_2 = |y_1|$

9. See Calculator Note 10C.

Problem Set 10.8

1. a. $11(4) + 3 = 47$ **b.** $(x - 1)(6x^3 + x^2 + 8x - 4) + 11$
c. $(x - 2)(x^2 + x - 8)$

2. a. $x^4 - 5x^3 + 15x^2 - 45x + 54$ **b.** $x^3 - 3x^2 + 9x - 27$
c. $x^2 + 9$ **d.** $\pm 3i$ **e.** (Calculator check)

3. a. 4 zeros   **b.** $-5, -1, 2, 1$ **c.** 10   **d.** $(x + 5)(x + 1)(x - 1)(x - 2)$

4. a. $\pm 2i, \pm 2, \pm 1$ **b.** $-7.011074, -0.942787, 0.45386126$
c. $6.605, 12.501, 17.556, 11.675 \pm 0.380i$ **d.** $-3.033, 2.634, -0.3 \pm 0.812i.$

5. a. $-3.079, 0, 3.079$ **b.** $-3.141, 0, 3.141$ **c.** As the pattern continues, the real roots approach 0 and $\pm\pi$.

6. Answers will vary.

7. Answers will vary.

Chapter Review

Problem Set 10.9

1. $1; 4; 10; 20; 35; \ldots$; the expression for n points is $\frac{1}{6}n^3 + \frac{1}{2}n^2 + \frac{1}{3}n$.

2. a. $y = 2x^2 - 8x - 8; y = 2(x - 4.828)(x + 0.828)$
b. $y = -3x^2 + 12x + 15; y = -3(x - 2)^2 + 27$
c. $y = (x + 1)(x + 2); y = (x + 1.5)^2 - 0.25$
d. $y = x^3 + 2x^2 - 11x - 12$
e. $y = 2(x + 3.386)(x - 0.886); y = 2(x + 1.25)^2 - 9.125$
f. $y = -x^2 - 14x - 51; y = -(x + 7 + 1.414i)(x + 7 - 1.414i)$

3. 3a.–d., use the information from Problem 2 a.–d.

a.   **b.**

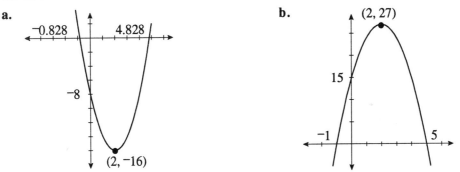

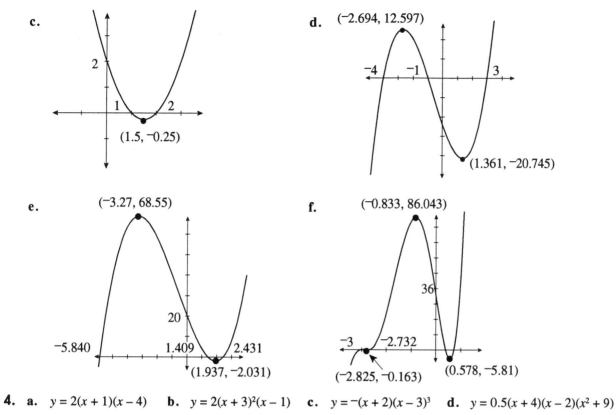

c. (1.5, ⁻0.25)

d. (⁻2.694, 12.597)   (1.361, ⁻20.745)

e. (⁻3.27, 68.55)   ⁻5.840   1.409   2.431   (1.937, ⁻2.031)   20

f. (⁻0.833, 86.043)   ⁻3   ⁻2.732   36   (⁻2.825, ⁻0.163)   (0.578, ⁻5.81)

4. a. $y = 2(x + 1)(x - 4)$ **b.** $y = 2(x + 3)^2(x - 1)$ **c.** $y = -(x + 2)(x - 3)^3$ **d.** $y = 0.5(x + 4)(x - 2)(x^2 + 9)$

5. 18 in. × 18 in. × 36 in.

6. Answers will vary.

7. Answers will vary.

Chapter 11

Problem Set 11.1

1. a. $8! = 40,320$ **b.** $7! = 5040$ **c.** $\frac{1}{8}$ **d.** Answers will vary.
   e. 0.5; answers will vary.   **f.** 1   **g.** 40,319
   h. 0.999975

2. a. 12   **b.** 7   **c.** $n + 1$ **d.** n
   e. $120(119) = 14,280$ **f.** $n(n - 1)$ **g.** $n + 1 = 15$; $n = 14$

3. a. Answers will vary.   **b.** $_7P_3 = \frac{7!}{4!}$; answers will vary.   **c.** Answers will vary.

4. a. 3,628,800   **b.** 0.1   **c.** 0.2   **d.** ≈ 0.01

5. 8,000,000

6.

N	Permutation (N!)	Time
5	120	0.00012 sec
10	3,628,800	3.6288 sec
12	479,001,600	≈ 8 min
13	6,227,020,800	≈ 1.7 hr
15	≈ $1.31 \cdot 10^{12}$	≈ 15 days
20	≈ $2.43 \cdot 10^{18}$	≈ 771 centuries

7. a. ≈ 0.07   **b.** ≈ 0.005   **c.** ≈ 0.16   **d.** $3.20

Problem Set 11.2

1. a. $_7P_2 = 2 \cdot {_7C_2}$ (2 = 2!)   **b.** $_7P_3 = 6 \cdot {_7C_3}$ (6 = 3!)   **c.** $_7P_4 = 24 \cdot {_7C_4}$ (24 = 4!)
     d. $_7P_7 = 5040 \cdot {_7C_7}$ (5040 = 7!)   **e.** $_nC_r = \frac{_nP_r}{n!}$

2. a. 120   **b.** 35   **c.** 105   **d.** 1

3. a. 120   **b.** 35   **c.** 105   **d.** 1

4. a. $_{10}C_4 = \frac{10!}{6!4!}$ **b.** $_{10}C_4 = {_{10}C_6}$ **c.** $\frac{10!}{6!4!} = \frac{10!}{4!6!}$ **d.** $_nC_r = \frac{n!}{r!(n-r)!}$

5. a.–d. Answers will vary.

6. a. 38,760   **b.** 3060   **c.** 0.08   **d.** Answers will vary.

7. a. 35   **b.** $\frac{4}{7}$

8. Answers will vary. $_5C_4(0.5)^5 = 0.15625$. There are $_5C_4$ or 5 arrangements of HHHHT, and each has a probability of $0.5^5 = 0.03125$.

9. a. $_7C_5(0.3)^5(0.7)^2 = 0.0250047$ **b.** $_7C_6(0.3)^6(0.7)^1 = 0.0035721$
     c. $_7C_7(0.3)^7(0.7)^0 = 0.0002187$ **d.** $0.0025 + 0.00357 + 0.00022 = 0.2879$

10. In a "combination" lock the order in which the numbers are entered does not matter. You could enter the correct three numbers in any order to open the lock.

Problem Set 11.3

1. a. HH, HT, TH, TT   **b.** HH, HT, TH, TT   **c.**
     d. The combination number $_2C_0$ is the number of times you get no tails when two coins are tossed; $_2C_1$ is the number of times you get 1 tail when two coins are tossed; $_2C_2$ is the number of times you get 2 tails when two coins are tossed.
     e. The terms represent the long-range distribution of 2 heads, 1 head, and 0 heads.

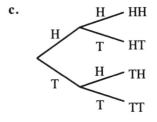

2. a. $x^4 + 4x^3y + 6x^2y^2 + 4xy^3 + y^4$ **b.** $p^5 + 5p^4q + 10p^3q^2 + 10p^2q^3 + 5pq^4 + q^5$
     c. $8x^3 + 36x^2 + 54x + 27$ **d.** $81x^4 - 432x^3 + 864x^2 - 768x + 256$

3. a. 1   **b.** Answers will vary.   **c.** 1
     d. Answers will vary.

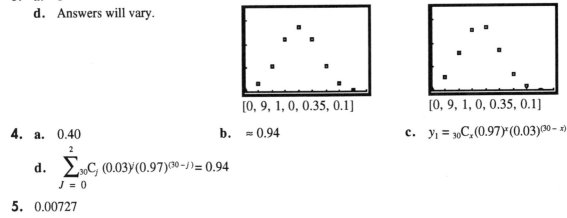

[0, 9, 1, 0, 0.35, 0.1]   [0, 9, 1, 0, 0.35, 0.1]

4. a. 0.40   **b.** ≈ 0.94   **c.** $y_1 = {_{30}C_x}(0.97)^x(0.03)^{(30-x)}$

     d. $\displaystyle\sum_{J=0}^{2} {_{30}C_j}\,(0.03)^j(0.97)^{(30-j)} = 0.94$

5. 0.00727

6. a. 0.00026   **b.** 0.445888   **c.** 0.98336

7. $_6C_1 + {_6C_2}\,{_6C_3}\,{_6C_4}\,{_6C_5}\,{_6C_6} = 63$

8. a. Answers will vary.
   b. Answers will vary. The horizontal shift can be found by tracing to the highest point of the binomial curve and finding the x-value. It should be $90(1 - p)$. The y-value of the maximum point should be the value of a in the exponential curve. The value of b will be less than 1, but not much less.

Problem Set 11.4

1. a. Answers will vary, but the second set has less spread.
   b. First set: mean = 35, standard deviation = 19.99; second set: mean = 117, standard deviation = 3.16
   c. Both the mean and the standard deviations are ten times the original numbers.
   d. The mean is ten more than the original mean, and the standard deviation is the same.

2. a. The set with the smallest standard deviation is any set with four of the same number, because each member of the set will be equal to the mean.
   b. The set {1, 1, 8, 8} has the largest standard deviation; answers will vary.

3. a. Answers will vary.
   b. This is clearly the French exam, which has the greatest standard deviation; answers will vary.
   c. Hans; answers will vary.

4. a. Answers will vary, but $\bar{x}$ should be close to 7, and σ should be close to 2.4.
   b. Close to 67   **c.** Close to 68%   **d.** Close to 95%

5. a.–c. Answers will vary. Figure a should have the largest standard deviation, and Figure c should have the smallest standard deviation.

6. a. Answers will vary.
   b. Presidents: mean = 54.9, σ = 6.21; vice-presidents: mean = 53.84, σ = 8.42
   c.

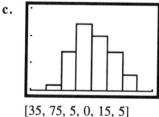
[35, 75, 5, 0, 15, 5]

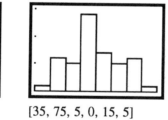
[35, 75, 5, 0, 15, 5]

   d. Calculator procedure
   e. For the presidents the range is from −1.92 to 2.27. The range for the vice-presidents is from −2.12 to 2.04.
   f.

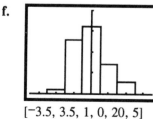
[−3.5, 3.5, 1, 0, 20, 5]

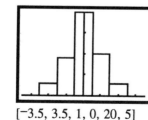
[−3.5, 3.5, 1, 0, 20, 5]

   g. Answers will vary. The graph for the vice-presidents is more symmetrical around the mean than the graph for the presidents.

7. a.

Heads (x)	0	1	2	3	4	5	6	7
$P(x)$	0.00003	0.00046	0.0032	0.01389	0.04166	0.09164	0.15274	0.19638
Frequency	0.02	0.23	1.6	6.94	20.83	45.82	76.37	98.19

Heads (x)	8	9	10	11	12	13	14	15
$P(x)$	0.19638	0.15274	0.09164	0.04166	0.01389	0.0032	0.00046	0.00003
Frequency	98.19	76.37	45.82	20.83	6.94	1.6	0.23	0.02

b.

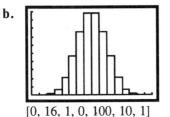

[0, 16, 1, 0, 100, 10, 1]

c. $\bar{x} = 7.5$, $\sigma = 1.94$

e. 69.6%

g. 100%

d. 348

f. 96.4%

8. Answers will vary.

Problem Set 11.5

1. a.

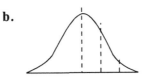

b.

Answers for part b will vary.

c. The distribution with the smaller standard deviation will be taller.

2.

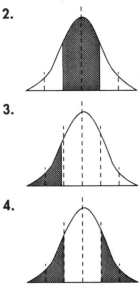

3.

4.

5. a. For $a = 75$, $b = 89$, and $n = 500$, the probability is 65.5%.

b. For $a = 67$, $b = 97$, and $n = 500$, the probability is 95.65%.

c. For $a = 60$, $b = 104$, and $n = 500$, the probability is 99.74%

6. a. $y = 0.054(0.991)^{(x-82)^2}$.

b. For $a = 75$, $b = 89$, $n = 500$, the area is approximately 0.66 or 66%.

c. For $a = 67$, $b = 97$, $n = 500$, the area is approximately 0.96 or 96%.

d. For $a = 60$, $b = 104$, $n = 500$, the area is approximately 1.00 or 100%.

7. a. $\bar{x} = 165$; $\sigma \approx 5.82$ **b.**

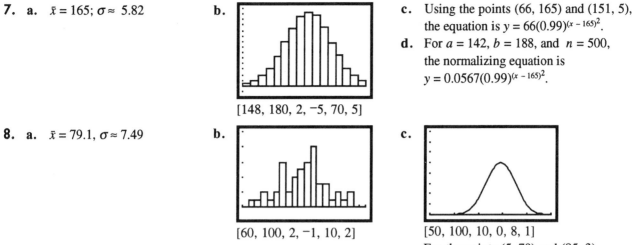

c. Using the points (66, 165) and (151, 5), the equation is $y = 66(0.99)^{(x-165)^2}$.

d. For $a = 142$, $b = 188$, and $n = 500$, the normalizing equation is $y = 0.0567(0.99)^{(x-165)^2}$.

[148, 180, 2, −5, 70, 5]

8. a. $\bar{x} = 79.1$, $\sigma \approx 7.49$ **b.**

[60, 100, 2, −1, 10, 2]

c.

[50, 100, 10, 0, 8, 1]

For the points (5, 79) and (85, 3), the equation is $y = 5(0.9859)^{(x-79)^2}$.

d. For $a = 49$, $b = 109$, and $n = 500$, the normalizing equation is $y = 0.0676(0.9859)^{(x-165)^2}$.

e. Answers will vary. The data does not appear to be normally distributed. It seems to be evenly distributed with several peaks.

9.

`:Prompt A,B,N`	Input values for the left endpoint, the right endpoint, and the number of divisions.
`:(B-A)/N→D`	Take the difference between the left and right endpoint, divide this difference by the number of divisions, and store this result in D.
`:0→S`	Store 0 in S.
`:For(J,0,N)`	For values of J from 0 to N (J is a counter).
`:S+Y₁(A+JD)→S`	Compute the value of the function, Y_1, at the endpoint of each interval, and add this result to the previous sum of function values. This sum represents the sum of the heights of all of the intervals.
`:End`	End the loop when $J = N$.
`:Disp (B-A)S/(N+1)`	$(B-A)$ represents the length of the interval. $S/(N+1)$ represents the average height of an interval. So the entire expression computes the area under the curve by multiplying the length of the interval by the average height.

Problem Set 11.6

1. 31%

2. a. 71.4 g   **b.** 69.3 g   **c.** 66.6 g

3. a. 0.0145   **b.** 0.0025

4. 0.439; answers will vary.

5. a. 12.96 oz   **b.** 23.3%

6. a. 0.08655   **b.** 86 or 87 groups   **c.** Calculator procedure   **d.** 4.3634

   e. 4.3763

7. a.

N	47	64	150	Your choice	Your choice
P	0.3	0.8	0.18	0.61	Your choice
M	14.1	51.2	27	Answers will vary.	Answers will vary.
S	3.14	3.2	4.7	Answers will vary.	Answers will vary.

b. They are the same graph.   **c.** Answers will vary.

Chapter Review

Problem Set 11.7

1. **a.** $12! = 479{,}001{,}600$ **b.** $\frac{5!7!}{12!} = 0.00126$ or 0.13%

2. 0.0217

3. $\displaystyle\sum_{i=17}^{20} {}_{20}C_i(0.65)^i(0.35)^{20-i} = 0.044$ or 4.4%

4. **a.** $100 - 800x + 2800x^2 - 5600x^3 + 7000x^4 - 5600x^5 + 2800x^6 - 800x^7 + 100x^8$
   b. $600 + 250x + 41.667x^2 + 3.4722x^3 + 0.14468x^4 + 0.002411x^5$

5. The mean is 67.8 in., and the standard deviation is 3.6 in. Approximately 67% of the adults in Normalville are between 64 in. and 71 in. tall.

6. $y = \frac{1}{8.5\sqrt{2\pi}}\left(1 - \frac{1}{2(8.5)^2}\right)^{(x-167)^2}$

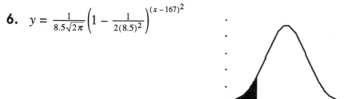

[140, 195, 5, 0, 0.05, 0.01]

7. 0.205

8. ${}_nC_r = \frac{n!}{r!(n-r)!}$; ${}_nP_r = \frac{n!}{(n-r)!}$

9. 0.00086

10. **a.** $y = \frac{1}{14\sqrt{2\pi}}\left(1 - \frac{1}{2(14)^2}\right)^{(x-175)^2}$ **b.** 14%
    c. 152 lb to 198 lb **d.** 32%

Chapter 12

Problem Set 12.1

1. **a.** $f(x) = \frac{1}{x} + 2$ **b.** $f(x) = \frac{1}{x-3}$ **c.** $f(x) = \frac{1}{x+4} - 1$

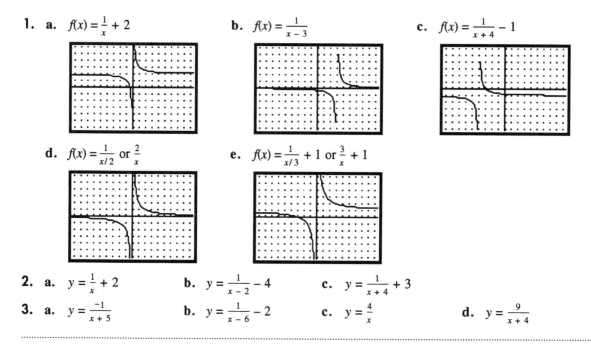

   d. $f(x) = \frac{1}{x/2}$ or $\frac{2}{x}$ **e.** $f(x) = \frac{1}{x/3} + 1$ or $\frac{3}{x} + 1$

2. **a.** $y = \frac{1}{x} + 2$ **b.** $y = \frac{1}{x-2} - 4$ **c.** $y = \frac{1}{x+4} + 3$

3. **a.** $y = \frac{-1}{x+5}$ **b.** $y = \frac{1}{x-6} - 2$ **c.** $y = \frac{4}{x}$ **d.** $y = \frac{9}{x+4}$

4. Answers will vary.

5. a. 20.9 ml

b. $f(x) = \frac{20.9 + x}{55 + x}$ and $g(x) = 0.64$

c. ≈ 39.72

d. The graph slowly approaches 1.0.

6. 12 games

7. ≈ 0.020 gal

8. a.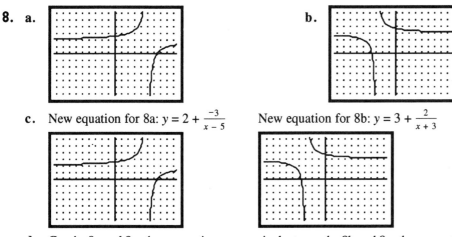

b.

c. New equation for 8a: $y = 2 + \frac{-3}{x - 5}$ New equation for 8b: $y = 3 + \frac{2}{x + 3}$

d. Graphs 8a and 8c: these equations are equivalent; graphs 8b and 8c: these equations are equivalent.

e. Graph 8a: The transformations alter $y = \frac{1}{x}$ by a vertical stretch of -3, a horizontal slide 5 units right, and a vertical slide 2 units up. Graph 8b: The transformations alter $y = \frac{1}{x}$ by a vertical stretch of 2, a horizontal slide 3 units left, and a vertical slide 3 units up.

Problem Set 12.2

1. a. 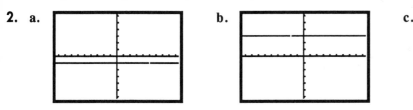   **b.**   **c.**

d. The first graph has a slant asymptote of $y = x - 2$, because for large absolute values of x, the term $\frac{1}{x}$ becomes insignificant and the equation is very nearly $y = x - 2$.

The second graph has a slant asymptote of $y = -2x + 3$, because for large absolute values of x, the term $\frac{2}{x}$ becomes insignificant and the equation is very nearly $y = -2x + 3$.

The third graph has a hole at $x = 2$, because the function is undefined there. For all other x-values, however, the equation is equivalent to $y = 3 + 1$ or $y = 4$.

2. a. 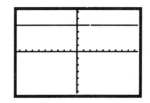   **b.**   **c.**

d. Graph 2a has a hole at $x = 5$ because the function is undefined at that point. Graph 2b has a hole at $x = -2$ because the function is undefined at that point. Graph 2c has a hole at $x = 4$ because the function is undefined at that point.

3. a. $y = 0 + \frac{x + 2}{x + 2}$ **b.** $y = -3 + \frac{x - 3}{x - 3}$ **c.** $y = \frac{(x + 2)(x + 1)}{x + 1}$

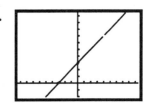

4. a. The graph of $y = \frac{4}{x}$ is translated 3 units right. This means it has a vertical asymptote at $x = 3$. The graph has a slant asymptote at $y = {}^-x$.

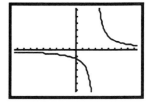

b. As you zoom out, the graph looks more and more like the line $y = {}^-x$.

c. The graph gets closer and closer to both sides of the vertical line $x = 3$.

d. ${}^-x + \frac{4}{x-3} = \frac{{}^-x(x-3)}{x-3} + \frac{4}{x-3} = \frac{{}^-x^2 + 3x + 4}{x-3}$

e. $4, {}^-1; 4, {}^-1$

5. a. The graph has a slant asymptote of $y = x$, vertical asymptote at $x = {}^-2$, and has been vertically stretched by ${}^-3$.

b. $y = x$

c. Answers will vary. One possibility is $y = \frac{1}{x+2}$.

d. Answers will vary. One possibility is $y = (x+3)(x-1)$.

e. $y = x + \frac{-3}{x+2}$ or $\frac{(x+3)(x-1)}{x+2}$

6. $y = \frac{-(x+2)(x-6)}{3(x-2)}$

7. a. The graph has x-intercepts at 1 and ${}^-4$ and vertical asymptotes at $x = 2$ and $x = {}^-3$. The y-intercept is $\frac{2}{3}$.

b. The graph has a horizontal asymptote at $y = 1$.

c.

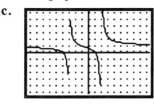

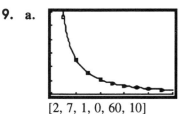

8. a. $x \approx 1.586$ and $x \approx 4.414$ **b.** No solutions   **c.** ${}^-7 \le x < {}^-2$

9. a.

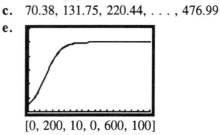

[2, 7, 1, 0, 60, 10]

b. If the volume is fixed, the height gets larger as the radius gets smaller. The radius $x > 2$.

c. $V = \pi x^2 h - 4\pi h$

d. $h = \frac{V}{\pi(x^2-4)}; f(x) = \frac{V}{\pi(x^2-4)}$

e. $V \approx 400$ in.^{3}

Problem Set 12.3

1. a. The unrestricted growth rate is 8% and the population limit is 500.

b. 53.6   **c.** 70.38, 131.75, 220.44, . . . , 476.99

d. 500   **e.**

[0, 200, 10, 0, 600, 100]

2. After 20 weeks the bacteria population is at 5000. This is a net rate increase of 26% per week.

3. Answers will vary, but the arguments should fit the information pictured in the table below, where n is the number of elapsed time periods and u_n is the number of daisies. The limit for the number of daisies is 750 over the interval described by this expression. The model used in the table and the graph is $u_{(n-1)} + 0.35\left(1 - \frac{u_{(n-1)}}{750}\right)u_{(n-1)}$.

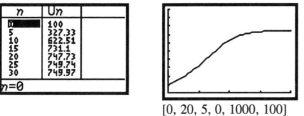

n	Un
0	100
5	327.33
10	622.51
15	731.1
20	747.73
25	749.74
30	749.97

$n=0$

[0, 20, 5, 0, 1000, 100]

4. Answers will vary

5. **a.** The deer population will disappear within 35 yr.   **b.** Answers will vary.

6. **a.** 8074 weeds   **b.** 8,237.3; 11,286; 8,237.3; 11,286; 8,237.3; 11,286

     c.   **d.** Answers will vary.

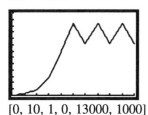

[0, 10, 1, 0, 13000, 1000]

7. Answers will vary. The frog population fluctuates and seems quite unpredictable without using the equation.

8. **a.**   **b.** Answers will vary.

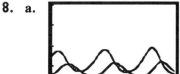

[0, 480, 50, 0, 100, 35]

Problem Set 12.4

1. **a.** The shortest possible distance occurs when the boat travels directly to point D.

     b. The boat would travel approximately 99.1 mi and the ambulance 0 mi.

     c. The shortest time (2.016 hr) occurs when $x \approx 5.218$. Using this point the boat travels approximately 15.88 mi and the ambulance approximately 92.782 mi.

2. **a.** $y = \sqrt{10^2 + x^2} + \sqrt{(20 - x)^2 + 13^2}$

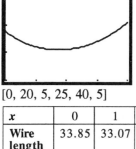

[0, 20, 5, 25, 40, 5]

x	0	1	2	3	4	5	6	7	8	9	10
Wire length	33.85	33.07	32.40	31.84	31.39	31.03	30.77	30.59	30.50	30.48	30.54

     b. $0 \le x \le 20$, $30 \le$ *wire length* ≤ 43

     c. Fasten it at $x \approx 8.696$ m for a minimum wire length of ≈ 30.48 m.

3. a. 12 sec

b.

Time (sec)	0	1	2	3	4	5	6
Height (ft)	24	23.92	23.66	23.24	22.63	21.82	20.78

Time (sec)	7	8	9	10	11	12
Height (ft)	19.49	17.89	15.87	13.27	9.59	0

c. No; the table and graph indicate that the rate of the ladder top moving down increases as you pull steadily at the bottom of the ladder.

d. i. $x_{1t} = 2t$ ii. $y_{1t} = \sqrt{24^2 - (2t)^2}$

e. Answers will vary.

4. a. 64 sec (0.125 mi/sec; distance = 8 mi)

b. $d = \sqrt{7^2 + (8 - 0.125t)^2}$

c.

Time (sec)	0	1	5	10	20	30	64
Ground distance (mi)	8	7.875	7.375	6.75	5.5	4.25	0
Actual distance (mi)	10.63	10.536	10.168	9.7243	8.9022	8.1892	7

d.

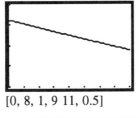

[0, 8, 1, 9 11, 0.5]

5. a. $y = \sqrt{(5 - x)^2 + (0.5x^2 + 1 + 3)^2}$

b. The minimum distance of about 6.02 units occurs at about (0.92, 1.42).

6. a. The parametric equations are $x = 50 \cos 12(t - 3.75)$ and $y = 50 \sin 12 (t - 3.75) + 55$.

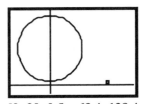

[0, 30, 0.5, −68.4, 138.4, 0, −12.4, 124, 0]

b. The parametric equations used to model the motion of the keys are $x = -55t \cos 70 + 90$ and $y = 55t \sin 70 + 4 - 16t^2$. It appears that Sandra can catch the keys.

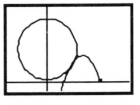

c. The distance equations are $x = t$ and $y = \sqrt{(x_{1t} - x_{2t})^2 + (y_{1t} - y_{2t})^2}$. She should be able to catch the keys because they are only 1.7 ft from her at 2.2 sec. They get as close as 0.253 ft at the 2.246 sec mark.

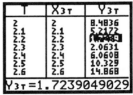

7. a. About 0.628 sec

b. If $x_{1t} = -2.5 \cos \frac{1800(t - 0.157)}{\pi}$ and $y_{1t} = 2.5 + 2.5 \sin \frac{1800(t - 0.157)}{\pi}$, then graph $x_{2t} = t$ and $y_{2t} = y_{1t}$.

c. If $x_{1t} = -2.5 \cos \frac{1800(t - 0.157)}{\pi}$ and $y_{1t} = 2.5 + 2.5 \sin \frac{1800(t - 0.157)}{\pi}$,

then graph $x_{2t} = 25t$ and $y_{2t} = y_{1t}$.

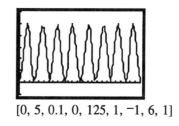

[0, 5, 0.1, 0, 125, 1, −1, 6, 1]

Problem Set 12.5

1. a. Center at $(0, 0)$ and radius 2.

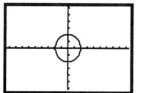

b. Center at $(3, 0)$ and radius 1.

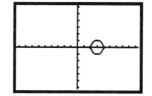

c. Center at $(-1, 2)$ and radius 3.

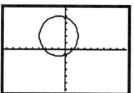

d. Center at $(0, 1.5)$ and radius 0.5.

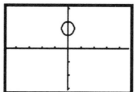

e. Center at $(1, 2)$ and radius 2.

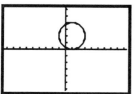

f. Center at $(-3, 0)$ and radius 4.

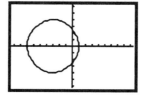

2. a. $x = 5 \cos t + 3$ and $y = 5 \sin t$ or $(x - 3)^2 + y^2 = 25$

b. $x = 3 \cos t - 1$ and $y = 3 \sin t + 2$ or $(x + 1)^2 + (y - 2)^2 = 9$

c. $x = 4 \cos t + 2.5$ and $y = 4 \sin t + 0.75$ or $(x - 2.5)^2 + (y - 0.75)^2 = 16$

d. $x = 0.5 \cos t + 2.5$ and $y = 0.5 \sin t + 2.5$ or $(x - 2.5)^2 + (y - 2.5)^2 = 0.25$

3. a. $(2, 0), (-2, 0), (0, 4), (0, -4)$

b. $(5, -2), (-1, -2), (2, -1), (2, -3)$

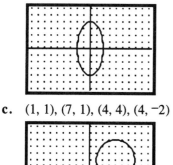

c. $(1, 1), (7, 1), (4, 4), (4, -2)$

d. $(-5, -1), (1, -1), (-2, 1), (-2, -3)$

e. $(-5, 3)$, $(3, 3)$, $(-1, 5)$, $(-1, 1)$ **f.** $(0, 0)$, $(6, 0)$, $(3, 5)$, $(3, -5)$

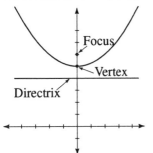

4. a. $x = 6 \cos t$ and $y = 3 \sin t$ or $\left(\frac{x}{6}\right)^2 + \left(\frac{y}{3}\right)^2 = 1$

b. $x = 2 \cos t + 3$ and $y = 5 \sin t$ or $\left(\frac{x-3}{2}\right)^2 + \left(\frac{y}{5}\right)^2 = 1$

c. $x = 4 \cos t - 1$ and $y = 3 \sin t + 2$ or $\left(\frac{x+1}{4}\right)^2 + \left(\frac{y-2}{3}\right)^2 = 1$

d. $x = 6 \cos t + 3$ and $y = 3 \sin t - 1$ or $\left(\frac{x-3}{6}\right)^2 + \left(\frac{y+1}{3}\right)^2 = 1$

5. a. Answers will vary. The equation $\left(\frac{x-493}{497}\right)^2 + \left(\frac{y}{63}\right)^2 = 1$ is a good fit.

b. ± 63 AU   **c.** 990 AU   **d.** $(986, 0)$

6. a. Answers will vary. The 16 cm string is tacked to the cardboard at F_1 and F_2. A pencil traces out an ellipse as it moves against the stretched string.

b. $(8, 0)$ and $(-8, 0)$ **c.** $\left(0, \sqrt{39}\right)$ and $\left(0, -\sqrt{39}\right)$ **d.** $\left(\frac{x}{8}\right)^2 + \left(\frac{y}{\sqrt{39}}\right)^2 = 1$

e. $y = \sqrt{(x-5)^2 + 39\left(1 - \left(\frac{x}{8}\right)^2\right)} + \sqrt{(x+5)^2 + 39\left(1 - \left(\frac{x}{8}\right)^2\right)}$. The values are always 16.

7. a. The string will be 12 units long.   **b.** $\left(3\sqrt{3}, 0\right)$ and $\left(-3\sqrt{3}, 0\right)$

8. $\left(\frac{x}{237,176.5}\right)^2 + \left(\frac{y}{236,667}\right)^2 = 1$

9. $\left(\frac{x-1}{5}\right)^2 + \left(\frac{y-1}{4}\right)^2 = 1$

Problem Set 12.6

1. a. Vertex $(0, 5)$; focus $(0, 6)$; directrix $y = 4$ **b.** Vertex $(-2, -2)$; focus $(-1.75, -2)$; directrix $x = -2.25$

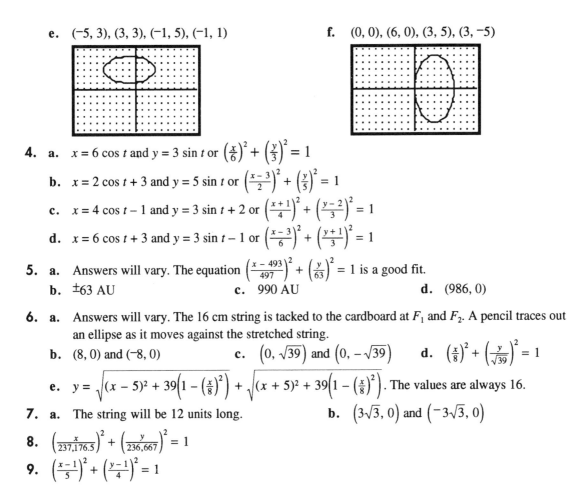

c. Vertex $(-3, 0.5)$; focus $(-3, 0)$; directrix $y = 1$ **d.** Vertex $(4, 0)$; focus $(3.875, 0)$; directrix $x = 4.125$

e. Vertex $(-1, 3)$; focus $(-1, 5)$; directrix $y = 1$

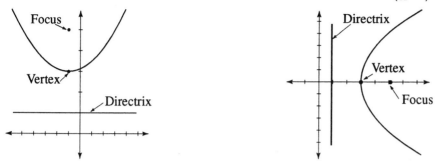

f. Vertex $(3, 0)$; focus $\left(\frac{61}{12}, 0\right)$; directrix $x = \frac{11}{12}$

2. a. $x = t^2$ and $y = t + 2$ or $x = (y - 2)^2$; vertex $(0, 2)$, focus $(0.25, 2)$, and directrix $x = -0.25$

b. $x = t$ and $y = -t^2 + 4$ or $y = -x^2 + 4$; vertex $(0, 4)$, focus $(0, 3.75)$, and directrix $y = 4.25$

c. $x = 2t + 3$ and $y = t^2 - 1$ or $y = \left(\frac{x - 3}{2}\right)^2$; vertex $(3, -1)$, focus $(3, 0)$, and directrix $y = -2$

d. $x = -t^2 - 6$ and $y = 3t + 2$ or $y = \pm 3\sqrt{-x - 6} + 2$ or $x = -\frac{1}{9}(y - 2)^2 - 6$; vertex $(-6, 2)$, focus $(-8.25, 2)$, and directrix $x = -3.75$

3. The path will be parabolic. The rock is the focus and the shoreline is the directrix.

4. a. The graph is a parabola with vertex $(0, 1)$, focus $(0, 3)$, and directrix $y = -1$.

b. $y = \frac{x^2}{8} + 1$ or $y = 0.125x^2 + 1$

c.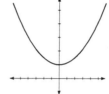

5. a. The graph is a parabola with vertex $(3, 4)$, focus $(3.5, 4)$, and directrix $x = 2.5$.

b. $y = \pm 2\sqrt{x - 3} + 4$

c.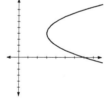

6. $y = -2.4x^2 + 21.12x - 44.164$

7. $x^2 + y^2 + 4x - 2y - 20 = 0$ or $(x + 2)^2 + (y - 1)^2 = 25$

Problem Set 12.7

1. a. The vertices are $(-2, 0)$ and $(2, 0)$. The equations of the asymptotes are $y = \pm 2x$.

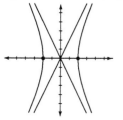

b. The vertices are $(2, -1)$ and $(2, -3)$. The equations of the asymptotes are $y = \pm\frac{1}{3}(x - 2) - 2$.

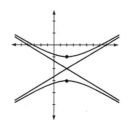

c. The vertices are (1, 1) and (7, 1). The equations of the asymptotes are $y = \pm(x - 4) + 1$.

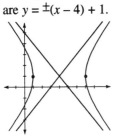

d. The vertices are (−2, 1) and (−2, −3). The equations of the asymptotes are $y = \pm\frac{2}{3}(x + 2) - 1$.

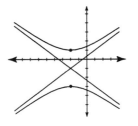

e. The vertices are (−5, 3) and (3, 3). The equations of the asymptotes are $y = \pm 0.5(x + 1) + 3$.

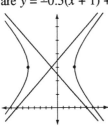

f. The vertices are (3, 5) and (3, −5). The equations of the asymptotes are $y = \pm\frac{5}{3}(x - 3)$.

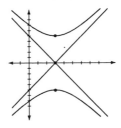

2. a. $x = \frac{2}{\cos t}$ and $y = \tan t$; $\left(\frac{x}{2}\right)^2 - \left(\frac{y}{1}\right)^2 = 1$; $y = \pm 0.5x$.

   b. $x = 2\tan t + 3$ and $y = \frac{2}{\cos t} - 3$; $\left(\frac{y+3}{2}\right)^2 - \left(\frac{x-3}{2}\right)^2 = 1$ $y = \pm(x - 3) - 3$

   c. $x = \frac{3}{\cos t} - 2$ and $y = 4\tan t + 1$; $\left(\frac{x+2}{3}\right)^2 - \left(\frac{y-1}{4}\right)^2 = 1$; $y = \pm\frac{4}{3}(x + 2) + 1$

   d. $x = 3\tan t - 2$ and $y = \frac{4}{\cos t} + 1$; $\left(\frac{y-1}{4}\right)^2 - \left(\frac{x+2}{3}\right)^2 = 1$; $y = \pm\frac{4}{3}(x + 2) + 1$

3. a. $\left(\pm\sqrt{2}, 0\right)$ **b.** $\left(2, -2 + \sqrt{10}\right)$ and $\left(2, -2 - \sqrt{10}\right)$

4. $\left| \sqrt{(x+2)^2 + (y-1)^2} - \sqrt{(x-4)^2 + (y-1)^2} \right| = 10$

5. $\left(\frac{y + 2.49}{3.95}\right)^2 - \left(\frac{x + 2.35}{2.63}\right)^2 = 1$

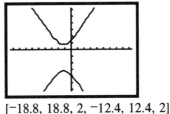

[−18.8, 18.8, 2, −12.4, 12.4, 2]

6.

x-value	5	10	20	40
Distance	0.41	0.25	0.14	0.07

7. a. A possible equation is $\left(\frac{y}{2.5}\right)^2 - \left(\frac{x - 9.5}{2.5}\right)^2 = 1$.

   b. The center is (9.5, 0).

   c. One explanation is that when the car has traveled 9.5 mi it is still 2.5 mi from the transmitter, and this is as close as the car will get.

8. Answers will vary.

Problem Set 12.8

1. a. $1x^2 + 0xy + 0y^2 + 14x - 9y + 148 = 0$ **b.** $1x^2 + 0xy + 9y^2 - 14x + 198y + 1129 = 0$

2. a. $a = 1.4$ **b.** $b = 0.7$ **c.** 0.49 **d.** 7.35 **e.** 0.7

3. a. False   **b.** True   **c.** True   **d.** False

4. a. iv   **b.** ii   **c.** iii   **d.** i

5. a. $\left(\frac{y}{5}\right)^2 - \left(\frac{x}{2}\right)^2 = 1.$ It is a hyperbola.   **b.** $(y + 2)^2 = \frac{5}{2}(x - 2).$ It is a parabola.

   c. $\left(\frac{x + 3}{\frac{1}{2}}\right)^2 + \left(\frac{y - 1}{\frac{1}{2}}\right)^2 = 1.$ It is a circle.   **d.** $\left(\frac{x - 2}{\sqrt{8}}\right)^2 + \left(\frac{y + 2}{\sqrt{4.8}}\right)^2 = 1.$ It is an ellipse.

6. a. $y = \dfrac{\pm\sqrt{400x^2 + 1600}}{-8}$ **b.** $y = \dfrac{-16 \pm \sqrt{160x - 320}}{8}$

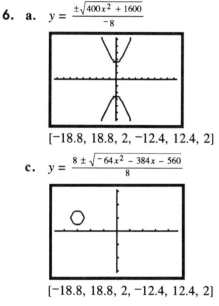

[−18.8, 18.8, 2, −12.4, 12.4, 2]   [−18.8, 18.8, 2, −12.4, 12.4, 2]

   c. $y = \dfrac{8 \pm \sqrt{-64x^2 - 384x - 560}}{8}$ **d.** $y = \dfrac{-20 \pm \sqrt{-60x^2 + 240x + 240}}{10}$

[−18.8, 18.8, 2, −12.4, 12.4, 2]   [−2.7, 6.7, 1, −5.1, 1.1, 1]

7. $y = 0.00115x^2 + 4$

8. Answers will vary.

Problem Set 12.9

1. a. $\begin{bmatrix} 0.866 & -0.5 \\ 0.5 & 0.866 \end{bmatrix}$ **b.** $\begin{bmatrix} -0.839 & -0.545 \\ 0.545 & -0.839 \end{bmatrix}$

   c. $\begin{bmatrix} 0 & 1 \\ -1 & 0 \end{bmatrix}$ **d.** $\begin{bmatrix} -0.839 & -0.545 \\ 0.545 & -0.839 \end{bmatrix}$

2. The vertices of the rotated triangle are $(2, 1)$, $(-5, 4)$, and $(2, 7)$.

3. a.

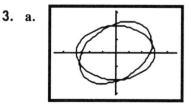

   b. $x_{1t} = 3 \cos t; \, y_{1t} = 2 \sin t$
      $x_{2t} = x_{1t} \cos 30° - y_{1t} \sin 30°$
      $y_{2t} = x_{1t} \sin 30° + y_{1t} \cos 30°$

4. a. The vertices of the rotated triangle are $(-1, -4)$, $(-7, -2)$, and $(-4, 1)$.
   b. A reflection over the x-axis followed by a reflection over the y-axis (or vice versa).

5. a. Reflection over x
   b. Reflection over y
   c. Rotate 90° counterclockwise.
   d. Rotate 180°.
   e. Reflect over $y = x$.

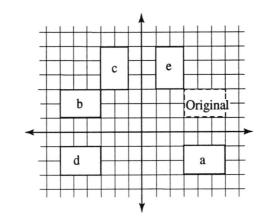

6. a. The graph is a unit hyperbola that opens vertically.
   b. The equations for x_2 and y_2 rotate the original hyperbola 50° counterclockwise.
   c.

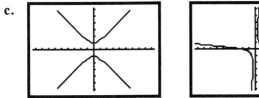

7. $y = \frac{4}{x}$ $x^2 - y^2 = 8$

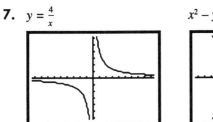

8. a.–b. Answers will vary.

Chapter Review

Problem Set 12.10

1. Approximately 10.34 oz

2. a. The slice is perpendicular to the axis of rotation.
   b. The slice intersects only one branch of the cone. The angle is not perpendicular to the axis of rotation.
   c. The slice intersects only one branch of the cone and is parallel to an edge.
   d. The slice intersects both branches of the cone but does not contain the vertex.
   e. The slice intersects at the vertex.
   f. The slice is along an edge.
   g. The axis of rotation is contained in the slice.

3. a. $\left(\frac{x-5}{3}\right)^2 + \left(\frac{y+2}{4}\right)^2 = 1$
   b. $x = 3 \cos t + 5$ and $y = 4 \sin t - 2$
   c. The center is $(5, -2)$. The foci are $\left(5, -2 + \sqrt{7}\right)$ and $\left(5, -2 - \sqrt{7}\right)$.
   d. $16x^2 + 9y^2 - 160x + 36y + 292 = 0$
   e. $x = (3 \cos t + 5) \cos 75 - (4 \sin t - 2) \sin 75$; $y = (3 \cos t + 5) \sin 75 + (4 \sin t - 2) \cos 75$
   f. $16(x \cos 75 - y \sin 75)^2 + 9(x \sin 75 + y \cos 75)^2 - 160(x \cos 75 - y \sin 75) + 36(x \sin 75 + y \cos 75) + 292 = 0$

4. a. $y = {}^\pm 0.5x$ **b.** $x^2 - 4y^2 - 4 = 0$ **c.** Distance $= 0.5x - \sqrt{\frac{x^2}{4} - 1}$

d.

x	0	1	2	10	...	20
Distance	None	None	1	0.101	...	0.050

5. a.

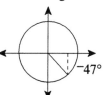

b. Distance $= \left| \frac{2x - 14}{x - 5} - 2 \right|$ **c.** Distance $= \left| 2 - \frac{2x - 14}{x - 5} \right|$

d.

x	0	3	5	10	...	20
Distance	0.8	2	None	0.8	...	0.27

6. Include $(x + 3)$ as a factor in both the numerator and denominator of the fraction.
$$y = \frac{(2x - 14)(x + 3)}{(x - 5)(x + 3)}$$

7. About 23.3 mi/hr and 43.3 mi/hr.

8. a. $y_1 = \frac{34}{x + 11} + \frac{13}{x}$

b.

$[-10, 10, 1, -10, 10, 1]$
There is a vertical asymptote at $x = -1$.
There is a horizontal asymptote at $y = 0$.

c. Answers will vary depending on how fast you think Eric can run (perhaps $2 < x < 10$ and $3 < y < 9$).

d. About 4.6 mi/hr

9. Answers will vary.

Chapter 13

Problem Set 13.1

1. a. $\sin 85° = 0.9962$
reference angle $= 85°$

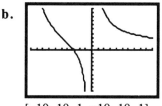

b. $\cos 147° = {}^-0.8387$
reference angle $= 33°$

c. $\sin 280° = {}^-0.9848$
reference angle $= 80°$

d. $\cos 310° = 0.6428$
reference angle $= 50°$

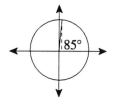

e. $\sin {}^-47° = {}^-0.7314$
reference angle $= 47°$

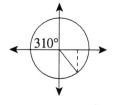

2. a. $y = \sin x$ **b.** The graph will shift up 2 units.

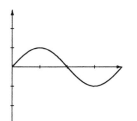

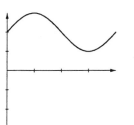

c. The graph will shift right 180°.

d. The graph will be stretched vertically by a factor of 2, shifted up 3 units, and shifted to the right 180°.

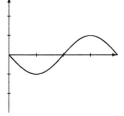

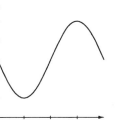

3. a.–b.

Angle A	0°	30°	60°	90°	120°	150°	180°
x-coordinate	1	0.8660	0.5	0	−0.5	−0.8660	−1
y-coordinate	0	0.5	0.8660	1	0.8660	0.5	0
Slope	0	0.5774	1.7321	Undefined	−1.7321	−0.5774	0
$\tan A$	0	0.5774	1.7321	Undefined	−1.7321	−0.5774	0

Angle A	210°	240°	270°	300°	315°	330°	360°
x-coordinate	−0.8660	−0.5	0	0.5	0.7071	0.8660	1
y-coordinate	−0.5	−0.8660	−1	−0.8660	−0.7071	−0.5	0
Slope	0.5774	1.7321	Undefined	−1.7321	−1	−0.5774	0
$\tan A$	0.5774	1.7321	Undefined	−1.7321	−1	−0.5774	0

c. The lengths of the legs of the reference triangle form the same ratio as the ratio of the x- and y-coordinates because lengths of the sides are the same as the coordinates, so the definition of a slope, $\frac{\text{rise}}{\text{run}}$, can be translated to $\frac{y\text{-coordinate}}{x\text{-coordinate}}$. Another name for the ratio of the legs is the tangent.

d. The tangents of the angles in the table in part a are the same as the slopes for the angles in the table.

e. $\tan A = \dfrac{\text{Height of lily pad}}{\text{Horizontal distance of lily pad from center}}$

4. a.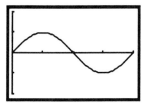

b. At $x = 90°$ the function does not exist. Answers will vary.

c. Tan 40° = tan 220° because if $\cos A = y$ and $\sin A = x$, then the slope equals $\frac{y}{x}$. In the case of 40° and 220°, $\cos 40° = {}^-\cos 220°$ and $\sin 40° = {}^-\sin 220°$, so $\frac{y}{x} = \frac{{}^-y}{{}^-x} = \frac{y}{x}$.

5. a. Period = 360°

b. Period = 360°

c. Period = 180°

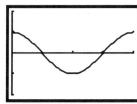

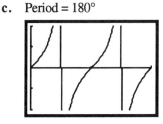

d. Period = 180°   **e.** Period = 60°

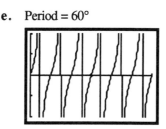

6. a. The value of a determines the period such that as a increases the period decreases.
   b. $\frac{360}{a}$ = period

7. a. 90°   **b.** 540°
   c. The change in period is similar to a horizontal stretch.

8. Answers will vary for the equations. Two possibilities are given for each.
   a. $y = \sin(2x) + 1$ or $y = \cos 2(x - 45) + 1$
   b. $y = {}^{-}\cos x$ or $y = \sin(x - 90)$
   c. $y = \tan(2x) - 1$ or $y = \tan 2(x + 90) - 1$
   d. $y = {}^{-}2\sin(2x)$ or $y = 2\cos 2(x + 45)$

9. a. 15 min   **b.** 10 mi   **c.** + 300 mi   **d.** $y = 10\sin 24x + 300$

Problem Set 13.2

1. a.

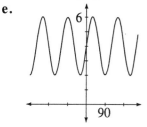

b. $y_1 = \sin(x - 90)$ or $y_1 = {}^{-}\cos x$
   $y_2 = \dfrac{1}{\sin(x - 90)}$ or $y_2 = \dfrac{1}{{}^{-}\cos x}$

2. a. $y = 0.5\csc(x) + 1$ or $y = 0.5\sec(x - 90) + 1$
   b. $y = {}^{-}\cot\left(\frac{1}{3}(x + 270)\right)$ or $y = \tan\left(\frac{1}{3}x\right)$
   c. $y = \cot(x + 90) + 1$ or $y = {}^{-}\tan(x) + 1$
   d. $y = \sin(2(x - 45)) - 0.5$ or $y = {}^{-}\cos(2x) - 0.5$

3. a. The d-value shifts the graph of the function up or down; a positive d-value shifts the function up, and a negative d-value shifts the function down.
   b. The a-value represents the amplitude. A value of 1 for a gives an amplitude of 1, and a value of 5 gives an amplitude of 5.
   c. The b-value determines the period such that as b increases the period decreases; $\frac{360}{b}$ = period.
   d. The c-value shifts the graph; a positive c-value shifts the graph to the left, and a negative c-value shifts the graph to the right.
   e.

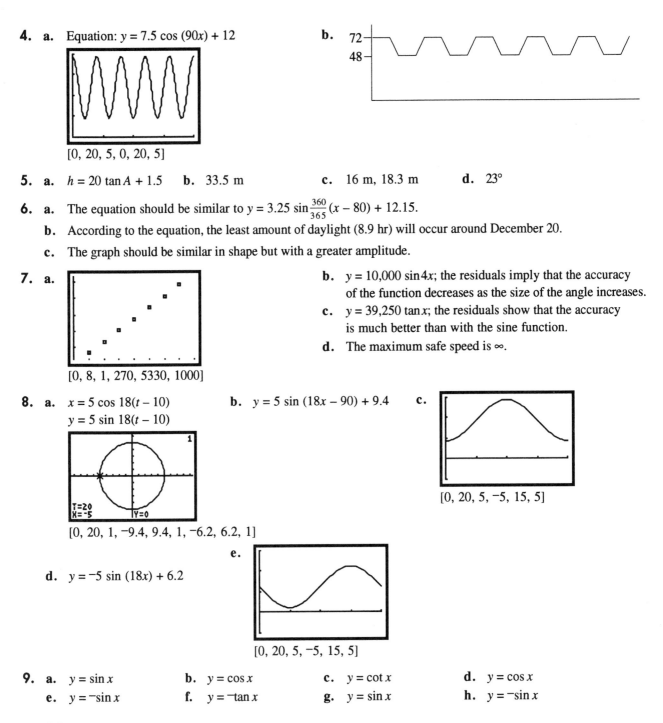

4. a. Equation: $y = 7.5 \cos (90x) + 12$

[0, 20, 5, 0, 20, 5]

b.

5. a. $h = 20 \tan A + 1.5$ **b.** 33.5 m   **c.** 16 m, 18.3 m   **d.** 23°

6. a. The equation should be similar to $y = 3.25 \sin \frac{360}{365}(x - 80) + 12.15$.

b. According to the equation, the least amount of daylight (8.9 hr) will occur around December 20.

c. The graph should be similar in shape but with a greater amplitude.

7. a.

[0, 8, 1, 270, 5330, 1000]

b. $y = 10,000 \sin 4x$; the residuals imply that the accuracy of the function decreases as the size of the angle increases.

c. $y = 39,250 \tan x$; the residuals show that the accuracy is much better than with the sine function.

d. The maximum safe speed is ∞.

8. a. $x = 5 \cos 18(t - 10)$
$y = 5 \sin 18(t - 10)$

b. $y = 5 \sin (18x - 90) + 9.4$ **c.**

[0, 20, 5, −5, 15, 5]

[0, 20, 1, −9.4, 9.4, 1, −6.2, 6.2, 1]

d. $y = {}^{-}5 \sin (18x) + 6.2$

e.

[0, 20, 5, −5, 15, 5]

9. a. $y = \sin x$ **b.** $y = \cos x$ **c.** $y = \cot x$ **d.** $y = \cos x$
   e. $y = {}^{-}\sin x$ **f.** $y = {}^{-}\tan x$ **g.** $y = \sin x$ **h.** $y = {}^{-}\sin x$

Problem Set 13.3

1. $y = \sin 8x$; $0° \le x \le 45°$, $-1 \le y \le 1$

2. a. Answers will vary.

b. Physical: $y = \sin 15.8695x$; emotional: $y = \sin 13.0357x$; intellectual: $y = \sin 11.0606x$

c. The plot depends on where your cycles are starting today.

d. 21,252 days or 58.22 yr

3. a.

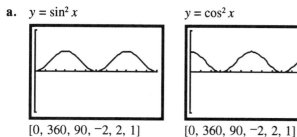

$[-360, 360, 90, -2, 2, 1]$

b.

x	0°	30°	60°	120°	150°	180°
$\cos^2 x + \sin^2 x$	1	1	1	1	1	1

A plot of all of these points would look like the line, $y = 1$.

c. $\cos^2 x + \sin^2 x = 1$

d. The function equation of a circle is $x^2 + y^2 = 1$. The parametric substitutions for x and y are $x = \cos t$ and $y = \sin t$. Substituting these expressions into the function equation, you get $(\cos t)^2 + (\sin t)^2 = 1$.

4. a. $y = 10 \sin 18(x + 15) + 12$

b. $y = 11 \sin 12(x + 22.5) + 23$

c. $y = (10 \sin 18(x + 15) + 12) + (11 \sin 12(x + 22.5) + 23) - 12$

d. 10 times

5. a. $y = \sin^2 x$ $y = \cos^2 x$

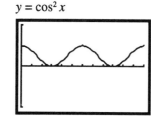

$[0, 360, 90, -2, 2, 1]$ $[0, 360, 90, -2, 2, 1]$

b.

x	0°	30°	60°	90°	120°	150°
$\cos^2 x - \sin^2 x$	1	0.5	−0.5	−1	−0.5	0.5

When plotted the points resemble a periodic function.

c. $y = \cos 2x$ **d.** $\cos^2 x - \sin^2 x = \cos 2x$

6. $\sin 2x = 2 \cos x \sin x$

7. a. $y = 1 - \sin 2x$ **b.** $y = (\sin x - \cos x)^2 = \sin^2 x + \cos^2 x - 2 \sin x \cos x = 1 - \sin 2x$

8. a.
$$y = 1 - \cos^2 x$$
$$= \sin^2 x + \cos^2 x - \cos^2 x$$
$$= \sin^2 x$$

b.
$$y = \tan^2 x + 1$$
$$= \frac{\sin^2 x}{\cos^2 x} + \frac{\cos^2 x}{\cos^2 x}$$
$$= \frac{1}{\cos^2 x} = \sec^2 x$$

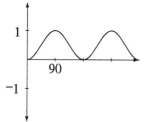

c. $y = \sec x - \sin x \tan x$

$ = \dfrac{1}{\cos x} - \sin x \left(\dfrac{\sin x}{\cos x}\right)$

$ = \dfrac{1 - \sin^2 x}{\cos x} = \dfrac{\cos^2 x}{\cos x} = \cos x$

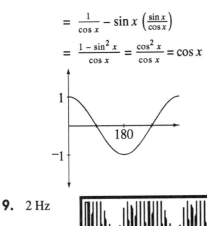

d. $y = \dfrac{1}{\sin^2 x} - \dfrac{1}{\tan^2 x}$

$ = \dfrac{1}{\sin^2 x} - \dfrac{\cos^2 x}{\sin^2 x}$

$ = \dfrac{1 - \cos^2 x}{\sin^2 x} = \dfrac{\sin^2 x}{\sin^2 x} = 1$

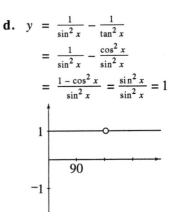

9. 2 Hz

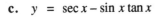

[0, 360, 0, −1, 1, 1]

Problem Set 13.4

1. a. $\triangle ABC$; $AB = 8.35$, $BC = 6.40$, $m\angle ABC = 25.5°$
  b. $\triangle DEF$; $DF = 6.46$, $m\angle EDF = 81.22$, $m\angle EFD = 52.68°$
  c. $\triangle GHI$; $m\angle HGI = 66.31°$, $m\angle GHI = 84.64°$, $m\angle GIH = 29.05°$
  d. $\triangle LKJ$; $m\angle LJK = 38.81°$, $m\angle JLK = 33.29°$, $JK = 4.76$

2. If the known parts include SAS or SSS, use the Law of Cosines. If the known parts include AAS, use the Law of Sines. If the known parts are SSA, you can use either law, but be careful if you use the Law of Sines to check whether you want an acute or obtuse angle.

3. 1659.8 mi

4. $m\angle B = 120°$; $m\angle C \approx 38.21°$; $m\angle A \approx 21.79°$

5. 57.85 cm

6. Heading $= 34°$; distance ≈ 2.5 mi

7. 149.3° from north

8. 5.46845 light-years from first position, 5.46847 light-years from second position.

Problem Set 13.5

1. a. $m\angle A = 106.8°$
  b. $m\angle B = 120.4°$

2. a. $x = t$; $y = \sin t$
  $0 \le t \le 360$

  $x = \sin t$; $y = t$
  $-90 \le t \le 90$

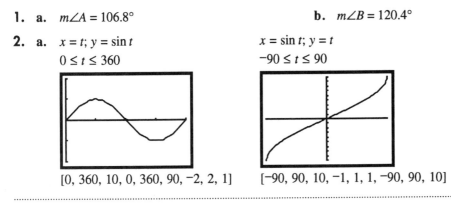

[0, 360, 10, 0, 360, 90, −2, 2, 1]   [−90, 90, 10, −1, 1, 1, −90, 90, 10]

b. $x = t; y = \sin 2t$
   $0 \le t \le 360$

$x = \sin 2t; y = \sin t$
$-45 \le t \le 45$

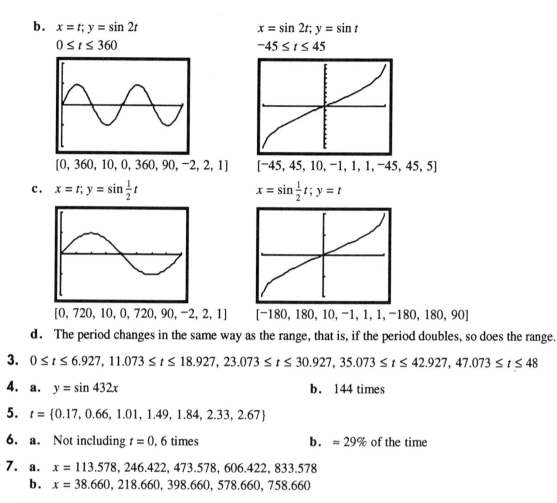

[0, 360, 10, 0, 360, 90, −2, 2, 1]   [−45, 45, 10, −1, 1, 1, −45, 45, 5]

c. $x = t; y = \sin \frac{1}{2}t$

$x = \sin \frac{1}{2}t; y = t$

[0, 720, 10, 0, 720, 90, −2, 2, 1]   [−180, 180, 10, −1, 1, 1, −180, 180, 90]

d. The period changes in the same way as the range, that is, if the period doubles, so does the range.

3. $0 \le t \le 6.927$, $11.073 \le t \le 18.927$, $23.073 \le t \le 30.927$, $35.073 \le t \le 42.927$, $47.073 \le t \le 48$

4. a. $y = \sin 432x$ **b.** 144 times

5. $t = \{0.17, 0.66, 1.01, 1.49, 1.84, 2.33, 2.67\}$

6. a. Not including $t = 0$, 6 times   **b.** $\approx 29\%$ of the time

7. a. $x = 113.578, 246.422, 473.578, 606.422, 833.578$
   b. $x = 38.660, 218.660, 398.660, 578.660, 758.660$

8. The domain of $(\sin x, x)$ is all real numbers. The domain of $y = \sin^{-1} x$ is $-90 \le x \le 90$. Both graphs look exactly the same for $-90 \le x \le 90$.

9. a. $y = 110 \sin 21600x$ **b.**

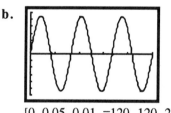

[0, 0.05, 0.01, −120, 120, 20]

0. a. $y_1 = 5 \cos 25.7(x - 12) + 11$
   b. $16.42 \le x \le 21.58$ and $30.42 \le x \le 35.58$ or between 4:25 and 9:35 p.m. and again between 6:25 and 11:35 a.m. the next day

Problem Set 13.6

1. $(2, 390°)$ and $(-2, -510°)$

2. $(3, 240°)$, $(-3, 300°)$ and $(3, -120°)$

3. a.

θ	0°	5°	10°	15°	20°	25°	30°	35°	40°	45°	50°	55°
r	3	2.90	2.60	2.12	1.5	0.78	0	−0.78	−1.5	−2.12	−2.60	−2.9

60°	65°	70°	75°	80°	85°	90°	95°	100°	105°	110°	115°	120°
−3	−2.90	−2.60	−2.12	−1.5	−0.78	0	0.78	1.5	2.12	2.60	2.90	3

125°	130°	135°	140°	145°	150°	155°	160°	165°	170°	175°	180°	185°
2.90	2.60	2.12	1.5	0.78	0	−0.78	−1.5	−2.12	−2.60	−2.90	−3	−2.90

190°	195°	200°	205°	210°	215°	220°	225°	230°	235°	240°	245°	250°
−2.60	−2.12	−1.5	−0.78	0	0.78	1.5	2.12	2.60	2.90	3	2.90	2.60

255°	260°	265°	270°	275°	280°	285°	290°	295°	300°	305°	310°	315°
2.12	1.5	0.78	0	−0.78	−1.5	−2.12	−2.60	−2.9	−3	−2.9	−2.60	−2.12

320°	325°	330°	335°	340°	345°	350°	355°	360°
−1.5	−0.78	0	0.78	1.5	2.12	2.60	2.90	3

b.

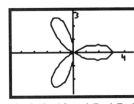

[0, 360, 10, −4.7, 4.7, 1, −3.1, 3.1, 1]

4. a.

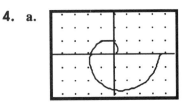

b. The graph is flipped over the *x*-axis.

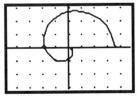

c. Rotation of 180°

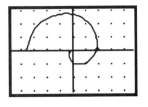

d. The spiral is stretched in all directions by a factor of 2.

5.
a. The graphs appear to be the same, but the starting point for each is different.
b. The graph is the same image rotated 90° counterclockwise.
c. The width at $y = 0$ is $2a$.

6.
a. This is better for audience noise because it "listens" only to the area in front, where the performers are.
b. The edge performers are 3 units away. The center is 4, and the others are 3.732 units away.

7.
a. $r = 3 \cos \theta: 0° \leq \theta \leq 180°$
b. $r = 3 \cos 2\theta, r = 2 \sin 2\theta: 0° \leq \theta \leq 360°$
c. $r = -2 (\cos \theta + 1): 0° \leq \theta \leq 360°$
d. $r = \pm 2 (\cos \theta + 1), r = 2: 0° \leq \theta \leq 360°$

8. a. $0° \le \theta \le 720°$

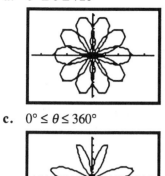

b. $0° \le \theta \le 720°$

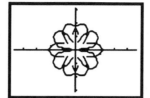

c. $0° \le \theta \le 360°$

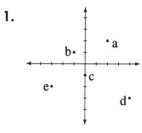

d. $0° \le \theta \le 2700°$

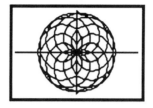

Problem Set 13.7

1.

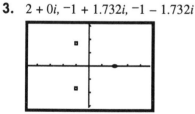

2. Answers will vary with different choices for θ.

   a. $2.828(\cos 45° + i \sin 45°)$ **b.** $1.414(\cos 135° + i \sin 135°)$

   c. $1(\cos {}^-90° + i \sin {}^-90°)$ **d.** $5(\cos {}^-36.87° + i \sin {}^-36.87°)$

   e. $3.606(\cos {}^-146.31° + i \sin {}^-146.31°)$

3. $2 + 0i, {}^-1 + 1.732i, {}^-1 - 1.732i$

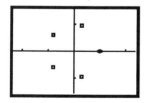

4. $1 + 0i, 0.309 + 0.951i, {}^-0.809 + 0.588i,$
$0.809 - 0.588i, 0.309 + {}^-0.951i$

5. a. $5 + 2i$ **b.** ${}^-64 + 0i$ **c.** $0.223 - 0.114i$ **d.** $\frac{4}{3} + 0i$

   e. ${}^-0.125 - 0.125i$ **f.** $0 + 12i$

6. a. Points continue to spiral out.

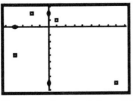

b. Points spiral in to origin.

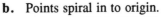
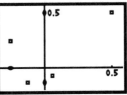

c. Because the modulus of $1 + i$ is more than 1, raising it to increasing powers will make each result larger. Because the modulus of $0.5 + 0.5i$ is less than 1, raising it to increasing powers will make each result smaller.

7. a. $r \approx 1.414$; $\theta = -135°$ or $225°$

b. $\left(\sqrt{2}\right)^t \cos 225t$; $y = \left(\sqrt{2}\right)^t \sin 225t$

c. $x = \left(\sqrt{2}\right)^t \cos 225t$; $y = \left(\sqrt{2}\right)^t \sin 225t$

t	0	1	2	3.	4	5	6	7	8	9	10
x	1	−1	0	2	−4	4	0	−8	16	−16	0
y	0	−1	2	−2	0	4	−8	0	−16	32	32

d.

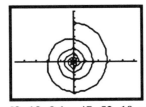

[0, 10, 0.1, −47, 52, 10, −25, 40, 5]

The graph is a spiral that is expanding exponentially.

8. a. For Problem 7a.–d.

    a. $r = 1$; $\theta = 60°$; $1(\cos 60° + i \sin 60°)$

    b. $(0.5 + 0.866)^t = 1^t(\cos 60t + i \sin 60t)$

    c. $x = \cos 60t$; $y = \sin 60t$

t	0	1	2	3	4	5	6
x	1	0.5	−0.5	−1	−0.5	0.5	1
y	0	0.866	0.866	0	−0.866	−0.866	0

t	7	8	9	10	11	12
x	0.5	−0.5	−1	−0.5	0.5	1
y	0.866	0.866	0	−0.866	−0.866	0

    d.

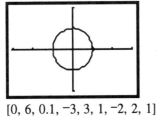

[0, 6, 0.1, −3, 3, 1, −2, 2, 1]

This number is one of the sixth roots of 1. All powers have a modulus of 1 and the pattern repeats every six.

b. (0.5, 0.866)

9. a. The table values repeat in groups of 5. The five points in the table represent the five roots of 32. The five roots are $2 + 0i$, $0 + 1.902i$, $-1.618 + 1.176i$, $-1.618 - 1.176i$, $0.618 - 1.902i$.

b. $x = 32^{1/6} \cos\left(\frac{360t}{6}\right)$; $y = 32^{1/6} \sin\left(\frac{360t}{6}\right)$. The six roots of 32 are $1.782 + 0i$, $0.891 + 1.543i$, $-0.891 + 1.543i$, $-1.782 + 0i$, $-0.891 - 1.543i$, $0.981 - 1.543i$.

0. a. Goes to $(1, 0)$ **b.** Goes to $(1, 0)$ **c.** Goes to $(1, 0)$ **d.** All points go to $(1, 0)$

1. The points iterate as shown below. Those colored black iterate to $(1, 0)$. Those left white iterate to $(-0.5, 0.866)$. The others iterate to $(-0.5, -0.866)$. If you try to find the point where it switches from one color to another, you will always find a point that goes to the other point. For example, while $-1.6 + 0i$ iterates to $(1, 0)$ and $-1.6 + 0i$ iterates to $(-0.5, 0.866)$, if you iterate $-1.6 + 0.0999i$, it goes to $(-0.5, -0.866)$.

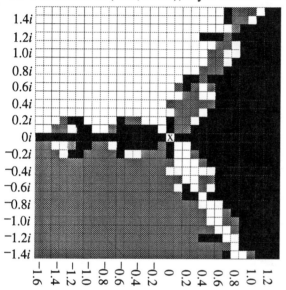

Chapter Review

Problem Set 13.8

1. a. Period $= 120°$, $y = -2 \cos 3(x - 120°)$ **b.** Period $= 90°$, $y = 3 \sin 4(x - 22.5°)$

c. Period $= 180°$, $y = \csc 2(x + 45°)$ **d.** Period $= \frac{180}{2} = 90$, $y = \cot 2(x - 45°) + 1$

2. a. $y = -2 \sin 2x - 1$ **b.** $y = \sin 0.5x + 1.5$ **c.** $y = 0.5 \tan(x - 45)$ **d.** $y = 0.5 \sec 2x$

3. a. The equation should be similar to $y = 1.92 \sin\frac{360}{365}(x - 80) + 12.13$.

b. Approximately June 19; 14.05 hr

c. Approximately March 17 and September 22.

4. a.

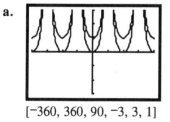

$[-360, 360, 90, -3, 3, 1]$

b. $\sec^2 x = \tan^2 x + 1$

5. a. $m\angle A \approx 74.5°$, $m\angle B \approx 58.4°$, $AB \approx 10.49$ cm **b.** $m\angle E = 52.55°$, $m\angle F = 17.45°$, $DE \approx 5.55$ cm

6. If the known parts include SAS or SSS, use the Law of Cosines. If the known parts include AAS, use the Law of Sines. If the known parts are SSA, you can use either law, but be careful if you use the Law of Sines to check whether you want an acute or obtuse angle.

7. $y = 100 \cos \frac{360}{105}(x - 10)$; 82.6 mi from the equator; passes over the launch site 41 times in 3 days.

8. $(5, -320°)$, $(5, 400°)$

9. a. $r = -2(\cos \theta + 1)$
   b. $r = 2(\sin \theta + 1)$

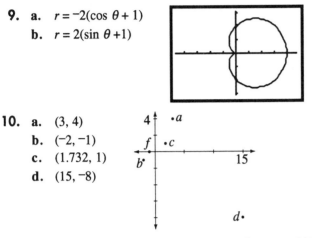

10. a. $(3, 4)$
   b. $(-2, -1)$
   c. $(1.732, 1)$
   d. $(15, -8)$

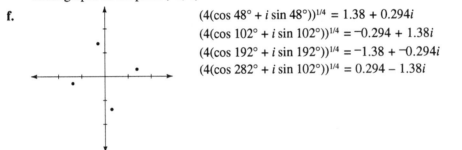

   e. $i^6 = (0 + i)^6 = [1(\cos 90° + i \sin 90°)]^6 = 1(\cos 540° + i \sin 540°) = 1(\cos 180° + i \sin 180°) = -1 + 0i$, which graphs as the point $(-1, 0)$

   f.

   $(4(\cos 48° + i \sin 48°))^{1/4} = 1.38 + 0.294i$
   $(4(\cos 102° + i \sin 102°))^{1/4} = -0.294 + 1.38i$
   $(4(\cos 192° + i \sin 192°))^{1/4} = -1.38 + -0.294i$
   $(4(\cos 282° + i \sin 102°))^{1/4} = 0.294 - 1.38i$

11. Points inside a circle of radius 1 centered at the origin iterate to $(0, 0)$. Points outside the circle become further and further away from the origin as they are iterated. Points on the circle stay on the circle. Some, such as $1 + i$, iterate to single point. Others, such as $\left(\sqrt{0.3}, \sqrt{0.7}\right)$ keep bouncing around the circle hitting various points on the circle.

Advanced Algebra
Through Data Exploration
Comment Form

Please help us correct and improve *Advanced Algebra*. If you find mistakes in the text or the teacher support materials, use this form to let us know. If you have general comments or suggestions about the materials, we'd like to hear those as well. Once you've filled out this form, all you have to do is fold it and drop it in the mail. We'll pay the postage. Thank you!

Your name _____

School _____

School address _____

City/State/Zip _____

Phone _____

Advanced Algebra student text

Page ____ Comment _____

Page ____ Comment _____

Page ____ Comment _____

Teacher's Guide and Answer Key

Section _____ Page ____ Comment_____

Section _____ Page ____ Comment_____

Section _____ Page ____ Comment_____

Teacher's Resource Book

Section _____ Page ____ Comment_____

Section _____ Page ____ Comment_____

Section _____ Page ____ Comment_____

Quizzes, Tests, and Exams

Section _____ Page ____ Comment_____

Section _____ Page ____ Comment_____

Section _____ Page ____ Comment_____

Solutions Manual

Section _____ Page ____ Comment_____

Section _____ Page ____ Comment_____

Calculator Notes (calculator model _____)

Section _____ Page ____ Comment_____

Section _____ Page ____ Comment_____

Do you have any other comments about *Advanced Algebra* or any suggestions for improving the student text or the teacher's material? _____

_____

_____

_____

Fold carefully along this line.

BUSINESS REPLY MAIL
FIRST CLASS   PERMIT NO. 151   BERKELEY, CA

POSTAGE WILL BE PAID BY ADDRESSEE

KEY CURRICULUM PRESS
P.O. Box 2304
Berkeley, CA 94702-9983

Attention: Editorial—*Advanced Algebra*

Fold carefully along this line.

Advanced Algebra
Through Data Exploration
Comment Form

Please help us correct and improve *Advanced Algebra*. If you find mistakes in the text or the teacher support materials, use this form to let us know. If you have general comments or suggestions about the materials, we'd like to hear those as well. Once you've filled out this form, all you have to do is fold it and drop it in the mail. We'll pay the postage. Thank you!

Your name _____

School _____

School address _____

City/State/Zip _____

Phone _____

Advanced Algebra student text

Page ____ Comment _____

Page ____ Comment _____

Page ____ Comment _____

Teacher's Guide and Answer Key

Section _____ Page ____ Comment_____

Section _____ Page ____ Comment_____

Section _____ Page ____ Comment_____

Teacher's Resource Book

Section _____ Page ____ Comment_____

Section _____ Page ____ Comment_____

Section _____ Page ____ Comment_____

Quizzes, Tests, and Exams

Section _____ Page ____ Comment_____

Section _____ Page ____ Comment_____

Section _____ Page ____ Comment_____

Solutions Manual

Section _____ Page ____ Comment_____

Section _____ Page ____ Comment_____

Calculator Notes (calculator model _____)

Section _____ Page ____ Comment_____

Section _____ Page ____ Comment_____

Do you have any other comments about *Advanced Algebra* or any suggestions for improving the student text or the teacher's material? _____

_____

_____

_____

Fold carefully along this line.

BUSINESS REPLY MAIL
FIRST CLASS   PERMIT NO. 151   BERKELEY, CA

POSTAGE WILL BE PAID BY ADDRESSEE

KEY CURRICULUM PRESS
P.O. Box 2304
Berkeley, CA 94702-9983

Attention: Editorial—*Advanced Algebra*

Fold carefully along this line.

Advanced Algebra
Through Data Exploration
Comment Form

Please help us correct and improve *Advanced Algebra*. If you find mistakes in the text or the teacher support materials, use this form to let us know. If you have general comments or suggestions about the materials, we'd like to hear those as well. Once you've filled out this form, all you have to do is fold it and drop it in the mail. We'll pay the postage. Thank you!

Your name _____

School _____

School address _____

City/State/Zip _____

Phone _____

Advanced Algebra student text

Page _____ Comment _____

Page _____ Comment _____

Page _____ Comment _____

Teacher's Guide and Answer Key

Section _____ Page _____ Comment _____

Section _____ Page _____ Comment _____

Section _____ Page _____ Comment _____

Teacher's Resource Book

Section _____ Page _____ Comment _____

Section _____ Page _____ Comment _____

Section _____ Page _____ Comment _____

Quizzes, Tests, and Exams

Section _____ Page _____ Comment _____

Section _____ Page _____ Comment _____

Section _____ Page _____ Comment _____

Solutions Manual

Section _____ Page _____ Comment _____

Section _____ Page _____ Comment _____

Calculator Notes (calculator model _____)

Section _____ Page _____ Comment _____

Section _____ Page _____ Comment _____

Do you have any other comments about *Advanced Algebra* or any suggestions for improving the student text or the teacher's material? _____

_____

_____

_____

Fold carefully along this line.

BUSINESS REPLY MAIL
FIRST CLASS   PERMIT NO. 151   BERKELEY, CA

POSTAGE WILL BE PAID BY ADDRESSEE

KEY CURRICULUM PRESS
P.O. Box 2304
Berkeley, CA 94702-9983

Attention: Editorial—*Advanced Algebra*

Fold carefully along this line.